MARKETING SCIENCE INSTITUTE SERIES

Multidimensional Scaling

Marketing Science Institute
1033 Massachusetts Avenue
Cambridge, Massachusetts 02138

The Marketing Science Institute was established in 1962 as a nonprofit organization to contribute to improved marketing performance through research designed to provide objective information about marketing practices and their effects. MSI's program includes studies aimed at developing more reliable research procedures; explorations of consumer behavior; and investigations of public policy issues related to marketing.

In October, 1968, the Institute's Board of Trustees approved the establishment of a new association between MSI and the Harvard Graduate School of Business. MSI retains its status as an independent research organization, but it can now benefit from the Business School's facilities, such as the computer center and the various libraries, and from working closely with Harvard faculty.

MSI is supported by member companies representing leading U.S. industries. The Institute's by-laws also permit acceptance of grants or gifts from foundations, associations, and governmental agencies.

Multidimensional Scaling
and Related Techniques
in Marketing Analysis

PAUL E. GREEN

University of Pennsylvania

FRANK J. CARMONE

Drexel University

ALLYN AND BACON, INC., BOSTON, MASSACHUSETTS

Printed in the United States of America

Library of Congress Catalog Card Number: 79-127370

Contents

Foreword: *xi*

Preface: *xiii*

INTRODUCTION AND PROBLEM SETTING: *1*

Format: *2*
The Problem Setting: *2*
Multidimensional Scaling: *3*
Summary: *6*
References: *6*

Chapter 1
MEASUREMENT THEORY AND OVERVIEW OF SCALING APPLICA-
TIONS: *7*

Measurement Theory: *7*
Types of Multidimensional Scaling: *10*
Typical Marketing Problems: *14*
Summary: *19*
References: *19*

Chapter 2
A CLASSIFICATION OF DATA AND SCALING TECHNIQUES: *21*

Multidimensional Scaling Fundamentals: *21*
Coombsian Data Classification: *27*
Nonmetric Multidimensional Scaling: *32*
An Illustrative Computer Algorithm: *37*
Specific Features of the TORSCA 8 Program: *40*
Summary: *40*
References: *41*

Chapter 3
ANALYSIS OF SIMILARITIES DATA: *42*

Similarities Responses and Distance Models: *42*
Synthetic Data Analyses: *48*
Data Collection Methods: *53*
Solution Interpretation in Multidimensional Scaling: *57*
Special Issues in the Analysis of Similarities Data: *61*
Summary: *68*
References: *68*

Chapter 4
ANALYSIS OF PREFERENCE DATA: *71*

Models of Preference Judgments: *71*
Synthetic Data Analyses: *82*
Data Collection Methods: *84*
Solution Interpretation in Joint Space Configurations: *86*
Special Issues in Preference Analysis: *91*
Summary: *94*
References: *95*

Chapter 5
DIMENSION-REDUCING METHODS AND CLUSTER ANALYSIS: *97*

The Data Matrix: *97*
Reduced Space Analysis: *99*
Cluster Analysis: *103*
An Application of Reduced Space and Cluster Analysis: *112*
Recent Developments in Clustering Techniques: *119*
Summary: *123*
References: *123*

Chapter 6
LIMITATIONS OF THE METHODOLOGY AND AREAS FOR
FURTHER RESEARCH: *125*

Computational Problems: *125*
Empirical Problems: *129*
Conceptual Problems: *133*
Summary: *137*
References: *138*

Appendix A
CAPSULE DESCRIPTIONS OF COMPUTER PROGRAMS: *141*

Traditional Scaling Procedures: *141*
Preprocessing Programs for Multidimensional Scaling: *143*

Multidimensional Scaling Programs: *144*
Analysis of Qualitative Data: *149*
Cluster Analytic Routines: *150*
Miscellaneous Programs: *154*
References: *158*

Appendix B
BIBLIOGRAPHY ON MULTIDIMENSIONAL SCALING
AND RELATED METHODS: *161*

Index: *197*

Foreword

This book deals with multidimensional scaling and related techniques, a relatively new, computer-based methodology for analyzing marketing behavior. Although the technique as described by Green and Carmone applies to marketing situations, the underlying theories were originally formulated in the behavioral sciences.

MSI has for several years sponsored the authors' research into multidimensional scaling and is pleased to be able to make available a synthesis of the results of this effort to date. One of the leading theorists in the scaling field, J. Douglas Carroll of Bell Telephone Laboratories, has commented: "Dr. Green and his students and colleagues . . . have most carefully and systematically explained virtually all facets of the methodology as it is related to the marketing area. . . . Their work is playing a vital role in establishing the groundwork for an approach that promises, in time, to realize the *full* potential of their scaling methods in the marketing area. I believe, too, that their work has already demonstrated important practical applications."

It is one of MSI's primary objectives to support investigations into new methods.

The results of careful and thorough evaluation of theories, which have been tested on a pilot scale, are then published by MSI for the use of marketing practitioners and educators.

I hope that the findings of Green and Carmone will stimulate further research into the applicability of scaling methods in marketing as well as other areas of applied behavioral science. It has been a source of great satisfaction for MSI to contribute to the publication of a work that should provide a valuable new tool for the marketing community.

Robert D. Buzzell
Executive Director, MSI

Preface

This monograph represents the outgrowth of over four years of research devoted to examining the applicability of multidimensional scaling and related techniques to substantive problems in marketing. Most of these techniques have been developed only since 1962 by researchers in the behavioral and life sciences. Much of the material has been available in only working paper form or in journals not usually scanned by marketing researchers or marketing teachers.

The general objectives of the monograph are set forth in the Introduction and Problem Setting. We can only say here that the experience of working in this rapidly evolving field has been both exciting and frustrating. It has been exciting because it seems to us that multidimensional scaling methodology provides a new perspective for approaching some particularly thorny problems in marketing. It has been frustrating because, as this preface is being written, we are aware that our statement will soon be obsolete—such is the pace with which technical developments in the field are occurring.

It is hoped, however, that even this transitory attempt to capture the "state of the art"—and its implications for marketing analysis—will make accessible to a wider audience a methodology of potential utility for researchers in business. This monograph, along with a collection of working papers and reprints entitled *Selected Studies in Multidimensional Scaling and Cluster Analysis* (available from the Marketing Science Institute, Cambridge, Mass.), should serve to give the interested reader both a broad exposure to the topic as well as in-depth description, should he wish to read about specific pilot applications.

One word of caution at the outset. If we have learned anything over the past four years, it has been an appreciation of the sizeable research commitment that is required for developing anything beyond a superficial understanding of scaling methodology. Fortunately for us, few policy decisions have hung in the balance during the course of our pilot level research. There are signs, however, that scaling methodology may become a research "fad" as a growing number of consulting firms and advertising agencies start to offer such services. It is our hope that this monograph will alert prospective users of these techniques to their limitations as well as their potential.

Acknowledgments

A large number of individuals—students, researchers and administrative staff—have influenced the preparation of this monograph. We are intellectually indebted to Clyde H. Coombs and James C. Lingoes, University of Michigan; J. Douglas Carroll, Stephen C. Johnson, Joseph B. Kruskal and Myron Wish, Bell Telephone Laboratories; Forrest W. Young, University of North Carolina; Warren S. Torgerson, Johns Hopkins University; Victor E. McGee, Dartmouth College; and Peter C. Fishburn, Research Analysis Corporation. All of these individuals were participants in a lecture series held at the University of Pennsylvania during the 1967-68 academic year.

In addition, we are grateful for the stimulating conversations that we have had with Roger N. Shepard, Stanford University; David Krantz, University of Michigan; and Amos Tversky and Louis Guttman of Hebrew University. Patrick J. Robinson, of Robinson and Naus, Inc., and J. Sayer Minas, of the University of Waterloo, deserve acknowledgment for their insight and interest in this work.

Dr. J. Douglas Carroll, of Bell Telephone Laboratories, deserves special thanks for serving as a continuous source of encouragement and advice; his own creativity in this area has done much to sustain our research interest. Mrs. J. J. Chang, also of Bell Telephone Laboratories, has been most helpful in the conversion of various computer programs.

Critical reviews of the manuscript were provided by J. Douglas Carroll, Bell Telephone Laboratories; Alvin Silk, Massachusetts Institute of Technology; and James R. Taylor, University of Michigan. Their comments are most appreciated and have added measurably to the monograph's completeness and clarity. The incisive technical comments of Dr. Carroll, particularly, have raised the accuracy level of our presentation; needless to say, however, only the authors are accountable for any residual errors that may remain.

Perhaps our largest debt of gratitude is owed to the senior author's graduate students. This small, enthusiastic army has participated in virtually all of our research projects. Those deserving special thanks are R. P. Fenwick, L. B. Fox, S. M. Gonzalez, J. M. W. Hogan, Robert McCracken, Arun Maheshwari, Thomas W. Morris and, last but not least, Vithala R. Rao. Thanks are also extended to Mollie Horowits and Mary Fulton who "mapped" often illegible scrawl into neat typescript.

We also wish to thank Prentice-Hall, Inc., for permission to utilize some material appearing in Paul E. Green and Donald S. Tull, *Research for Marketing Decisions* (second edition, 1970).

The major part of the work described here was financially supported by the Marketing Science Institute. Dr. Robert D. Buzzell, Executive Director of MSI, deserves special thanks for his continuing interest in this work. More recently we have also been aided by a research grant received from the A.A.A.A. Educational Foundation. We hope that their trust, and dollars, have not been misplaced.

Only the authors should be—and are—responsible for the use which we have made of all this help. We hope that our belief in the potential of this methodology has not led us to place undue emphasis on its virtues at the expense of appropriate recognition of its current limitations.

Paul E. Green
University of Pennsylvania

Frank J. Carmone
Drexel University

Introduction and
Problem Setting

The purpose of this monograph is to acquaint marketing practitioners and teachers with a recently developed methodology—multidimensional scaling and related techniques—for analyzing marketing behavior. This methodology is computer-based and had its origins in the behavioral and life sciences. While some of these technqiues can be broadly classified under the traditional rubric of "attitude or image research," the methods extend well beyond the familiar use of rating scales, semantic differentials and other such devices historically used in the measurement of perception and preference.

For the most part, the techniques are less than a decade old. Sufficient evidence has been gathered, however, to suggest that their implications be taken seriously and, indeed, that the need for further test and evaluation could justify at least small-scale applications in both consumer and industrial marketing research.

The objectives of this monograph are to describe these procedures and their implications for marketing analysis. In addition, since the methodology is probably unfamiliar to most readers, we include (in Appendix A) a brief description of each of the principal computer programs used in this project and a "directory" of program developers. The reader may then wish to secure more information (and, perhaps, the programs themselves) from the original sources.

Finally, we discuss current limitations of the methodology and problems for future research. While our general enthusiasm about the potential of these techniques in marketing is seldom concealed, it should be made clear at the beginning that the methodology itself is still evolving and, furthermore, that much more empirical application is required if it is to make good on its promise. This monograph has been prepared to further that aim by attempting to provide in one place an integration of materials heretofore scattered over a variety of journals and unpublished working papers not normally perused by either the marketing practitioner or marketing academic.

1

FORMAT OF THE MONOGRAPH

The format of the monograph consists of five main sections:

1. Chapter 1 sets the stage for later discussion by reviewing some of the fundamentals of measurement theory and some historical background on multidimensional scaling. In addition, a description of several potential applications of scaling methods is presented as motivation for subsequent chapters.
2. Chapter 2 introduces some of the more formal characteristics of scaling methodology and provides a classification system, due to Coombs [2], for the analysis of behavioral data.
3. Chapters 3, 4 and 5 describe, respectively: (a) the analysis of similarities data; (b) preference data analysis; and (c) reduced space and clustering methods.
4. Chapter 6 describes current limitations of the techniques used and areas for additional research—computational, empirical and conceptual.
5. The Appendices contain two sections: (a) short descriptions of current multidimensional scaling and related computer programs and (b) an extensive bibliography of the field.

Throughout the monograph, the reader will note repeated references to computer methodology, although the technical level of our presentation will not be high. In a very real sense the methodology to be described here owes its existence to the types of computation and complex data handling provided only by computer-based algorithms. Our de-emphasis of technical and mathematical detail, however, is prompted by the hoped-for audience of this monograph—the potential applier of this methodology to marketing research. Such awareness is a necessary step for eventual test and evaluation of these procedures in field-level marketing problems.

THE PROBLEM SETTING

Two still recent ideas in marketing—the marketing concept and market segmentation—continue to be enjoying a kind of vogue in both marketing practice and research. The *marketing concept* emphasizes the firm's role in the satisfaction (and stimulation) of buyers' wants. Under this point of view, such corporate activities as research and development, production, finance, and even personnel administration are to be (ultimately) customer-oriented and supportive to marketing efforts, As such, the marketing concept is integrative in nature; all activities of the firm are ultimately connected with the shaping and satisfaction of buyers' desires. These efforts take place in a variety of competitive and cooperative environments, are intended to "create and retain customers" and are expected to lead, ultimately, to growth and profits for the firm in question.

The concept of *market segmentation* recognizes the diversity of buyers' wants and the assumption that different buyers respond differentially to various marketing strategies. As such, the concept is disaggregative in nature; the firm (integrated, in the sense used above) attempts to shape its marketing strategy so as to appeal differentially to diverse market segments. In so doing, it is assumed that total profits can be increased. Problems concern the identification of relevant segments and the prediction of consequences stemming from the employment of different strategies for different segments.

Perceptions and Preferences

The analysis of buyer perceptions and preferences regarding products and services is congenial with both the marketing concept and market segmentation. First, buyer perception and preference scaling can provide operational measures of how the product or service is being seen and evaluated by the firm's clientele, actual or potential. Second, the fact that neither perceptions nor preferences need be homogeneous over buyers can suggest opportunities for segmentation strategy. As we shall try to show, perceptual and preference measurement can provide an operational procedure for implementing both concepts.

Perception and preference are two fundamental phenomena of all human behavior. Constantly we are making perceptual judgments about similarities and differences among the myriad stimuli with which we are confronted. Is a Ford Mustang more similar to a Chevrolet Camaro than it is to a Mercury Cougar? How is the Du Pont Company perceived by the typical purchaser of nylon carpet? Our perceptions of various entities are necessary factors in the process of choice and represent a more or less continuous part of our behavior.

Preferences are no less ubiquitous. Buyers may perceive products or services similarly while displaying differences in preferences. Clearly, the fact that one brand or supplier rarely dominates a particular market is some evidence of the heterogeneity of buyer preferences.

MULTIDIMENSIONAL SCALING

Multidimensional scaling and related techniques are concerned primarily with the *spatial* representation of relationships among behavioral data—in our case, buyer perceptions and preferences. While we shall be presenting a somewhat more formal description of multidimensional scaling methods in succeeding chapters, some of the basic concepts are presented here at an intuitive and content-oriented level.

Attribute Space

Any product or service can be visualized as composed of both objective and perceived attributes or "dimensions." A firm may conduct extensive laboratory tests on its brand, leading to an objective description of it in chemical or physical terms. Such objective attribute "spaces," in which various brands are viewed as points positioned somewhere in the space, will usually not agree with the buyer's perceived space. The perceived space, in contrast, consists of brand or supplier positions as related to dimensions which reflect the buyer's perception of the product or service class—those attributes which he uses in making discrimination judgments among brands or suppliers [1].

Two characteristics of perceived space, and its relationship to objective space, should be mentioned. First, the *dimensions* of perceived space need not agree with those of objective space. Second, even if they do agree with (some subset of) the set of objective dimensions, the projections of the points on the various dimensions may not agree with their objective counterparts. That is, the two *configurations* of points may differ even if the dimensions agree.[1]

Thus, a set of more or less common stimuli—brands of toothpaste, banking services, electric motors, and so on—can be assumed to occupy positions in both objective and perceptual space. The perceptual "maps" of brands or specific suppliers of services may, of course, vary over individual perceivers and vary over time and context within the same individual. Moreover, the dimensionality of this space—the "richness" of the typical perceptual map—may vary over stimulus classes.

In some cases, e.g., industrial products, the perceived configuration of brands may agree rather closely with an objectively constructed configuration in which measurements of such characteristics as size, speed, efficiency and reliability can be made rather straightforwardly. In other instances—brands of coffee, headache remedies, toothpastes—the perceived dimensions may differ markedly from the physical and chemical characteristics of the products. This disparity, of course, is partly a reflection of such factors as advertising content, supplier reputation and other "external" influences that contribute to the buyer's overall image of the brand or service.

Nevertheless, from the viewpoint of consumer choice, the *perceived* dimensions are the relevant ones; clearly, brands physically and chemically identical may be perceived differently and, conversely, chemically and physically distinct brands may be perceived similarly. This possible disparity between objective and perceived attributes suggests the need to consider not only perceived dimensions but "objective" dimensions as well—and the function by which one set can be related to the other.

Ideal Points

Individuals, as well, may be characterized as having an ideal stimulus in a subjective (perceived) attribute space. If so, what is the interpretation? One rather compelling interpretation is that individuals prefer some particular combination of values on the perceived product or service dimensions to all other combinations within a given product-service class. In one formulation of this concept,

---

[1] The configurations may disagree in two ways: a) the ratios of scale separations between point projections may be different on the psychological dimensions versus the objective dimensions, even though the order of projections is maintained; or b) the order of point projections may differ. In the first case the "psychophysical" transform relating psychological scale values to objective scale values is monotonic but nonlinear. In the second case the "psychophysical" transform is not even monotonic.

brands or suppliers "closer" to an individual's *ideal point* will tend to be preferred to those farther away [2]. Moreover, the individual may differentially weight the dimensions in terms of their relative importance to him in an evaluative context. If such is the case, the distance of specific brands or services from his ideal point is assumed to reflect the differential "stretching" which he applies to the dimensions of interest—often termed the *saliences* of the dimensions, as *now* considered in evaluative space.

As the reader will probably gather, the concept of attribute space is central to the techniques to be described in this monograph. Under some circumstances the "nearness" of any two brands or services in this space can be formulated as an operational measure of their competitiveness. Finally, buyers can be positioned in an evaluative attribute space as well, this interpretation being usually construed as their respective ideal points—that combination of attribute levels which for a given buyer would tend to be preferred to all other combinations.

We believe that analytical power derives from the above, rather simple geometrical notion of attribute space. As we have noted, however, several types of spaces are relevant:

1. The "objective" attribute space in which brands or services are positioned in terms of hard data, such as physical and chemical composition, price, number of service suppliers, etc.

2. The set of subjective attribute spaces that reflect perceived dimensions of brands or suppliers. These may vary:
   a. Over individuals at any point in time.
   b. Over time for any specific individual.
   c. Over individuals and time by specific situations, e.g., uses to which the product is to be put.

3. The set of subjective attribute spaces that reflect common perceived positions of brands or suppliers but not necessarily common saliences and/or ideal point positions of individuals. These "evaluative" spaces may vary, again:
   a. Over individuals at any point in time.
   b. Over time for any specific individual.
   c. Over individuals and time by specific situations.

Finally, one requires a transformation which links selected distances in evaluative attribute space to brand choice. In one type of model formulation this might be accomplished by construction of a function which relates probability of choice to distance of stimulus (brand or service) from a buyer's ideal point in evaluative space.

Consequently, predictions of buyer response to corporate policy variables (changes in product, package, promotion, price and distribution) would thus proceed through the links: (a) objective attribute space; (b) perceived attribute space; (c) evaluative attribute space of stimuli and ideal points; (d) choice response function; and (e) aggregation over individual types of buyers and specific purchase situations.

SUMMARY

In this introductory section we have tried to outline, at an intuitive level, the notion of attribute space and its relevance to the spatial description of brands and suppliers of services. Our interest from a content standpoint primarily consists of the measurement of perceptions and preferences. In so doing, we must distinguish between objective and perceived attribute spaces. Finally, the concepts of attribute salience and *ideal point* enter as a means of portraying, geometrically, preferred combinations of "scores" on the evaluative dimensions by which brands or suppliers of services are compared.

In principle, then, the methodology could be used to predict the effect of brand or service supplier changes (in objective space) on: (a) brand or supplier positions in perceived space; (b) ideal point or stimulus positions in evaluative space; and, ultimately, (c) share of choices. The remainder of this monograph will be largely concerned with the difficulties surrounding the implementation of this predictive model and the analytical procedures that are relevant for at least making a start in this direction.

REFERENCES

1. K. E. Boulding, *The Image* (Ann Arbor, Mich.: The University of Michigan Press, 1968).
2. C. H. Coombs, *A Theory of Data* (New York: John Wiley & Sons, Inc., 1964).

CHAPTER ONE

Measurement Theory and Overview of Scaling Applications

This chapter, like "Introduction and Problem Setting," has been prepared at a somewhat intuitive level. Our purpose here is to elaborate on the problem setting discussed in the preceding section. As such, the orientation is primarily substantive rather than methodological.

Specifically, we first introduce some of the rudiments of measurement theory so as to provide background for later discussion of potential scaling applications. This is followed by a brief description of the evolution of multidimensional scaling methods. Two pilot studies are then discussed at an informal level in order to give the reader some idea of the results of applying the methodology. (We leave to later chapters a more technical discussion of how and why the techniques work.)

We then turn to a presentation of capsule descriptions of a variety of applied problems in marketing which could be—and, in some cases, have been—researched by means of multidimensional scaling methodology. Our description of these problems is motivated by the desire to provide a substantive base for application of the formal models to be described in subsequent chapters.

MEASUREMENT THEORY

In its broadest context measurement consists of the assignment of one set of entities, usually mathematical entities such as numbers, to another set of entities, usually empirical phenomena. In making such assignments, the researcher is assuming that basic relationships among the mathematical entities are descriptive of relationships among the empirical entities. If the correspondence holds well enough to be useful, the known properties of the mathematical system can serve as a model for describing the empirical system.

Now it is a common observation in marketing research that people can *order* objects or concepts according to some criterion. That is, they can say whether object A has (a) more, (b) the same, or (c) less, of property X than object B has. Such data are collected in a variety of marketing research studies dealing with buyer attitudes, beliefs, and preferences. While we could assign numbers to the objects so the order is preserved, any set of numbers that did not violate the ranking relationship would do. Such data are only ordinal scaled and will be often called "nonmetric" in this monograph.

A more common impression of measurement, however, assumes that the *difference* between the scale numbers of any two objects should meaningfully measure their difference on property X. Thus, we would like to be able to define a unit which enables numerical comparisons of the difference between any pair of objects. Such considerations involve an *interval*, or "metric," scale.

If we can also fix a unique zero or natural origin point, we have a *ratio* scale, the usual type of scaling associated with physical properties like height, weight, and length. The ratio scale is another type of metric scale, but one which is hard to justify in the measurement of buyer perceptions and evaluations. Nor in many instances does the researcher require this strong a metric. For example, most of the common forms of statistical tests assume only interval scaled data [11].

Permissible Transformations

Another way of looking at the differences among ordinal, interval, and ratio scales is in terms of their uniqueness under certain types of transformations. Ordinal scales are unique up to a (strictly) monotonic increasing transformation, as shown in **Figure 1-1a**. Any transformation which preserves rank order (monotonicity) is appropriate; that is, any order preserving transformation of the original scale is just as good a representation of the empirical relationships as the original.

Permissible transformations of interval scales are constrained to be positive linear, i.e.,

$$y = a + bx; \quad b > 0$$

Figure 1-1b illustrates this type of function. A conventional illustration of interval scaling involves temperature, as measured on the centigrade or Fahrenheit scales. We recall that each represents a linear transformation of the other.

Ratio scales are unique up to a positive proportionality transformation, i.e., we are allowed only to change the unit of measurement.

$$y = cx; \quad c > 0$$

Figure 1-1c illustrates this case. Note that the transformation is linear, but the linear function is constrained to pass through the origin. While we would like to be able to measure various classes of psychological and social phenomena on ratio scales, the fact of the matter is that such possibilities are rare. Furthermore, it is often the case that interval scale measurements are sufficiently "strong" for various research purposes and policy objectives as well.

FIGURE 1-1
PERMISSIBLE TRANSFORMATION BY SCALE TYPE

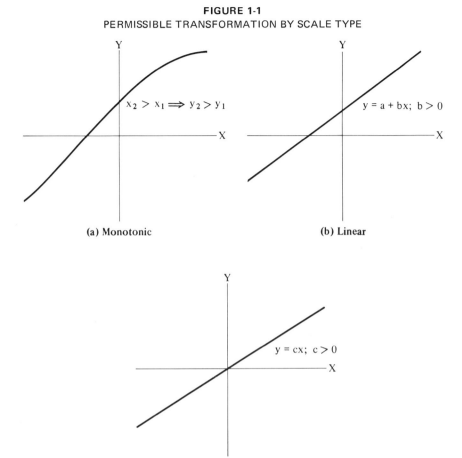

(a) Monotonic

(b) Linear

(c) Proportionality

Ordered Metric Scales

While ordinal, interval, and ratio scales represent the more familiar types, a less common scale, of particular significance to certain classes of multidimensional scaling techniques, is the ordered metric.[1] An ordered metric scale is one

[1]Some authors (e.g., S. S. Stevens, "Mathematics, Measurement and Psychophysics," in S. S. Stevens (ed.), *Handbook of Experimental Psychology* (New York: John Wiley & Sons, 1951) include nominal classification as a type of scale. Such scales are unique up to a permutation transformation; the numbers serve only as individual (or perhaps class) labels.

Finally, some authors discuss "absolute" scales, such as probabilities or numbers used in counting; these are unique up to an identity transformation. One way to differentiate this type of scale from others is to say that: (a) in ordinal scales no ratios of scale differences or scale values are meaningful; (b) in interval scales ratios of scale differences (only) are meaningful; (c) in ratio scales ratios of scale values are meaningful; and (d) in "absolute" scales, the scale values themselves are meaningful (i.e., the ratios of the scale values to some fixed value, say, unity are meaningful).

in which all possible intervals between scale positions can be ranked. Suppose we have ordered five objects, A, B, C, D, and E, along a continuum. Also assume that we can order all ten interpoint distances $\overline{AB}$, $\overline{AC}$, . . . , $\overline{DE}$, of the five objects taken two at a time. The scale is still a ranking or ordinal scale, but the order is on all *distances* separating pairs of points. Moreover, in the limit (by adding more and more points on the continuum whose end points are A and E) we will obtain an interval scale.

While a single ordering of objects which differ in only one aspect provides no basis for developing a stronger representation of the data (e.g., an interval scale), it turns out that orderings of *pairs* of points (objects), or interpoint "distances," imply more information about the scale positions of the points than might be first imagined. Similarly, several orderings (not all of which are the same) of a set of objects by *different respondents* can (asymptotically) provide metric (interval scaled or stronger) information about both objects and people by requiring that parameter values of the fitted measurement model be consistent with the whole set of data.

The above are both illustrations of conjoint measurement [13]. An outcome or event is conjoint if it represents a combination of two or more elements. Response to relationships involving pairs of objects is conjoint as is also the case of response to a pair of items involving a person and an object. If we can establish an order relation on such pairs, *we may be able to "upgrade" the data to some stronger form of scale.* This is one of the major objectives of *nonmetric* (or ordinal) multidimensional scaling.

TYPES OF MULTIDIMENSIONAL SCALING

Multidimensional scaling methods, considered generally, attempt to represent certain types of data as relations on points in a multidimensional space. The dimensions of the space are assumed to represent attributes or properties along which the objects (stimuli) are compared. As we shall see later, the stimuli may be real (e.g., brands of toothpaste, corporate names, advertisements), or hypothetical (e.g., an "ideal" stimulus [3] which possesses a particular combination of attribute levels that the respondent would prefer to any other combination).

The Development of Nonmetric Scaling

The history of ordinal or nonmetric methods of multidimensional scaling is short; the first conceptual paper and computer program by Roger Shepard appeared in 1962 [15]. Since that time, however, progress in algorithm development has been rapid. Some appreciation for the versatility of these newer methods might be gained by contrasting them with precursor approaches: (a) fully metric, and (b) fully nonmetric, multidimensional scaling.

Fully metric methods, as the name suggests, require ratio-scaled distances to begin with. (In practice, however, only interval scale values are required if a procedure for estimating an "additive constant" is used.) The principal task of these techniques (which utilize a factor analytic approach) is as follows: given a set of interpoint distances, find the dimensionality and configuration of points whose distances most closely match the *numerical* input values (up to a positive proportionality transformation). Fully metric methods go back to 1938 and are based on a set of theorems proved by Young and Householder [19]. In general such methods—since they are based on the linear factor model—will require *higher* dimensionality of solution if the relationship between input data and output distances is nonlinear (but still monotonic). Early multidimensional scaling work by Richardson [14], Klingberg [12], and Torgerson [17] used this type of approach and these methods are still in use today.

Fully nonmetric methods do not assume more than a rank order of the input "distances." The objective of this class of methods is to find a space of minimum dimensionality and the rank order (in the multidimensional case) of each point on each dimension in turn. Thus, one does *not* obtain the configuration of points (i.e., their positions in the space) but only the rank order of stimulus projections on each dimension, in turn. These methods were originally developed by Coombs [2] and Bennett and Hays [1]. While the techniques require only nonmetric (ordinal) input data, unfortunately in the multidimensional case they also yield nonmetric output.

Nonmetric multidimensional methods, the chief concern of this monograph, combine the best of both previous approaches—ordinal input and metric output. Given only a rank order of "psychological distance" data, the objective of these approaches is to find a configuration whose rank order of (ratio-scaled) distances best reproduces the original input *ranks*. One tries to do this in the lowest dimensionality that produces a "close enough" ordinal fit.

Pilot Applications of Multidimensional Scaling

In order to give the reader some intuitive feel for the results of applying multidimensional scaling techniques, we describe briefly two pilot applications of nonmetric methods. At this point we purposely ignore questions of methodology, and focus, instead, on the *outcomes* of the methodology. In this way the substantive issues are kept uppermost while still enabling us to demonstrate some of the rudiments of the techniques.

Graduate Business School Perceptions. In one pilot study (conducted in the Fall of 1966) we were interested in how first-year graduate students at the Wharton School of Finance and Commerce perceived alternate graduate schools of business as being "similar" or "different" [4]. Clearly, one could measure various aspects of graduate schools in terms of faculty/student ratios, starting salaries of graduates, size of student body, and so on. Which of a myriad group of attributes do prospective students *actually* use in making similarity and difference judgments and what is the outcome of their perceptions?

Approximately fifty first-year Wharton graduate business students were given a questionnaire in which they were asked to respond to the following kind of question:

> Using criteria of your choice, which two of the following graduate business schools are most similar? Least similar?
> Harvard Business School
> Wharton School of Finance and Commerce
> Carnegie-Mellon University

The above questions were repeated for all possible triples of six business schools: (a) Carnegie-Mellon; (b) Chicago; (c) Harvard; (d) M.I.T.; (e) Stanford; and (f) Wharton.

From simple tasks such as the above, one can eventually rank order each school *pair* in terms of "subjective" similarity. The rank order of similarities is then submitted to a computer algorithm which develops a spatial configuration representing the ranked data. In subsequent chapters we shall discuss these algorithms more thoroughly. For the moment, however, we show (**Figure 1-2**) only the two-space configuration which was derived from data pooled over all respondents.

FIGURE 1-2

SIMILARITIES MAP OF SIX GRADUATE BUSINESS SCHOOLS

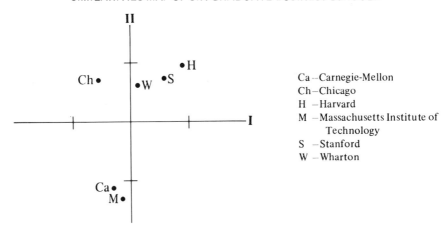

We note from Figure 1-2 that the two schools perceived to be most similar are Carnegie-Mellon and M.I.T.; the two least similar are M.I.T. and Harvard. From other information obtained from the questionnaire, the vertical axis can be labeled "qualitativeness of the school's curriculum"—Harvard being perceived to be the most qualitative and M.I.T. the least qualitative. The horizontal axis can be labeled as "school prestige or market value of the MBA degree"—Harvard being perceived to be the most prestigious and Chicago the least prestigious. Such "labels," however, are *not* found by the technique; the problem of axis labeling is discussed in subsequent chapters.

For purposes of this chapter, the interesting conclusion is that *only* two attributes were needed to describe Wharton students' perceptions of graduate business schools. Moreover, the geometrical distance between each school pair can be viewed as a metric measure of similarity—the notion of school "image" has been quantified and portrayed geometrically from nonmetric (rank order) input data alone.

Professional Journals. A second pilot study was conducted among a small sample of Wharton marketing faculty members and Marketing Science Institute research personnel [5]. In this instance the "stimuli" were eight professional journals: (a) *Commentary*; (b) *Harvard Business Review*; (c) *Journal of Advertising Research;* (d) *Journal of Business;* (e) *Journal of Marketing;* (f) *Journal of Marketing Research*; (g) *Management Science*; and (h) *Public Opinion Quarterly.* These journals were all familiar to the respondents and, to a greater or lesser extent, represent sources of professional marketing literature.

In this study *both* similarities and preference data were obtained from each subject. Thus, in terms of previous discussion, our interest was in developing a similarities-preference space of stimuli and individuals' ideal points with regard to various combinations of journal attributes most preferred by the respondents.

Figure 1-3 shows a two-space map of ideal points and stimuli which was obtained for a subset of respondents from the analysis of both similarities and preference data. Looking first at the stimuli (professional journals) we note that the *Journal of Advertising Research* and the *Journal of Marketing Research* were perceived to be most alike, while the *Journal of Marketing* and *Management Science* were perceived to be least alike. From other information obtained in the study, one might label the vertical axis "technical level"—*Management Science* being the most technically oriented journal. Similarly, the horizontal axis appears to be "specific-general" with the *Journal of Advertising Research* being the most specific and *Harvard Business Review* being the most general with regard to content material, at least as perceived by this respondent group.

The position of respondent ideal points is also of interest. Respondent 9, for example, most prefers *Management Science* and least prefers the *Journal of Marketing.* Respondent 3, on the other hand, displays a predilection for the "general" journals, *Journal of Business* and *Harvard Business Review.* Finally, it is of interest to note that the "average" respondent appears to evince a preference for the technical-specific journals, *Management Science, Journal of Advertising Research*, and *Journal of Marketing Research.*

In later chapters we shall go into more detail regarding the computer algorithms from which the configuration of Figure 1-3 was prepared. For present purposes, however, suffice it to say that, for this group of respondents, the similarities-preference map yielded fairly straightforward and simple results. Again, we may view distances between stimuli (journals) as (ratio-scaled) measures of their psychological closeness and distances between stimuli and a given ideal point as indicative of preference—the closer a stimulus to a given ideal point, the more it is preferred.

FIGURE 1-3
SUBJECTS' IDEAL POINTS AND SIMILARITIES CONFIGURATION OF
EIGHT PROFESSIONAL JOURNALS

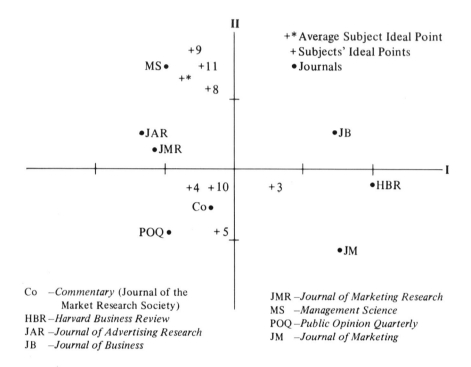

Co —*Commentary* (Journal of the
    Market Research Society)
HBR—*Harvard Business Review*
JAR —*Journal of Advertising Research*
JB —*Journal of Business*

JMR —*Journal of Marketing Research*
MS —*Management Science*
POQ—*Public Opinion Quarterly*
JM —*Journal of Marketing*

The foregoing remarks remain at a very general, intuitive level. In subsequent chapters these heuristic notions will be made more precise and operational. At this point, however, it may be useful to imagine some of the problems for which this type of approach may be applicable.

TYPICAL MARKETING PROBLEMS

Several perennial marketing problems might be viewed in a new way by using the conceptual framework briefly described above. We discuss below a series of illustrative problems in which multidimensional scaling and related methods might be utilized.

Product Life Cycle Analysis

Traditionally the analysis of product life cycles has utilized such notions as the "life cycle curve," in which some (typically S-shaped) curve is assumed to represent the behavior of, say, sales of some product or brand as a function of time. Suppose, alternatively, that we characterize each "brand" as a vector of performance characteristics. In such industrial product classes as electric motors, computers, gasoline engines, etc., reasonably hard data may exist. (In many consumer products, however, the brand's "scores" on each characteristic may be highly subjective.)

In any event, we might characterize a group of related brands as points in a multidimensional performance space. Points "near each other" would be presumed to be similar with respect to either objective or subjective characteristics. Indeed, as a first approximation, we might view their closeness in performance space as an operational measure of competitiveness.

With the above type of representation, one can next conceive of the points *moving through time* in performance space—or, if you will, a series of snapshots of the performance space of some reasonable and interpretable dimensionality. Each snapshot would show the relative positions of competing brands in a specific time period. To portray these performance spaces multidimensional scaling methods are required. Finally, one might like to relate movement along various performance axes to some "success" measure like sales or market share.

While this approach is still under development, a recent analysis of the computer market [6] has demonstrated its feasibility. We would speculate that this conceptualization of the product life cycle will receive increased attention, particularly in the analysis of industrial markets. In our judgment it provides a more meaningful and detailed portrayal of change than that described by empirical representations of growth curves.

Market Segmentation

A second area of potential application for nonmetric scaling methods is market segmentation. Suppose one could characterize a product class and its buyers as points in a similarities-preference space whose dimensions are perceived product characteristics. Each brand could be represented as a stimulus point and each buyer as an ideal point in the same attribute space. Actually, however, this would be a "superspace" in the sense that different buyers may perceive the same stimuli differently as well as occupy different ideal point positions in the space which is perceived.

Conceptually, then, a market segment might be viewed as a subspace in which all members:

1. Perceive the stimuli similarly, and
2. Possess the "same" ideal point position and dimension saliences.

We could, of course, also have the other two cases where: (a) individuals exhibit similar perceptions but possess differing dimension saliences and/or ideal point positions; and (b) neither stimulus perception nor ideal point position nor dimension salience is common over individuals.[2] Further, we might be interested

---

[2]We omit the fourth case of commonality of preference and differences in perception. Here we shall assume that the arguments of the preference function are the (possibly differentially weighted) perceived dimensions. Some dimensions may, of course, receive zero weight in the context of preference.

in the relationship of stimulus and ideal point position to other characteristics of the buyer, e.g., the usual socioeconomic, personality, and demographic variables [10].

Partitioning the superspace of ideal points and stimuli into reasonably homogeneous subspaces—and identifying the characteristics of consumers who exhibit commonality of perception and preference—appears to be in the spirit of market segmentation strategy. Perhaps such analyses would show "empty regions" where high concentrations of ideal points exist but no close brands are found. At the very least, the analysis should point out the competitive position of a firm's brand with other brands as viewed *perceptually* by different market segments—regardless of the brand's similarity with respect to physical or chemical characteristics.

From the marketer's point of view, the task is to modify his product, package, advertising, etc., for the purposes of either: (a) moving his brand toward some region in the space which has a high "concentration" of ideal points; or (b) attempting to move the ideal points themselves toward his brand. We might also conceive of the possibility of reorienting the whole configuration, including its dimensions, as might be the case in truly "innovative" brands. Or the manufacturer might try to move consumers (through "identification with reference group" advertising) from an unfavorable market segment to a favorable one.

Again, this approach is highly speculative, but appears provocative enough for further study and small-scale experimentation. Perhaps it is not too fool-hardy to speculate that such spatial representations might even be tracked through time—a perceptual and preference characterization analogous to a Nielsen-type audit of goods movement.

Allied with the above approach is the potential use of multidimensional scaling in intracorporate research. Do the advertising department, field sales, product development staff, and the firm's distributors have *congruent* images of the company's product or service? If so, do these perceptions agree with those of the ultimate buyer's? If not, what are the implications of such in-consistency for the effectiveness of interrelated policy decisions regarding pricing, advertising theme, product design, and distribution practice?

Vendor Evaluations

Another intriguing area for potential application may be found in the empirical estimation of "evaluation functions." By this is meant the weights that people use to derive simple preference orders from partially ordered alternatives. As an example, consider the industrial purchasing agent who must choose among alternative vendors. Vendor A may be low in price, fair on maintaining delivery promises, poor in technical service, and low in technical innovation. Vendor B might be high in price but excellent on delivery promises, and so on.

Each vendor might be characterized as a vector of dimension "scores," only the individual components of which can be ordered across alternatives.

Clearly, purchasing agents (and other decision makers) somehow "collapse" partially ordered alternatives into complete (overall) orders—they must do so, at least implicitly, so as to make a choice. What we would like to find out are the implicit weights which make up the evaluation function. Are some characteristics suppressed entirely, are strong interactions evident—in short, what is the relative importance of each characteristic and how do these weights differ among individuals and over time? Such knowledge would be undoubtedly useful in the design of vendor sales strategies.

To date, relatively little marketing research has been devoted to the evaluation function problem, although a pilot study [18] has demonstrated its feasibility.

Advertising Evaluation

The perennial problem of ad pretesting might also be profitably explored by the use of multidimensional scaling methods. Several basic questions come to mind: (a) Are "good" ads more similar to each other than "good" ads are to "bad" ads? (b) Do predictive experts (advertising personnel) exhibit interperson reliability in making similarity judgments? (c) What are the dimensions along which ads are judged, and their respective saliences in contributing to overall similarity or overall preference?

To the authors' knowledge, no extensive work on the use of nonmetric methods in ad pretesting has appeared, although a small scale study of the problem has been completed [7]. Again, we would speculate that nonmetric methodology might be useful in this area—and in the more general field of communication.

Related to the above comments is the question of media selection strategy. One early application [8] was concerned with developing medical journal and physician readership profiles. Nonmetric scaling was used to develop both journal configurations—in which those medical journals "near" each other in the space tended to "go together" in terms of physician readership—and, conversely, physician profiles in terms of journal readership. In addition, physician readership profiles were related to their prescribing activity in an attempt to determine correspondence between these two classes of behavior.

Studies such as the above could be extended to the problem of advertisement and vehicle matching. For example, what advertisements seem to "go with" what magazines? One could investigate this problem through content analysis or through experiments in which the consumer is asked to match specific advertisements with specific magazines. The incidence of such matchings could be taken as a measure of the commonality of specific types of advertisements and specific types of vehicles. This approach might be useful in getting some quantitative feel for the "vehicle effect" in media selection strategy; again, a pilot study has indicated its feasibility [9].

Test Marketing

Another problem area of significance to corporate strategy is test marketing. Multidimensional scaling methods may be employed both as guides to research and development of new products and in the prediction of market share for new entrants.

In the first case, similarities and preference mapping could be used to characterize the perceived structure of the product class and to identify clusters of ideal points. The position of a firm's current brand in this space would indicate which brands represent nearest competitors. Moreover, ideal point clusters (with few surrounding products) could suggest opportunities for new product development.

Candidate products could then be evaluated on a test basis by having buyers compare them to existing brands in order to see how product changes are actually perceived. The proportion of preferences going to each new brand would represent an indicant of its commercial success [16]. Moreover, additional information could be ascertained regarding those existing brands (including the firm's current brand) most likely to lose market share to the new entrant.

Salesman and Store Image Research

In some product classes the influence of the company salesman may be dominant in the choice of suppliers. Multidimensional scaling techniques would appear to be just as applicable to the perception of corporate sales representatives as they are to the perception of brands. It would be interesting to find out if the image which the salesman projects to the prospective client is consistent with that resulting from other corporate efforts. The question of congruence (or lack thereof) may present important implications for marketing planning and the coordination of promotional activities.

Similar remarks pertain to image research in the area of distribution channels. What is the dealer's image of the brand and the consumer's image of both brand and dealer? Disparateness of image at various links in the distribution chain may adversely affect ultimate sales and distributor relations. Such incongruity of image could be ascertained via multidimensional scaling methods.

Brand Switching Research

Considerable interest has been generated over the past few years on the phenomenon of buyer brand switching. The availability of large-scale panel data has provided the means for studying brand switching patterns quantitatively.

It might be of interest to couple studies of brand switching with ·those of similarities and preference analysis. Do brand switchers perceive products differently from brand loyal consumers? What are the characteristics of preference structures for both brand switching and brand loyal types? Similar questions relate to "opinion leaders" and other indirect influences on brand choice.

Attitude Scaling

The use of attitude scaling is quite common in marketing research. Attitude scales are often developed on a rather *ad hoc* basis by gathering a large number of statements and then asking "judges" to group them into ordered categories which purport to measure the intensity of each statement along an assumed underlying attitude continuum. However, the possibility exists that the statements may tap various portions of an attitude *space* of two or more dimensions rather than represent intensity levels of a single unidimensional scale.

In such cases, multidimensional scaling techniques could be used to develop the appropriate dimensionality and configuration of the attitude space. For example, one could obtain judgments of the following type: assume a person agrees strongly with statement A; how likely is it that he will also agree strongly with statement B? With statement C? and so on. From the similarities data developed from statement pairs, one could construct a multidimensional configuration of the statements and attempt to interpret the dimensions of this configuration as various components of the multidimensional attitude space. If desired, one could then select subsets of statements whose positions in the space could be approximated by a unidimensional scale.

Of course, all of the above areas of application are mentioned only suggestively and speculatively. Little marketing research using similarities and preference mapping has been published as yet. It is primarily in the spirit of getting more people to think about application areas that the above topics have been suggested.

SUMMARY

In this chapter we have tried to portray some of the central notions of measurement theory, attribute space, and similarities-preference mapping in an intuitive manner, emphasizing such applied problem areas as market segmentation, product life cycle analysis, and test marketing. We leave to later chapters a more formal discussion of the methodology itself. This chapter has been primarily motivational in intent but, it is hoped, suggestive of the breadth of possible applications of multidimensional scaling procedures to the study of marketing behavior.

REFERENCES

1. J. F. Bennett and W. L. Hays, "Multidimensional Unfolding: Determining the Dimensionality of Ranked Preference Data," *Psychometrika*, Vol. 25 (1960), pp. 27–43.

2. C. H. Coombs, "Psychological Scaling Without a Unit of Measurement," *Psychological Review*, Vol. 57 (1950), pp. 148–58.

3. C. H. Coombs, *A Theory of Data* (New York: John Wiley & Sons, 1964).

4. P. E. Green and F. J. Carmone, "Perceptual Structure of Graduate Business Schools—An Application of Multidimensional Scaling," working paper, University of Pennsylvania, June 1967.

5. P. E. Green and F. J. Carmone, "Perceptual and Preference Mapping of Professional Journals," working paper, University of Pennsylvania, May 1967.

6. P. E. Green and F. J. Carmone, "The Performance Structure of the Computer Market—A Multivariate Approach," *Economics and Business Bulletin*, Vol. 21 (Fall 1968), pp. 1–11.

7. P. E. Green and F. J. Carmone, "Advertisement Perception and Evaluation: An Application of Multidimensional Scaling," working paper, University of Pennsylvania, May 1968.

8. P. E. Green and F. J. Carmone, "A Reduced Space and Cluster Analysis of Physicians' Media Reading Habits," working paper, University of Pennsylvania, September 1967.

9. P. E. Green, F. J. Carmone, and P. J. Robinson, "A Comparison of Perceptual Mapping Via Confusions Data and Direct Similarity Judgments," in R. L. King (ed.), Proceedings of the Denver Conference of the American Marketing Association (Chicago: American Marketing Association, 1968), pp. 323–34.

10. P. E. Green and T. W. Morris, "Individual Differences Models in Multidimensional Scaling: An Empirical Comparison," working paper, University of Pennsylvania, April 1969.

11. P. E. Green and D. S. Tull, *Research for Marketing Decisions* (Englewood Cliffs, N. J.: Prentice-Hall, 1966), Chapter 7.

12. F. L. Klingberg, "Studies in Measurement of the Relations Among Sovereign States," *Psychometrika*, Vol. 6 (December 1941), pp. 335–52.

13. R. D. Luce and J. W. Tukey, "Simultaneous Conjoint Measurement: A New Type of Fundamental Measurement," *Journal of Mathematical Psychology*, Vol. 1 (1964), pp. 1–27.

14. M. W. Richardson, "Multidimensional Psychophysics," *Psychological Bulletin*, Vol. 35 (1938), pp. 659–60.

15. R. N. Shepard, "The Analysis of Proximities: Multidimensional Scaling with an Unknown Distance Function," Part One, *Psychometrika*, Vol. 27 (1962), pp. 125–39.

16. Volney Stefflre, "Market Structure Studies: New Products for Old Markets and New Markets (Foreign) for Old Products," in Frank Bass, C. M. King, and E. A. Pessemier (eds.), *Applications of the Sciences in Marketing Management* (New York: John Wiley & Sons, Inc., 1960).

17. W. S. Torgerson, *Theory and Methods of Scaling* (New York: John Wiley & Sons, Inc., 1958).

18. Yoram Wind, P. E. Green, and P. J. Robinson, "The Determinants of Vendor Selection: The Evaluation Function Approach," *Journal of Purchasing*, Vol. 4 (August 1968), pp. 29–41.

19. G. Young and A. S. Householder, "Discussion of a Set of Points in Terms of Their Mutual Distances," *Psychometrika*, Vol. 3 (March 1938), pp. 19–22.

CHAPTER TWO

A Classification of Data and Scaling Techniques

This chapter begins a more formal discussion of multidimensional scaling techniques, the type of discussion which is continued in subsequent chapters. As suggested earlier, behavioral data will be viewed as relations on points in some type of geometric space. Stimuli (brands, etc.) are typically represented as points in the space, and relationships between stimuli as distances in the space. Historically, the geometric "space" involved only one-dimensional scales, but recent developments have extended scaling methodology to handle higher dimensional spaces.

In the first section of the chapter we discuss multidimensional scaling fundamentals in terms of *dominance* and *consonance* relations on subsets of entities drawn from the same or different sets. Our emphasis on portraying these relations geometrically leads to a discussion of distance functions, including, but not restricted to, Euclidean distances.

We then turn to a discussion of classes of data, as formulated elegantly and succinctly by Coombs. Each of Coombs' four major classes of data are described in turn and illustrated with examples drawn from the behavioral field. This section concludes with a discussion of the major types of data matrices and the classes of data implied by these matrices.

With the preceding framework in mind, we then review, in somewhat more detail than in the previous chapter, the various types of multidimensional scaling approaches—fully metric, fully nonmetric, and nonmetric. We show conceptually how nonmetric scaling can "convert" ordinally scaled dissimilarities into metrically scaled distances. The chapter concludes with a somewhat more technical discussion of one (illustrative) algorithm which has been developed to execute this task.

MULTIDIMENSIONAL SCALING FUNDAMENTALS

All of the scaling techniques that we shall be discussing in this chapter deal with *relations* on elements or pairs of elements. The elements can be characteristics of stimuli, people, or both. As described by Coombs [3], the two basic relations which characterize psychological data are:

1. Dominance—in this case we *order* (strictly) the set of elements with respect to some property level, as would be the case where we are asked to rank a set of fruit drinks in terms of their tartness. For each pair of elements A and B (e.g., fruit drinks) we are asked to say which of the following is true:

   A is "higher" than B with respect to property X

   B is "higher" than A with respect to property X

2. Consonance—in this case we attempt to see if two elements *match* with respect to some property level, as would be the case where we are asked to say whether two fruit drinks are alike (or different) in terms of tartness. For each pair of elements A and B we are asked to say which of the following is true:

   A equals B with respect to property X

   A is not equal to B with respect to property X

It is perhaps surprising that virtually all scaling studies involve one or the other of the above tasks. For example, the collection of preference data (if no ties are allowed) is an instance of employing the dominance relation, but so may be the scaling of aptitude scores in which, for example, an arithmetic problem is "passed" by a subject if and only if he possesses more of the aptitude than the level being tapped by the problem. Data obtained from consonance relationships are no less prevalent—rating a product as falling in the category of "superior quality" can imply that the perceived attribute level of the product and that of the label, superior quality, represent the best match of the alternative response categories available to the subject.[1] Finally, if one permits ties in the preference ordering, one obtains both dominance and consonance relations on the same data set.

The concept of dominance or ordering implies a common unidimensional continuum for any pair of elements so that the terms "precedes" or "is higher than" have meaning. The notion of consonance or matching can also be construed as an interval along a continuum *within* which the subject is willing to assume that all points are indistinguishable.

So far it would seem that we are dealing with unidimensional scales rather than multidimensional ones. However, as we shall soon see, we may find it useful to characterize stimuli or people in several dimensions in a geometrical space. The ordering (or matching) of *distances between pairs of points provides the appropriate unidimensional continuum (viz., "distance") which leads to the construction of multidimensional configurations.*

An Example

To illustrate, assume that an individual is asked to make certain preference judgments about various automobile models. **Figure 2-1** shows a "picture" of

---

[1]Of course, one could say that the *agreement* between product and label is greater than that of the same product and any other label in the set; under this interpretation, a dominance relation is appropriate. Thus, an element of possible ambiguity exists in the use of the terms "dominance" and "consonance."

FIGURE 2-1

ILLUSTRATION OF SIMILARITIES-PREFERENCE SPACE OF IDEAL
POINTS AND STIMULI

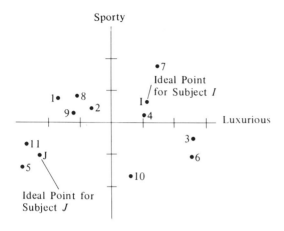

Stimuli—1968 Car Models

1. Ford Mustang 6
2. Mercury Cougar V8
3. Lincoln Continental V8
4. Ford Thunderbird V8
5. Ford Falcon 6
6. Chrysler Imperial V8
7. Jaguar Sedan
8. AMC Javelin V8
9. Plymouth Barracuda V8
10. Buick Le Sabre V8
11. Chevrolet Corvair

his response.[2] Assume that for this subject only two characteristics of cars—their degree of "luxuriousness" and their degree of "sportiness"—are important in his evaluative judgments. His *ideal point*, a concept first proposed by Coombs, is assumed to be located at point I, in the upper right quadrant of the chart. By "ideal point" is meant a hypothetical car model possessing just that combination of luxuriousness and sportiness represented by the amounts measured on each dimension of the chart, which he most prefers.

Let us imagine "measuring" the distance between each car model and the person's ideal point in this two-dimensional space by constructing a series of rods of varying lengths connecting the points. Next, let us lay out these eleven distances two at a time on a unidimensional "distance" continuum. In so doing we can compare the length of each rod with every other and, ultimately, rank their lengths. Note that in this instance the rod connecting the ideal point *I* with *Ford Falcon* is longest.

By using interpoint distances as our unidimensional scale—the relation is on *pairs of pairs* of points—we can depict either dominance or consonance relations. For example, we may say that individual *I* prefers *Thunderbird* to *Cougar* if the distance from point *I* to the point labeled *Thunderbird* is less than that from point *I* to the point labeled *Cougar*. That is, we could postulate that individuals will prefer real items whose combination of attribute levels is closer to their ideal point to those items whose combinations are farther away.

By the same token, we can compare the relative similarities of pairs of real cars in terms of their interpoint distances. For example, *Continental* and *Imperial* could be said to be more "similar" to each other than, say, *Jaguar* and *Mustang* if the distance connecting the former pair is less than that connecting the latter.

[2] This illustration is based on a study by P. E. Green, Arun Maheshwari, and V. R. Rao, "Dimensional Interpretation and Configuration Invariance in Multidimensional Scaling," *Multivariate Behavioral Research*, Vol. 4 (April 1969), pp. 159-80.

Notice, further, that a consonance relation can be described in this illustration. We do this by assuming some small difference in distances, $\Delta_{i, \, jk}$, such that if the (absolute) *difference* in distances between ideal point I, for example, and *Thunderbird* (j) and ideal point I and *Cougar* (k) is less than $\Delta_{i, \, jk}$, then the individual is not able to state a preference. The (absolute) quantity, $\Delta_{i, \, jk}$, can be viewed as individual I's perceptual threshhold.

Many assumptions have been introduced in our discussion of the above example. It seems appropriate now to discuss the nature of some of these assumptions from a somewhat more formal point of view.

The Properties of Distance Functions

Earlier we elected to view psychological data as relations—those of dominance or consonance—on pairs of points (or, alternatively, on pairs of pairs of points) in a metric space. The points could all be from the same set (e.g., real car models) or from different sets (e.g., an ideal car model versus real car models). But what do we mean by a *metric* space?

A metric space [1] is one in which there exists a well-defined distance function which possesses the following properties: for any points x, y and z,

1. $d(x, x) = 0$ and $d(x, y) > 0$ the distance between a point and itself is zero, while the distance between distinct points is positive.

2. $d(x, y) = d(y, x)$ distance must be symmetric.

3. $d(x, y) \leqslant d(x, z) + d(z, y)$ the distance from point x to point y must be less than or equal to the distance from x to y indirectly through point z. This property is known as the triangle inequality.

Euclidean Distances. In order to examine the additional properties of an important subclass of metrics—namely, vector forms—let us introduce an elementary formula for finding the distance between two points in the Euclidean plane. We recall from elementary geometry that the distance between two points i and j in the plane is given by:

$$d_{ij} = [(x_{i1} - x_{j1})^2 + (x_{i2} - x_{j2})^2]^{1/2}$$

That is, we first compute the difference of each pair of points on each dimension, in turn, and square the differences. We then add these two squared differences together and finally take the square root of the result. **Figure 2-2a** illustrates this procedure in terms of the Pythagorean theorem of high school geometry. This set of operations leads to two additional properties shared by all distance functions, Euclidean or otherwise, which are general Minkowski metrics (see below).

1. The distance between two points depends only on the (absolute) *differences* $|x_{i1} - x_{j1}|$ and $|x_{i2} - x_{j2}|$ in their coordinates, dimension by dimension. The distance between two points is not altered when both points are shifted by the same amount in the same direction (since this constant would drop out

when differences are taken). This is known as the property of *translation invariance*, i.e., an interval scale is appropriate for describing the scales (axes), as shown in **Figure 2-2c**.

2. If we next imagine two points lying on a vector going through the origin O (see **Figure 2-2d**) where point i has coordinates x_{i1} and x_{i2} and point j has coordinates ax_{i1} and ax_{i2} (where $a > 0$), then the distance of point j from the origin O is

$$d(O, j) = a\,[d(O, i)]$$

This is known as the *homogeneity* property.

FIGURE 2-2
ILLUSTRATION OF SELECTED PROPERTIES OF (EUCLIDEAN)
DISTANCE FUNCTION

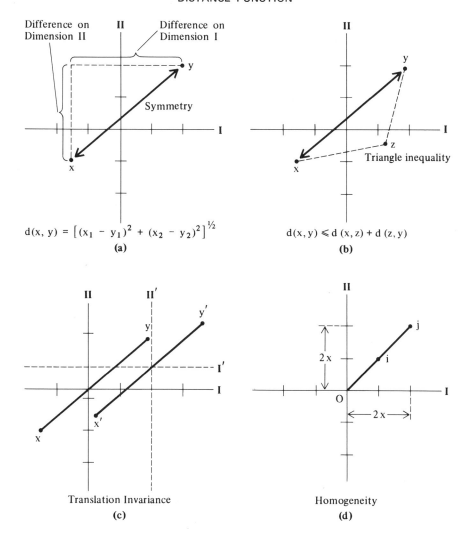

$$d(x, y) = \left[(x_1 - y_1)^2 + (x_2 - y_2)^2\right]^{1/2}$$

(a)

$$d(x, y) \leqslant d(x, z) + d(z, y)$$

(b)

Translation Invariance
(c)

Homogeneity
(d)

Although our high school geometry lessons concentrated on two dimensions, it should be pointed out that the Euclidean distance between a pair of points generalizes easily to more than two dimensions by the formula:

$$d_{ij} = \left[\sum_{k=1}^{r} (x_{ik} - x_{jk})^2 \right]^{1/2}$$

where we square each difference in coordinates on dimension $k(k = 1, 2, \ldots, r)$, add these quantities up and finally take the square root of the total.[3]

Other Distance Functions. While we are most familiar with the Euclidean distance function, it turns out that other distance functions obey the five properties described above. For example, if we can move only from point i to point j in the four main compass directions of north, south, east, and west, the type of distance so defined is called the *city block metric*. The distance between two points under this metric is merely the sum of the absolute difference of their projections on each separate dimension. This function and the Euclidean distance function are but special cases of a still more general function, the Minkowski p-metric [9], which still possesses the five properties enumerated earlier. (The Euclidean distance, however, is the only one which satisfies rotational invariance.)

The Minkowski p-metric can be written as:

$$d_{ij}(p) = \left[\sum_{k=1}^{r} \left| x_{ik} - x_{jk} \right|^p \right]^{1/p} ; p \geqslant 1$$

We require $p \geqslant 1$ so as to satisfy the triangle inequality. When $p = 1$ we have the city block metric; when $p = 2$ we have the familiar Euclidean metric. While most applications have involved the Euclidean metric, it is appropriate to point out that many nonmetric multidimensional scaling programs provide the flexibility to fit any type of Minkowski p-metric to the data.

Isosimilarity Contours

It is of interest to examine the type of isosimilarity contours implied by various special cases of the Minkowski p-metric. By "isosimilarity" is meant those points which are equal with respect to their similarity to a given reference point. **Figure 2-3** shows graphically the kind of notion we have in mind. For example, suppose we were working with the Euclidean metric. Points one unit distant from the center (reference point) all lie on the circumference of a circle with unit radius. On the other hand, the city block metric leads to a diamond-shaped isosimilarity contour. Finally, if we let p approach infinity, the isosimilarity contour approaches the square. In this case the *largest* difference,

---

[3]As Beckenbach and Bellman [1, p. 100] point out, the Euclidean measure also has the unique property of rotational invariance—in this example we can rotate the configuration through some angle around the origin without altering the interpoint distances.

FIGURE 2-3

ISOSIMILARITY CONTOURS FOR SELECTED MINKOWSKI *P*-METRICS

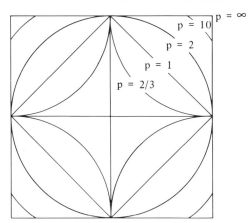

dimension by dimension, would receive all the weight in the computation of interpoint distance.

At the other extreme, if the concave pattern (for $p = \frac{2}{3}$) of Figure 2-3 were operative we would be dealing with the case where the triangle inequality was violated; hence, we would not have a metric space.

The implied weights given to the various differences on each dimension are also of interest. Only the city block metric gives equal weight to each dimensional difference. The more familiar Euclidean metric actually weights the differences on each dimension by the differences themselves. That is, large differences will receive greater weight than small differences in contributing to the overall distance between two points. In general, the distance $d_{ij(p)}$ in a Minkowski *p*-metric may be viewed as a weighted sum where each component difference, $|x_{ik} - x_{jk}|$, is weighted by its own size, raised to the $p - 1$ power [3]. As *p* approaches infinity, only the *largest* difference on any dimension contributes to the interpoint distance $d_{ij(p=\infty)}$. The square, shown in Figure 2-3, illustrates this case.

We can also see, in the case of two dimensions, why interpoint distance—with the exception of the Euclidean case—is not invariant under rotation. As can be noted from Figure 2-3, a rotation of 45° would change the city block metric ($p = 1$) into the "supremum" metric ($p = \infty$) if the scalar multiplier $\sqrt{2}$ were used; that is, the metric would no longer be unique [3]. (We shall return to a discussion of the rotational "freedom" provided by the Euclidean metric in subsequent chapters.)

COOMBSIAN DATA CLASSIFICATION

Now that we have commented on some of the representational aspects of data as relations on points in a metric space, our attention turns to the *classes* of psychological data that can be so represented. We have already used in our previous discussion three descriptors by which data can be organized:

1. Whether the relation is one of dominance or consonance.
2. Whether the points are from one set (e.g., stimuli) or from two different sets (e.g., people's ideal points and stimuli).
3. Whether the relation is on a pair of points or on a pair of pairs of points (e.g., an order relation on psychological "distances").

Coombs [3] uses the latter two descriptors to develop an elegant and parsimonious classification system by means of which he can classify various types of scaling techniques, either of a unidimensional or a multidimensional type. (Descriptor 1 is then used to distinguish various types of data *within* each of the four cells.) **Figure 2-4** shows Coombs' fourfold classification scheme using the second and third of the above dichotomous descriptors. In illustrating the four quadrants we will focus on dominance relations, but the reader should bear in mind that consonance relations could be established as well on each of the four data classes.

FIGURE 2-4

FOUR MAIN QUADRANTS OF THE COOMBSIAN CLASSIFICATION SYSTEM

	Pairs of Points	*Pairs of Pairs*
Points From Two Different Sets	*Quadrant II* Single Stimulus	*Quadrant I* Preferential Choice
Points From Same Set	*Quadrant III* Stimulus Comparison	*Quadrant IV* Similarities

Source: Adapted from C. H. Coombs, *A Theory of Data* (New York: John Wiley & Sons, 1964), p. 21 and p. 28.

Quadrant I Data

Data in this quadrant are characterized as involving relations on pairs of pairs of points (e.g., relations involving "distances") from two different sets. To illustrate, let us return to the spatial representation of the subject I's ideal point and the set of stimuli (automobile models), positioned in a common metric space whose dimensions are assumed to represent salient attributes which underlie his *evaluative judgments*.

If we again assume that subject I's ideal point is positioned at point I in **Figure 2-1** and that the subject prefers *Thunderbird* over *Continental* if and only if *Thunderbird* is nearer his ideal point than *Continental*, then we can say we are treating preference data as relations (in this case dominance relations) on pairs of pairs of points (with one member of each pair having a point in common, namely, the ideal point) drawn from two different sets. Such pairs of pairs of points are interpreted as defining pairs of psychological distances. If this model holds, we would expect to find the preference ordering: *Thunderbird, Cougar, . . . , Corvair, Ford Falcon*, in the order most to least preferred.

Some other individual, however, may most like a particular combination of the two attributes of luxuriousness and sportiness which places him nearest to *Corvair* (say, at point *J* in Figure 2-1). If so, *Corvair* would be most preferred and *Continental* would be least preferred, according to the previous argument.

Quadrant I, then, provides a way of characterizing preference data which is capable of handling a diversity of preferences over individuals for the same set of stimuli. Individual differences in preference orders are handled by assuming different ideal point locations. This lack of commonality of preferences is typically observed in marketing research (or, for that matter, behavioral science generally) and constitutes the empirical basis which underlies the concept of a *joint* space of stimuli and ideal (or "person") points.

Quadrant II Data

Quadrant II data are typed by Coombs as relations on pairs of points from two different sets. To illustrate the characteristics of data described by this quadrant, suppose we had a set of attitude statements regarding the brand, Product A. Each statement is presumed to tap a different degree of "favorableness of attitude toward Product A."

In practice, a large number of individuals (presumably with differences in their favorableness of attitude) would be asked to participate in the attitude survey. If the universe of content is scalable along a unidimensional continuum, we would expect any person possessing a higher degree of favorableness of attitude than is being tapped by a given statement to respond favorably to the statement. Those possessing less would be assumed to respond unfavorably.[4]

The objective of *single stimulus* data—in which the stimuli (e.g., attitude statements) are presented singly for evaluation by the subject—is to arrange both person points and statement points along a *single* continuum ranging from, say, "very unfavorable" to "very favorable." Such a joint scale of statements and people may only be ordinal. While representations of Quadrant II data are not constrained solely to unidimensional scales, most of the applications to date—e.g., of Guttman scalogram analysis [8]—have involved assumptions of unidimensionality.

Quadrant III Data

Data in this quadrant are characterized by relations on pairs of points drawn from the same set. An illustration of this class of data is Thurstone's law of comparative judgment [11] which, again, typically leads to a unidimensional (in this case interval) scale. The scale is developed from the frequencies of response with

[4]We are assuming that the statements are phrased "monotonically" [3].

which each element of a stimulus pair is asserted to possess more of some pre-designated property than the other member of the pair.

There is no need to review here the mechanics of Thurstonian comparative judgment scaling. For purposes of Coombsian data theory we note that a basic assumption of the Thurstonian model is that the individual says "i dominates j" if and only if the (momentary) magnitude of the person's "discriminal process" associated with stimulus i exceeds that associated with stimulus j. Such differences in magnitude are assumed to be normally distributed, and the individual, on any specific trial, is also assumed to have selected one "difference" from that distribution.

We note, then, that both Q-II and Q-III data, involving relations on pairs of points, often lead to unidimensional scales.[5] These two classes of data constituted the main focus of earlier research in scaling techniques, but are less relevant for the objectives of this monograph than Quadrants I and IV.

Quadrant IV Data

Coombs calls Q-IV data "similarities," a way of suggesting that this class of data involves the structure of appearance—how people perceive stimuli as being similar or different. Such data involve relations on pairs of pairs of points from the same set (usually stimuli). Similarities data are the kinds of data that would be obtained if a subject were asked to indicate which of the following pairs of automobile models is more similar:

Continental and *Imperial*, or

Falcon and *Barracuda*

Notice here that the criteria constituting "overall similarity" are left to the subject, i.e., no attempt is made to specify a particular criterion by which the relative similarity of the two pairs is to be judged. This class of data enables the analyst to develop "perceptual" maps of stimuli, the dimensions of which are assumed to represent the attributes along which each stimulus is compared. In some cases a single attribute will be involved, but in other cases, a multidimensional characterization of the data is more appropriate.

The focus of this monograph will be on Q-IV and Q-I data which deal, respectively, with the structure of perception and evaluation. Moreover, we shall show that Q-IV and Q-I representations will often (but not necessarily) be multidimensional rather than unidimensional.

Proximity Matrices

A complementary way to organize classes of data is to describe the various types of data matrices with which we shall be dealing. Coombs [3] considers

---

[5] Some care should be taken in interpreting this statement. As we shall see in later chapters, multidimensional scales *can* be constructed from either Q-II or Q-III data, e.g., representations obtained from the factor analysis of Q-II data. Moreover, one can obtain *unidimensional* scales in the analysis of Q-I and Q-IV data.

four main types of proximity matrices, a proximity being defined as an empirical measure of closeness or similarity between pairs of pairs of points (what we have also called, as anti-proximity measures, "psychological distance"). However, we shall use the term proximities in a *generic* sense to cover similarities or dissimilarities.

The four major types of proximity matrices are best represented in diagram form, as shown in **Figure 2-5**. To start off with the simplest case first, suppose

FIGURE 2-5
MAJOR TYPES OF PROXIMITY MATRICES

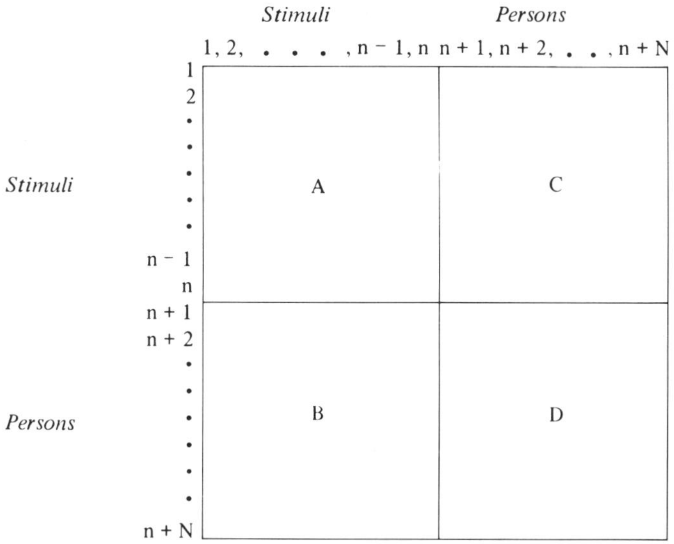

we had a single individual rank all $\frac{1}{2} n(n-1)$ distinct pairs of n items on the basis of similarity of the pairs. This type of proximity matrix is represented by the submatrix A in Figure 2-5. It would be called an *intact, unconditional* proximity matrix. The matrix is intact in the sense that each cell (excluding the main diagonal) has an entry which involves comparisons over items drawn from the same set. It is unconditional in the sense that each cell—above or below the main diagonal, since we also assume that the matrix is symmetric— can be compared to any other. (Unconditional matrices need *not* be symmetrical, however.)

Now consider the possibility that a single person merely ranked the remaining $n-1$ stimuli in terms of decreasing similarity to each row stimulus serving, in turn, as a reference item. In this case only cell entries *within* each row of the submatrix A are comparable. This would be called an *intact, conditional* proximity matrix. Again the points are drawn from the same set but proximities are comparable only within—not across—rows.

Next, suppose N individuals ranked the same n stimuli (say, on the basis of preference or some other "dominance" relation) as indicated by submatrix B. In this case we are dealing with an *off-diagonal, conditional* proximity matrix where values are comparable only within each row *and* the pairs of points are drawn from two different sets. Finally, if we could collect data of the form: individual i prefers stimulus j more than individual i' prefers stimulus j', we would have the case of an *off-diagonal unconditional* proximity matrix. In this case, then, we are assuming interpersonal comparisons of utility. Obviously such data are difficult to justify.

Interestingly enough, intact proximity matrices can be related to Quadrants III and IV in Coombs system (Figure 2-4), while off-diagonal proximity matrices can be related to Quadrants I and II. However, the *same* set of empirical observations can be analyzed from different viewpoints, as based on the researcher's model of the process assumed to underlie the generation of the observations.

Up to this point we have not discussed submatrices C and D where, respectively: (a) stimuli order individuals, and (b) pairs of individuals are ordered. Empirical situations where stimuli order individuals occur, for example, in various types of examination questions or attitude statements. Empirical situations where pairs of individuals may be ordered occur in Q-technique factor analyses and as input data for cluster analyses.

Cases in which *all* cell entries of the "supermatrix" are experimentally obtained would be extremely rare. In the usual case (e.g., where preference data of the type illustrated by submatrix B are obtained), the remaining submatrices (A, C, and D) are treated as missing data or "passive cells." Various computer programs can scale the $n + N$ points by using only the constraints which are obtained experimentally (submatrix B). The *derived* interpoint distances for submatrices A, C, and D thus have meaning only if one assumes the model to hold in its complete form. We shall elaborate on a number of these issues and extensions to multi-way matrices in later chapters.

NONMETRIC MULTIDIMENSIONAL SCALING

Our previous discussions of Coombs' classification system and distance functions have been by way of providing a framework for positioning the various techniques of multidimensional scaling—particularly nonmetric methods. As explained, by "nonmetric" we mean that the input data consist only of *ordinal* relations (usually on pairs of pairs of elements) but the output information is metric—interval scaled or stronger.

From our discussion of distance functions and data matrices, the broad objectives of multidimensional scaling should now be evident. We start out with a set of experimentally obtained proximities (similarities, dissimilarities, "psychological distances") and attempt to represent these empirical data geometrically as points in some type of metric space. Of interest are both the dimensionality of that space and the configuration. As will be shown below, the type of algorithm used will depend on what we are willing to assume about the scaling properties of the input data and the type of geometrical model "representing" the empirical relations.

The computer algorithms underlying nonmetric scaling date only from 1962 with publication of Roger Shepard's innovative paper [10]. Since that time a variety of procedures have been developed for converting nonmetric input data into metric output information. In the preceding chapter we discussed briefly the evolution of nonmetric scaling techniques. This earlier discussion is elaborated below.

Fully Metric Methods

As motivation for this discussion, assume that a respondent has been given the task of judging pairs of car names—the models shown in Figure 2-1—in terms of overall similarity. To be more specific, suppose the respondent is shown a set of 55 cards. On each card appear the names of two of the car models; all possible distinct pairs (55) of 11 items appear once. The subject is first asked to place the cards into two classes, namely, pairs of cars which he feels are more or less similar versus pairs of cars which are more or less different, according to criteria of his own choosing.

After this step the subject is asked to separate the "similar" pile into two subpiles—highly similar car pairs and somewhat similar car pairs. He is then asked to make two subpiles of the "different" pile—somewhat different pairs and highly different pairs of car models. Each subpile may then contain about 12 to 15 cards.

The subject is then asked to choose the most highly similar pair *within* the highly similar subpile, then the next most similar pair, until all cards in the first subpile are ranked. He then ranks the pairs in subpiles two, three, and four. (Before settling on this final ranking he is allowed to shift cards from subpile to subpile if he so desires.) By means of this stepwise procedure a simple rank order of the 55 car pairs is eventually obtained; one such rank order is shown in **Table 2-1**.

TABLE 2-1
RANK ORDER OF DISSIMILARITIES BETWEEN PAIRS OF CAR MODELS*

Stimuli	1	2	3	4	5	6	7	8	9	10	11
1	—	8	50	31	12	48	36	2	5	39	10
2		—	38	9	33	37	22	6	4	14	32
3			—	11	55	1	23	46	41	17	52
4				—	44	13	16	19	25	18	42
5					—	54	53	30	28	45	7
6						—	26	47	40	24	51
7							—	29	35	34	49
8								—	3	27	15
9									—	20	21
10										—	43
11											—

*The rank number "1" represents the most similar pair.

Now suppose, for a moment, that the 55 rank numbers ("1," most similar, to "55," least similar) are more "strongly" scaled than just ranks; that is, let us assume that the data of Table 2-1 really represent *ratio-scaled distances*. This is the crucial assumption of fully metric methods.[6] These methods use ratio-scaled distances to find a configuration (in Euclidean space) whose interpoint distances are proportional to these.

As shown earlier, it is a simple matter to compute interpoint Euclidean distances between all pairs of points *if we know their coordinates*, i.e., the configuration. The converse, however, is not so easy and represents the principal task of fully metric methods: given a set of interpoint distances, find the dimensionality and configuration of points whose distances most closely match the input values. In our usual appeal for parsimony, we would, of course, like to do this in the smallest possible number of dimensions.

Computational methods for finding the desired configuration entail the factor analysis of distances converted into scalar products. The techniques yield a configuration whose interpoint distances come as close as possible to reproducing (up to a positive proportionality transformation) the *numerical* values of Table 2-1.

Figure 2-6 shows the configuration resulting from the application of fully metric methods to the data of Table 2-1. Note that is is quite similar to the configuration of Figure 2-1 which, as we shall show, was obtained by a *non-metric* procedure from the same input data (but where the data were treated *only* as ranks). The essential point, however, is that fully metric methods assume that the input data are ratio-scaled distances. In turn, they yield metric

FIGURE 2-6

FULLY METRIC SCALING SOLUTION BASED ON DATA OF TABLE 2-1

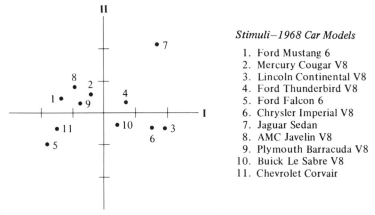

Stimuli—1968 Car Models

1. Ford Mustang 6
2. Mercury Cougar V8
3. Lincoln Continental V8
4. Ford Thunderbird V8
5. Ford Falcon 6
6. Chrysler Imperial V8
7. Jaguar Sedan
8. AMC Javelin V8
9. Plymouth Barracuda V8
10. Buick Le Sabre V8
11. Chevrolet Corvair

[6]Fully metric methods can take interval-scaled data and estimate an "additive constant" which makes the data ratio-scaled [11]. In any event, the "final" input data are assumed to be ratio-scaled distances; solutions are invariant up to *linear* transformations of the *original* data, however.

output information, namely, the type of configuration illustrated by Figure 2-6. If we were to compute the interpoint distances of all pairs of points in Figure 2-6—and if the configuration were a perfect fit to the data—the resulting numbers would *equal* those of Table 2-1 up to a positive proportionality transformation.

What happens, however, if we *cannot* assume that the subject is able to report ratio-scaled distances? Now suppose, as is reasonable, given the manner in which the data were collected in this example, that the numbers of Table 2-1 merely define a *rank order* of the 55 pairs.

Fully Nonmetric Methods

The above case is precisely the problem that Coombs attacked, namely, how to scale data when one does not assume more than rank order on the input "distances." Coombs [4] and, later, Bennett and Hays [2] addressed themselves to solving the nonmetric problem, both unidimensionally and (subsequently) multidimensionally.

Their approaches are known as *unfolding methods*. The objective of these methods is: given a set of conditional proximities (illustrated by submatrix *B* in Figure 2-5), find a Euclidean space of minimum dimensionality and the *rank order* (in the multidimensional case) of each point on each dimension of the configuration.

But notice here that the output is nonmetric as well. That is, by this approach we *cannot find a configuration,* similar to those shown in Figures 2-1 and 2-6, but only the rank order of the projections of each point on each dimension in turn. What is gained in the use of weaker assumptions about the "quality" of the input data appears to be balanced by the limitations of the solution, viz., rank orders only of point projections.

Moreover, fully nonmetric methods do *not* appear to lend themselves as readily to precise algorithm development as either the fully metric procedures, already discussed, or the nonmetric procedures, to be described next. In a sense, the fully nonmetric methods of Coombs and his colleagues provided a large part of the *conceptual* groundwork for subsequent, computer-based developments. But from an operational point of view the later developments yield more (asymptotically metric output) for the same assumption base (nonmetric input). Thus, we do not consider fully nonmetric methods beyond this point.

Nonmetric Methods

Prior to the publication of Shepard's paper on nonmetric multidimensional scaling, the extant procedures were either fully metric or fully nonmetric. It was Shepard who combined the best of both precursor approaches—rank order input data and metric solutions. Moreover, he provided the first computer algorithm for implementing this objective. (It can truly be said that a necessary condition in the development of *nonmetric* scaling is the availability of high-speed computer processing.)

The objective of nonmetric multidimensional scaling can be stated somewhat nonrigorously as: given a rank order of proximity data (similar to that shown in Table 2-1), find a configuration whose rank order of (ratio-scaled) distances—in a specified dimensionality—best reproduces the original rank order of the input data. As innocuous as this may sound, this objective has spawned a whole series of computer programs which are still being modified and expanded to cover an increasing variety of scaling applications.

The *conceptual* basis of nonmetric scaling, however, is not difficult to grasp intuitively. Let us return to the rank order data of Table 2-1. We note that the table is composed of rank numbers, ranging from the most similar pair, *Continental* and *Imperial* with rank "1," to the least similar pair, *Continental* and *Falcon* with rank "55." As the number of stimuli, n, increases, the number of rank order constraints increases almost with the square of n—actually as $\frac{1}{2}n(n-1)$. However, to portray a set of points in r dimensions we need only rn numbers, namely, the coordinate of each point on each dimension.[7] For example, if $r = 2$, we need only 22 numbers to fix the 11 points. In contrast, we have 55 ranks from the relationships shown in Table 2-1.

As the number of inequalities increases relative to the number of rn numbers needed to specify a configuration, the inequalities serve to restrict the movement of the n points so that with "enough" inequalities we obtain, for all practical purposes, a unique configuration. This means that we have little freedom to move one or more points around without violating at least one of the inequalities. Remember that moving just one point changes its distances with the remaining $n-1$ points.

Shepard demonstrated, via a series of synthetic data analyses, that with as few as 8 points the correlation between the interpoint distances of a known two-space configuration was 0.99, on the average, with the interpoint distances of a configuration constructed by his computer program from rank order information alone [9]. For $n \geqslant 15$ the two configurations were virtually indistinguishable.

A word should be said about what is meant by a "unique" configuration in this context. This means a configuration which can be operated on only by what is known as a *similarity* transform. In the case of the Euclidean metric a similarity transform permits: (a) rotation of the configuration about the origin; (b) translation of the origin (by adding a constant to each coordinate value); (c) reflection (flipping the configuration across one or more axes of the configuration); or (d) uniform stretching (or compression) of the axes. None of these operations will change the rank order of the interpoint distances which, after all, is the constraint under which this class of computer programs operates. That is, for a specified dimensionality the programs try to find a

---

[7]Technically speaking, fewer ($rn - [r(r+1)/2] - 1$) numbers are needed, given the invariance of solutions up to a similarity transformation.

configuration of points whose interpoint distances are monotone—that is, have the same (or possibly the inverse) ranks as the input data.

In general, as one increases the dimensionality of the space, the chances of finding such a configuration increase. As a matter of fact, any set of rank orders (including ties) on pairs of n points can be satisfied by a configuration in $n - 1$ dimensions [2]. The point at issue, however, is to find the *lowest* dimensionality for which the monotonicity constraint is "closely" met. That is, the analyst may wish to trade off the objective of perfect monotonicity for a solution of lower dimensionality whose distances are *almost* monotone with the original rank order data.

Currently, a rather wide variety of computer programs exist for performing various types of nonmetric scaling. We shall be considering many of them in subsequent chapters. We shall primarily emphasize nonmetric methods but shall also discuss fully metric methods where appropriate. The latter set of methods—like fully nonmetric techniques—assume that the distance function is Euclidean, while nonmetric techniques are not so restricted. But in practice the Euclidean function is most often used, and we shall also confine our discussion to that type of metric.

AN ILLUSTRATIVE COMPUTER ALGORITHM

Although we shall be discussing several different nonmetric scaling algorithms in later chapters, it seems useful here to illustrate how a prototypical program works. As will be shown later, most of the programs are quite similar in objective but differ in computational detail. Gleason [5] has pointed out their theoretical correspondences, and we have done a number of comparative Monte Carlo studies which indicate that the algorithms produce quite similar numerical results when applied to a common set of input data. For illustrative purposes we describe Torgerson and Young's TORSCA 8 program [12] as representative of these procedures. We follow their development closely.

For expository purposes assume that we have a set of ranked pairs $\delta_{ij}(i = 1,2,\ldots,n - 1; j = 2,3,\ldots,n)$. We can call the δ_{ij} dissimilarities, or psychological "distances." Our objective is to find a configuration $X = \{x_1,x_2,\ldots,x_n\}$ consisting of n vectors in a space of r dimensions. The coordinates of a given vector x_i can be specified as:

$$x_i = (x_{i1},x_{i2},\ldots,x_{ir})$$

For each x_i, x_j in X we can compute a distance d_{ij}. If X is a "good" configuration in that the ranks of its distances d_{ij} approximately reproduce the input ranks δ_{ij}, then that configuration should be "final" or close thereto for representing the δ_{ij} in a specified dimensionality.

The appropriate numbers (they may not be distances) which *are* perfectly monotone with the δ_{ij} can be denoted as $\hat{d}_{ij}$. The TORSCA algorithm considers, then, relationships among the three sets:

1. The δ_{ij}—the input data ranks.
2. The d_{ij}—computed distances between all pairs of points in the configuration X.
3. The $\hat{d}_{ij}$—a set of ratio-scaled numbers, *chosen to be as close to their respective d_{ij} as possible*, subject to being monotone with the δ_{ij}. That is, $\hat{d}_{ij} < \hat{d}_{kl}$ whenever $\delta_{ij} < \delta_{kl}$

All of these algorithms must then consider two problems: (a) the development of an index of fit by which one can tell if the configuration X is an appropriate one for representing the input data, δ_{ij}; and (b) a procedure for moving the points x_i, x_j to some "better" configuration if the current index of fit is poor.

Index of Fit

Most all of the nonmetric scaling algorithms provide an index of fit which represents some variant of Kruskal's stress measure [6].

$$S = \left[\frac{\sum_{\substack{i \neq j}}^{n} (d_{ij} - \hat{d}_{ij})^2}{\sum_{\substack{i \neq j}} d_{ij}^2} \right]^{1/2}$$

The numerator of this index consists of the sum of squares of the discrepancies between each computed d_{ij} for some configuration X and a set of numbers $\hat{d}_{ij}$ chosen to be as close to their respective d_{ij} as possible, subject to being monotone with the original δ_{ij}'s. If the $\hat{d}_{ij}$ equal their d_{ij} counterparts, the numerator of the expression becomes zero and, hence, stress is also zero, indicating a perfect fit.

The denominator of the expression is merely a normalizing value, computed to allow comparisons of the fit measure across different dimensionalities since, in general, the d_{ij} will increase with increasing dimensionality. More recent versions of the stress formula [7] place the quantity:

$$\sum_{\substack{i \neq j}}^{n} (d_{ij} - \bar{d})^2$$

(where $\bar{d}$ equals the mean distance) in the denominator. While there are theoretical advantages ascribed to this second formulation, in practice both versions of the formula are used.

Suppose, however, that the stress S of a particular configuration is high; that is, the monotonic fit is poor. The next feature of these algorithms consists of finding a new configuration X whose ranks of interpoint distances are more closely monotone to the original δ_{ij} than the previously ranked distances.

Improving the Configuration

Assume now that we wish to move the points around to make their distance ranks closer to the input data ranks than those found in the previous configuration. In particular, consider a specific point i and its relationship to each of the points j in turn. We would like to move the point i so as to decrease the average discrepancy between the distances d_{ij} and the numbers $\hat{d}_{ij}$, the latter set of numbers being monotone with the δ_{ij}.

If d_{ij} is larger than $\hat{d}_{ij}$ we could move point i towards point j by an amount which is proportional to the size of the discrepancy. Conversely, if $\hat{d}_{ij}$ is larger than d_{ij}, then point i is to be moved away from point j by an amount proportional to the discrepancy. Suppose we let α represent the coefficient of proportionality ($0 < \alpha < 1$) or step size. (Often α is set at 0.2.)

To find a new coordinate $x'_{ia(j)}$ for point i on axis a, as related to point j, we can use the formula:

$$x'_{ia(j)} = x_{ia(j)} + \alpha \left(1 - \frac{\hat{d}_{ij}}{d_{ij}} \right)(x_{ja} - x_{ia})$$

The above formula would move point i in the appropriate direction with respect to point j, but we must consider all $n - 1$ points insofar as their effect on point i is concerned.

To do this we merely use the expression

$$x'_{ia} = x_{ia} + \frac{\alpha}{n-1} \sum_{\substack{j \neq 1 \\ j \neq i}}^{n} \left(1 - \frac{\hat{d}_{ij}}{d_{ij}} \right)(x_{ja} - x_{ia})$$

Note that we move point i along axis a in such a way as to take into account the discrepancies involving all other points. This is, of course, done for all points in all dimensions.

The procedure can be summarized, then, as involving the following steps:

1. For a given dimensionality, select some initial configuration X_0.
2. Compute d_{ij} between the vectors x_i, x_j of the configuration X_0 and also compute $\hat{d}_{ij}$, chosen to be as close as possible to the original d_{ij}, subject to being monotone with the δ_{ij} (input data).[8]
3. Evaluate the fit measure S, the stress of the configuration.
4. If $S > \epsilon$ (some small "cutoff" value, say 0.01) find a new configuration X_1 whose ranks of the d_{ij} are closer to the δ_{ij}.
5. Repeat the process until successive configurations $X_0, X_1, X_2, \ldots, X_p$ converge such that S is satisfactorily "small," (e.g., $S \leqslant \epsilon$).
6. Repeat the above process in the next lower dimensionality, and so on.
7. Choose the lowest dimensionality for which S is satisfactorily "small."

---

[8]It is important to realize that this "monotone regression" step, while stated briefly here, is the *core* notion of many of the techniques to be discussed in subsequent chapters.

Although specific fit measures and procedures for moving the points differ among the various algorithms, they all seem to be based on the above, rather straightforward concepts.

SPECIFIC FEATURES OF THE TORSCA 8 PROGRAM

The TORSCA 8 program displays a number of features which should be mentioned in passing.

1. The initial configuration X_0 is obtained by factor analytic methods and, hence, is a type of fully metric method. However, since points can then be moved by nonmetric criteria, the complete method is of a nonmetric variety.
2. Latest versions (Version 9) of the program permit solutions in any type of Minkowski p-metric, including, of course, the Euclidean and city block metrics as special cases.
3. The program possesses a "passive cell" feature which enables the researcher to scale input data that display missing entries.
4. The program provides a history of the computation, configuration plots and "Shepard" diagrams which are scatter plots of the δ_{ij} versus, in turn, the d_{ij} and $\hat{d}_{ij}$. These scatter plots show the particular type of monotonic function that links the interpoint distances of the solution with the original input data.
5. Optional printout includes the d_{ij} and the $\hat{d}_{ij}$, expressed in tabular form.
6. Depending upon computer size, up to 60 or more points can be scaled in up to 10 dimensions.

We shall return in subsequent chapters to some of the specific features of this program when we discuss the analysis of similarities and preference data in more detail.

SUMMARY

In this chapter we constructed a frame of reference which will be useful for more detailed discussion of similarities and preference data, as well as reduced space and cluster analysis—topics to be covered in later chapters. We first described the relations of dominance and consonance as applied to pairs of points or pairs of proximities drawn from the same versus two different sets. This presentation led us into a discussion of distance functions and isosimilarity contours.

The Coombsian system of data classification was then described and illustrated by various types of behavioral data. It was then noted that our area of concentration will be on Q-I (preference) and Q-IV (similarities) data which lead often, but not necessarily, to multidimensional scales.

We then turned to a comparison of multidimensional scaling approaches, including fully metric, fully nonmetric, and nonmetric techniques. The conceptual rationale of each class was outlined and one specific algorithm for performing nonmetric scaling was described in some detail.

REFERENCES

1. Edwin Beckenbach and Richard Bellman, *An Introduction to Inequalities* (New York: Random House, 1961).

2. J. F. Bennett and W. L. Hays, "Multidimensional Unfolding: Determining the Dimensionality of Ranked Preference Data," *Psychometrika*, Vol. 25 (1960), pp. 27–43.

3. C. H. Coombs, "Scaling and Data Theory," Department of Psychology, University of Michigan, May 1966 (mimeographed); also see C. H. Coombs, *A Theory of Data* (New York: John Wiley & Sons, Inc., 1964).

4. C. H. Coombs, "Psychological Scaling Without a Unit of Measurement," *Psychological Review*, Vol. 57 (1950), pp. 148–58.

5. T. C. Gleason, "A General Model for Nonmetric Multidimensional Scaling," MMPP 67-3, Department of Psychology, University of Michigan, June 1967 (mimeographed).

6. J. B. Kruskal, "Multidimensional Scaling by Optimizing Goodness of Fit to a Nonmetric Hypothesis," *Psychometrika*, Vol. 29 (1964), pp. 1–27.

7. J. B. Kruskal, "How to Use M-D-SCAL, a Program to do Multidimensional Scaling and Multidimensional Unfolding" (Version 4 and 4M FORTRAN IV), Bell Telephone Laboratories, Murray Hill, New Jersey, 1968 (mimeographed).

8. E. A. Richards, "A Commercial Application of Guttman Attitude Scaling Techniques," *Journal of Marketing*, Vol. 22 (October 1959), pp. 166–73.

9. R. N. Shepard, "Metric Structures in Ordinal Data," *Journal of Mathematical Psychology*, Vol. 3 (1966), pp. 287–315.

10. R. N. Shepard, "The Analysis of Proximities: Multidimensional Scaling with an Unknown Distance Function," Part One, *Psychometrika*, Vol. 27 (1962), pp. 125–39.

11. W. S. Torgerson, *Theory and Methods of Scaling* (New York: John Wiley & Sons, Inc., 1958), pp. 271–77.

12. F. W. Young and W. S. Torgerson, "TORSCA, a FORTRAN IV Program for Shepard-Kruskal Multidimensional Scaling Analysis," *Behavioral Science*, Vol. 12 (1967), p. 498.

CHAPTER THREE

Analysis of
Similarities Data

In this chapter we describe models for the analysis of similarities data. Our discussion is based on the following progression of topics: (a) conceptual structure and assumptions underlying similarities models; (b) computational procedures and the results of analyses of synthetic data; (c) empirical problems, including data collection procedures and solution interpretation; and (d) specific issues, including individual differences models and scenario effects on similarities judgments.

We first discuss the general concept of similarity and its relationship to distance models and "perception." This leads to a description of various types of similarities matrices and algorithms which have been developed for portraying similarity relations geometrically. The results are then shown of using some of the major scaling algorithms in the context of analyzing synthetic data of known characteristics.

The next section of the chapter deals with a variety of empirical problems encountered in analyzing similarities data; these include means of handling various types of direct judgment data, direct behavioral indexes of similarity, and derived similarity measures. Discussion of data collection alternatives is followed by a description of problems encountered in the interpretation of scaling solutions.

The concluding section of the chapter takes up a variety of special issues in similarities analysis, including individual differences models, rotation of alternative scaling solutions to congruence, changes in the composition of the stimulus set on configuration stability, and extensions of scaling methods to multi-way matrices.

SIMILARITIES RESPONSES AND DISTANCE MODELS

The major model used in the analysis of similarities data is the distance model, described briefly in the preceding chapter. Certain intuitive niceties link the empirical notion of similarity with the formal notion of distance. For example, it seems reasonable to assume that an item is more similar to itself than it is to any other item and that the similarity of A to B is the same as the similarity of B to A. (Empirically, however, we can find instances where the symmetry property is violated, e.g., where the incidence of confusion of response j with stimulus i does *not* equal the incidence of confusion of response i with stimulus j.)

Even more important, it is well to consider the psychological theory implied by the use of distance models as representations of similarities (or dissimilarities) data. Virtually all distance models considered in mathematical psychology assert that the dissimilarity between a pair of stimuli is some function of their partial dissimilarities with respect to each of several perceptual dimensions. Moreover, the models assume that partial dissimilarities do *not* depend on the actual location of the points but only on their (absolute) differences, dimension by dimension. While for expository purposes one is tempted to call scaling solutions "perceptual maps," it should be made clear that relatively little research has been done to test the relevance of distance models as psychological models of perception.[1] Nor will such research be easy to carry out.

When a spatial representation of a set of similarities data is obtained, the interpoint distances are considered to be ratio-scaled. The axes of the configuration are assumed to be multidimensional interval scales with a common unit. As we pointed out in the preceding chapter, translation of the origin as well as choice of a common unit are permitted transformations in nonmetric methods. In the case of the Euclidean metric, the axes may be rotated as well, since interpoint distances, in this case, are invariant over the configuration's orientation in the space.

Types of Proximities Matrices

Our previous discussion (Chapter 2) of classes of proximity matrices listed the following types:

1. Intact, unconditional
2. Intact, conditional
3. Off-diagonal, unconditional
4. Off-diagonal, conditional

The types of proximity matrices usually associated with similarities (or dissimilarities) data are: (a) the intact, unconditional; and (b) the intact, conditional. As has been mentioned, in the first case it is assumed that all cell values of the $\frac{1}{2} n(n-1)$ distinct pairs are comparable. In the second case it is assumed that only entries *within* a given row are comparable. In the latter case—represented by a variety of data collection methods—the data are "conjoint" [7] in that an order relation on any pair of pairs always has a common element in each pair; for example:

$$\overline{AB} < \overline{AC}.$$

[1] Beals, Krantz and Tversky [1] have commented quite extensively on the formal properties of nonmetric scaling; they also raise a series of questions about the psychological theory implied by the distance model.

This would be interpreted as "the dissimilarity of the pair A and B is less than that of the pair A and C." Or, alternatively, "B is closer to A than C is."

Illustrative forms that a proximities matrix may assume are shown in **Figure 3-1**. Case (a) is probably the most common type in which all cell values

FIGURE 3-1
ALTERNATIVE PROXIMITIES MATRICES

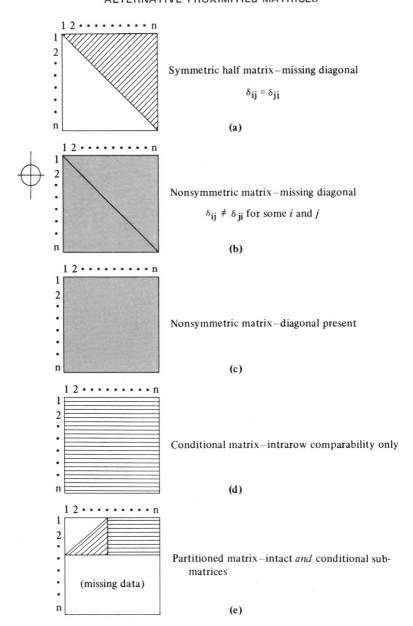

Symmetric half matrix–missing diagonal

$$\delta_{ij} = \delta_{ji}$$

(a)

Nonsymmetric matrix–missing diagonal

$$\delta_{ij} \neq \delta_{ji} \text{ for some } i \text{ and } j$$

(b)

Nonsymmetric matrix–diagonal present

(c)

Conditional matrix–intrarow comparability only

(d)

Partitioned matrix–intact *and* conditional sub-matrices

(missing data)

(e)

are assumed to be comparable and self-dissimilarities are assumed to be equal to each other and less than any off-diagonal entry. Moreover, the matrix is assumed to be symmetric. Case (b) illustrates the situation that may arise in the collection of confusions data (to be discussed later) where the incidence with which response j is confused with stimulus i does not equal the confusion incidence of response i with stimulus j. Case (c) can also arise in the collection of confusions data where the incidence of response i to stimulus i may be experimentally less than the incidence in which some off-diagonal response is obtained.

Case (d) represents a quite common form of original data collection and illustrates the case in which conjoint data (each pair of proximities having a stimulus in common) are obtained. Case (e) typifies a situation where all unconditional proximities are obtained from a subset (a core set) of the stimuli, while the remaining proximities are obtained on the basis of being conditional upon each core stimulus, in turn.

Many other varieties of proximity matrices are possible, given the possibility of omitting certain stimulus comparisons experimentally. Since most of the scaling algorithms possess "missing data" features, no problem arises so long as the absolute number of data entries is "large" relative to the number of coordinate values needed to specify the configuration in some selected dimensionality. A workable rule of thumb is to have three times as many stimuli to be scaled as the number of dimensions believed necessary to portray the relationships adequately, i.e., exhibit a low value of stress [18]. Moreover, the cells that *are* filled by experimentally obtained data values should be chosen to assure connectivity over subsets of proximities.

Scaling Algorithms for Proximities Data

A variety of scaling algorithms exists for portraying experimental similarities or dissimilarities as relations on points in geometric space. These include:

1. Factor analytic procedures [27, 31, 32]
2. Kruskal's M-D-SCAL programs [18, 19]
3. Torgerson and Young's TORSCA programs [31, 32]
4. Guttman and Lingoes' SSA program series [20]
5. McGee's programs [22, 23]
6. Carroll and Chang's parametric mapping program [26]

Space does not permit an extensive discussion of the special features of each program. (Capsule program descriptions appear in Appendix A.) Here we are concerned with the circumstances under which each major type of algorithm is appropriate.

Factor Analytic and Simple Scaling Methods. As recalled from the preceding chapter, fully metric methods, using a factor analysis of distances converted to scalar products, are appropriate if the data are considered to be ratio-scaled distances to begin with. Moreover, if the data are assumed to be only interval-scaled, various procedures are available for estimating an additive constant which will convert the input data to distances. It should be reiterated that the TORSCA programs incorporate a factor analytic approach for obtaining a starting configuration and also, if desired, a type of "quasi-nonmetric" feature that entails a series of factor analyses of successive distance matrices (converted to scalar products) whose distance entries are chosen to be monotone with the original input data.

More recently, Kruskal has incorporated a "simple scaling" feature in version IV of his program which enables the researcher to fit linear functions (with or without intercept) as well as prespecified polynomial functions (up to the fourth degree). As such, Kruskal's M-D-SCAL IV program can also be used for metric (as well as nonmetric) analysis.

It is often the case that metric methods provide excellent approximations to nonmetric solutions—particularly if the monotonic function can be closely approximated by a linear one—and are not subject to the types of local minima and degeneracy problems sometimes encountered in using ordinal methods. In our own research, at least, we have found it useful to compute *both* metric and nonmetric solutions.

Some researchers [16] have appeared to rely on metric methods almost exclusively. We do not find this choice congenial to our own research interests since it can easily be the case that the function linking distance with dissimilarity is highly nonlinear (but monotonic). Rather than *assuming* linearity, we prefer to run analyses both metrically and nonmetrically; the TORSCA (versions 8 and 9) and M-D-SCAL IV programs permit one to do this quite simply and efficiently.

Ordinal Approaches

All of the major programs—M-D-SCAL III and IV, TORSCA 8 and 9, the SSA series and McGee's programs—can handle the usual symmetric half matrix (Figure 3-1a). In addition, Kruskal's M-D-SCAL IV program can handle cases (b) and (c) as well. In this case a type of symmetrization is performed *within* the program since the output of the program—the configuration and its interpoint distances—must, of course, obey the metric axioms. On the other hand, if the researcher has obtained a nonsymmetric matrix experimentally, he may wish to assume that a symmetric model (coupled with random error) is most appropriate. If so, he may symmetrize this matrix by summing across the corresponding diagonal entries *before* scaling the data.[2]

The conditional proximity matrix (Figure 3-1d) is quite common in some data collection methods, e.g., the method of n-dimensional rank order. The M-D-SCAL IV program and the SSA-II program can be used to scale such data directly. The TORSCA 8 and 9 and the M-D-SCAL III programs may be used as well (by taking advantage of their passive cell feature) but, if so, the assumption is made that *all* cell values (i.e., those across rows) are comparable. As such, the proximity matrix would be treated as unconditional.

---

[2]It should be mentioned that various types of averaging, including geometric means, may be used in the symmetrization procedure.

An alternative procedure is to convert the conditional proximity matrix to an unconditional (and symmetric) one by triangularization. The authors have prepared such a program [2] which is best suited for data collected by the method of n-dimensional rank order. One version of the program will find the "best" complete order of all pairs (using a method due to Phillips [25]) from conditional proximity data. The behavior of this approach to the conversion of conditional proximities has been compared to direct scaling by the M-D-SCAL IV program, with similar results [9]. While the two-step procedures of triangularization, followed by scaling the resulting completely ordered vector of pairwise dissimilarities, is more time consuming, it seems less susceptible to problems of degeneracy or local optima. Moreover, the matrix consisting of subjects by dissimilarities can be useful in its own right, as will be shown later.

The scaling of partitioned matrices (like the one illustrated in Figure 3-1e) can arise in cases where core set methods are used. For example, a subject can be asked to give similarity responses on all $\frac{1}{2} k(k-1)$ pairs of k out of n items and, for the remaining $n - k$ stimuli, merely asked to rank order them from each of the k core items, in turn. Other procedures can be used which lead to partitioned matrices in which cell values are comparable only within submatrices. (Actually, the conditional proximity matrix, partitioned by rows, is a special case of this class.) The M-D-SCAL IV program, by sublist splitting, and one version of SSA-I permit the scaling of partitioned matrices. Guttman and Lingoes' SSAP-II program [21] also performs this task in the special case where one is dealing with a subject by variables matrix.

In summary, the M-D-SCAL IV program appears to be the most flexible in its ability to perform both metric and nonmetric analyses as well as being able to scale a variety of special forms of proximity matrices. The Guttman-Lingoes series of several programs seems to provide the next most flexible package. And all of the programs, of course, handle the most common case (Figure 3-1a) of the intact, unconditional half-matrix of similarities (dissimilarities) with missing main diagonal.

Continuity Approaches

Before this section is concluded, mention should be made of Carroll and Chang's parametric mapping program which is based on a different principle than monotone regression methods. In parametric mapping the function relating manifest proximities data to the solution space need only be relatively "smooth"— not necessarily a monotonic function of distances in this space. While monotonicity of proximities and distances tends to be preserved, at least locally, the program is *not* based on this principle. Parametric mapping often leads to the most parsimonious representation of proximities data—particularly if the assumed underlying distances are derived from points lying on some curved manifold embedded in a higher dimensional space.

Unfortunately, the properties of this program seem to be less well understood than those of the monotone algorithms; its empirical application to date has been relatively minor. We would speculate, however, that it will receive increased attention in the future as more researchers start to examine its properties. Moreover, it can be used in tandem (or sequentially) with metric or ordinal methods. At the current state of the art such dual approaches appear prudent to follow and underscore the value of not "locking in" on a particular method of data analysis—metric, ordinal, or otherwise.

SYNTHETIC DATA ANALYSES

One useful way to get some intuitive feel for the behavior of various algorithms in the scaling of similarities data is to examine their application to cases where the characteristics of the input data are known. To illustrate the ability of non-metric algorithms to "recover" known configurations, we present in this section the results of a few illustrative analyses.

Input Data

The configuration to be recovered by nonmetric methods is shown in **Figure 3-2**. It consists of the letter "R" made up of 27 points positioned in 2

FIGURE 3-2

ORIGINAL CONFIGURATION OF 27 POINTS USED IN SCALING ANALYSES

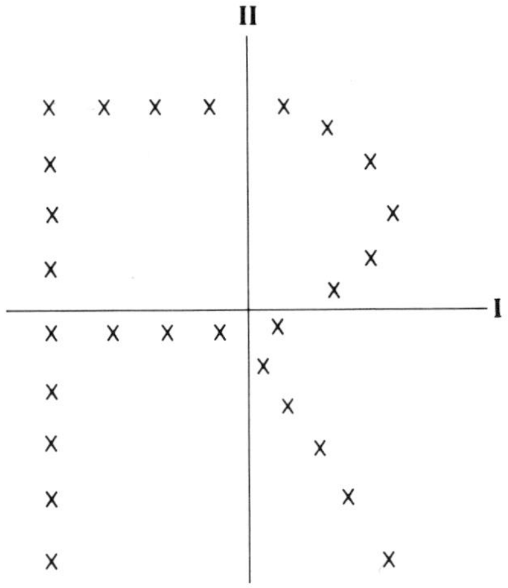

dimensions.[3] All 351 interpoint distances were computed for the pairs of points and then subjected to the following simple monotonic transformation:

$$y_{ij} = (d_{ij})^2 + 5$$

[3]The authors are grateful to V. R. Rao who performed the analyses underlying the exposition of this section of the chapter.

The resulting transformed data were then submitted independently to: (a) the TORSCA program (version 8); (b) the M-D-SCAL IV program; and (c) the SSA-I program. Solutions were sought in two dimensions and a plot of the monotone function linking dissimilarities with derived interpoint distances was also obtained; see Figures 3-3 and 3-4.

Scaling Results

We note from **Figure 3-3** that all three algorithms yield very good recoveries of the original configuration, albeit with different orientations. As might be expected, the fit measures, Kruskal's stress in the first two instances and Guttman

FIGURE 3-3
"RECOVERED" CONFIGURATIONS UNDER ERROR-FREE CONDITIONS

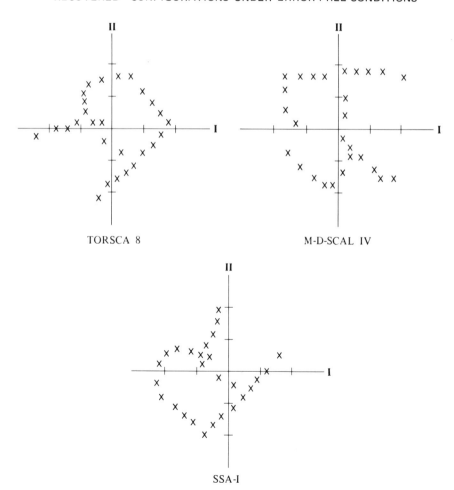

FIGURE 3-4

MONOTONE FUNCTION "RECOVERY" UNDER ERROR-FREE CONDITIONS

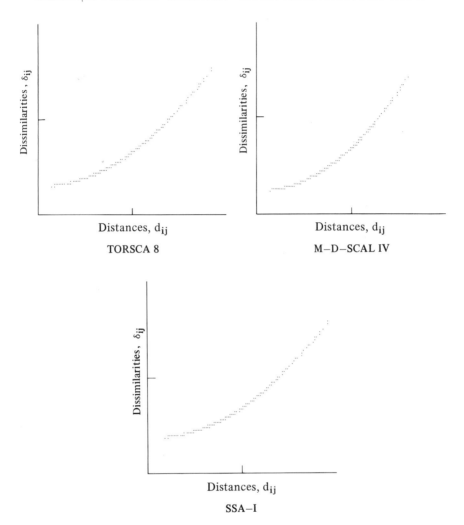

TORSCA 8   M–D–SCAL IV

SSA–I

and Lingoes' normalized phi coefficient in the third instance, indicated virtually perfect recovery. The TORSCA stress value was 0.002, the M-D-SCAL IV stress value was 0.009, and the SSA-I normalized phi coefficient was 0.0.

Finally we note that the monotone transformation function $y_{ij} = (d_{ij})^2 + 5$, is approximated quite accurately by the plots shown in **Figure 3-4**. While the algorithms differ in computational detail, it is evident that they produce quite similar results in the analysis shown here. Moreover, by a combination of reflection and rotation, each configuration in Figure 3-3 could be oriented to agree with the original orientation of Figure 3-2.

Adding Error to the Distances

In order to ascertain the effect of "noise" on configuration recovery, the original 351 interpoint distances were next transformed by the function:

$$y'_{ij} = (d_{ij})^2 + 5 + \epsilon_{ij}$$

where: ϵ represents a normally distributed error term with a mean of zero and a standard deviation equal to one-fifth of the mean of the original interpoint distances. The same three programs used above were again used here.

Results of Scaling the "Noisy" Data

The results of scaling the noisy data appear in Figures 3-5 and 3-6. Again we note from **Figure 3-5** that orientation of the configurations differs over the three

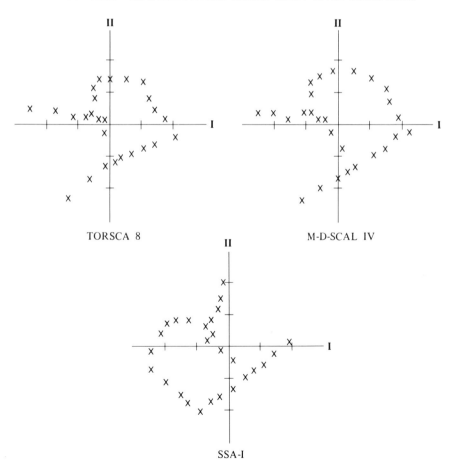

FIGURE 3-5
"RECOVERED" CONFIGURATIONS UNDER NOISY DATA CONDITIONS

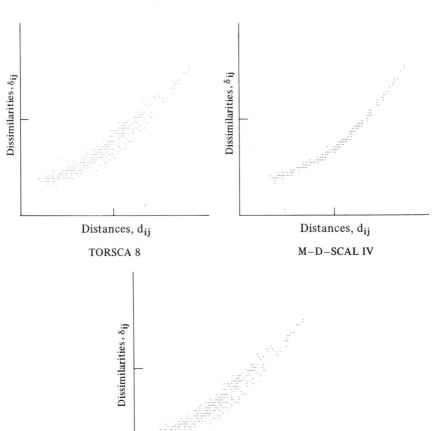

FIGURE 3-6
MONOTONE FUNCTION "RECOVERY" UNDER NOISY DATA CONDITIONS

algorithms but recovery of the original configuration is still quite remarkable. In this case the TORSCA stress value was 0.09, the M-D-SCAL IV stress value was 0.12, and the SSA-I normalized phi value was 0.002, all rather "fair" values with regard to goodness of fit. Still the configuration has been recovered with relatively little distortion.

Plots of the monotone function, shown in **Figure 3-6** reveal that the addition of random error distorts the monotonic function somewhat but its general shape still appears quite clear, even in the presence of moderate amounts of noise.

In both cases—error free and noisy data—all three algorithms performed rather similarly. Since the computation of the fit measures differs among the three approaches: stress formula 1 for TORSCA 8 [18], stress formula 2 for M-D-SCAL IV [19], and normalized phi for SSA-I [20], one cannot readily use this indicator to ascertain the relative recovery "power" among the three algorithms. Nor, in this case, would such comparisons be particularly revealing since all three approaches yield quite accurate recoveries, as shown by Figures 3-3 and 3-5.

DATA COLLECTION METHODS

The preceding sections of the chapter have dealt with the more or less conceptual and computational aspects of the algorithms. We now discuss a number of empirical problems surrounding their application to the portrayal of similarities data as geometrical relations on points in a metric space. One class of such problems concerns the choice of an appropriate data collection method.

A variety of data collection procedures exist for the collection of similarities data; some type of classification system has, therefore, to be constructed. Coombs [7, Chapter 2] classifies data collection techniques as involving either: (a) picking k out of n items or (b) ordering k out of n items. While we shall refer to this system, for our purposes a somewhat more detailed set of categories appears to be called for. Throughout we keep in mind the desire, wherever possible, to end up with a complete rank order of all distinct pairs. While our scheme is not exhaustive, it does serve to illustrate the large number of data collection procedures which can be employed in gathering similarities data.

Figure 3-7 presents the major descriptors of the classification. Note that the first dichotomy concerns whether the pairwise measures are obtained directly or are "built up" from correspondences in interstimulus profile "scores." The

FIGURE 3-7
A CLASSIFICATION OF PROCEDURES FOR COLLECTING SIMILARITIES DATA

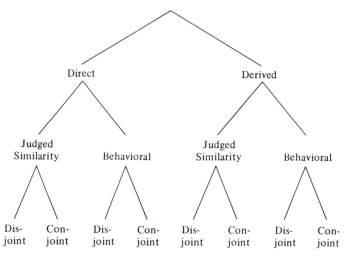

second dichotomy—judged similarity versus behavioral—refers to whether the response of the subject consists of his subjective judgment or is some behavioral response that we take to be an indicant of psychological similarity. The third descriptor, disjoint versus conjoint [7] comparisons, appears most relevant within the cross-category "direct judged similarity," although instances can be imagined under each of the other categories where either conjoint or disjoint data can be obtained. We discuss each of the major categories in turn.

Direct Measures of Similarity

By far the most often used method of obtaining similarities data involves the case of direct (pairwise) measures. Typically, these are obtained by having respondents give judged similarities on stimulus pairs, although other approaches (here called behavioral) can be used as well. Approaches included in this second sub-category have been used in studies of, for example: (a) confusions data; (b) discrimination time; and (c) response amplitude.

Direct, Behavioral Methods. Confusions data can be collected under a variety of tasks. For example, the subject may be asked to assign individual advertisements (of origin known by the experimenter) to one of several magazines [8]. Or, the subject may be given pairs of unidentified brands of soft drinks and asked to indicate whether each pair is the "same" or "different." An alternative form of this task would be to have the respondent assign each unidentified drink to one of a prespecified set of branded categories. The frequency with which object i is confused with object j is taken to be a behavioral measure of their "psychological" similarity. Through replication, a confusions matrix can be developed for a single subject, enabling the researcher to obtain his specific similarities configuration. More frequently, however, the data are pooled over subjects and a type of group configuration is obtained. In the latter case one usually assumes that the respondents are homogeneous with regard to "perceptual" dimensions and discriminating acuity as well.

Other behavioral tasks can be developed. For example, slides of two package designs could be flashed momentarily on a screen and the subject asked to indicate whether the members of the pair are the same or different. The mean exposure time required for the subject to make some prespecified percentage of correct responses could be taken as an indicant of each pair's similarity. In still other tasks, the strength (amplitude) of the subject's response, e.g., as measured on a psychogalvanometer, could be taken as an indicant of interstimulus similarity. It should be noted that one can obtain either unconditional (and symmetric) or conditional proximities, depending upon the type of task employed.

Direct Judged Similarities—Disjoint Data. Most applied studies in which similarities data are collected make use of direct judgments of pairwise similarity. A variety of procedures, yielding disjoint comparisons, are possible. For example, the subject may be given pairs of pairs of stimuli and asked to indicate which is the more similar pair. Or, of course, he may be given all pairs at the outset and asked to rank them in terms of decreasing (or increasing) similarity. Alternatively, he may be asked to rate each pair on, say, a 9-point similarity/dissimilarity scale. Or, he may be given each pair and asked to indicate whether it is "similar" or "different," a special case of the rating scale in which response categories are constrained to be dichotomous. (Note here, however, that in all cases the stimuli are identified.)

In subjective clustering methods the subject would be asked to sort the stimuli into groups such that those in any given group are thought to be more similar to each other than they are to any stimuli not in the group. An "incidence" matrix could then be constructed in which a "1" would be inserted if any two stimuli appear in the same group and a "0" otherwise. In this and the immediately preceding procedure, data typically would be aggregated across subjects to overcome the large number of ties, since individual responses are limited to those of the zero-one type.

All of the preceding methods will yield disjoint data, either in individual subject or aggregated form. Since the programs can handle missing data, it is also possible for the experimenter to forego some comparisons if the number of stimuli is large. While the problem of which, and how many, comparisons to forego has not been solved analytically as yet, intuitively we would probably want: (a) an equal number of representations of each stimulus and (b) maintenance of "connectivity" among groups of comparisons so that the stimuli cannot be partitioned into two or more subsets with no comparisons being available across subsets.

Direct Judged Similarities—Conjoint Data. Many procedures exist for the collection of similarity judgments involving conjoint data, where each pair of pairs has a stimulus in common. Since the number of pairs of pairs is the number of combinations of $\frac{1}{2} n(n-1)$ object pairs, taken two at a time ($\frac{1}{8} [n(n-1) (n-2) (n+1)]$, it is clear that with, say, $n > 10$, the number of tetrads becomes unwieldy. Conjoint data procedures can reduce the comparison task markedly, the trade-off being that disjoint comparisons, where feasible, must be inferred from conjoint comparisons *and* the assumption of transitivity.

The *method of triads*: "pick the two stimuli out of the triple which you think are most similar; now pick the two which are least similar"; the *method of anchor point ordering*: "which is more similar to A, stimulus B or stimulus C?"; the *method of* n-*dimensional rank order*, and several others are illustrations of what Coombs [7, Chapter 2] calls "cartwheel data." Such data lead to conditional proximity matrices which can be either scaled directly or triangularized, as described earlier. In any case, the *model* being fitted obtains interpoint distances for all pairs of points, thus implicitly assuming disjoint as well as conjoint comparisons.

In our own research we have tended to employ triangularization methods in cases where conjoint data have been obtained. In this way a larger number of order constraints are available for "fixing" the configuration but, of course, the level of input data has been upgraded by invoking the assumption of transitivity over pairs of pairs not obtained from the subject directly.

One other procedure should be mentioned in connection with conjoint data, namely, the procedure of anchor point clustering. In this method the subject is asked to pick those k out of $n - 1$ items (where k is usually specified by the experimenter) which are most similar to the anchor item. Each of the n stimuli serves, in turn, as an anchor item. The resulting matrix of ones and zeroes is a conditional proximity matrix and, of course, need not be symmetric. Moreover, in this approach, responses are usually pooled over subjects in order to mitigate the problem of ties. (A variation of the procedure would entail pooling over subsets of subjects after first partitioning them into subgroups, based on their relative similarity to each other over the whole zero-one response matrix.)

While the above methods are not exhaustive of the many procedures available for collecting direct similarities data, they are representative of the principal ones. Clearly, much more applied research is required to ascertain their correspondence over various groups of subjects and stimulus sets. Part of our own research [11, 13] has been devoted to inter-technique comparisons, a topic also explored by Greenberg [14].

Derived Measures of Similarity

By "derived" similarity measures we mean those which are *computed* for each pair of objects over the objects' profile scores. For example, one could construct a series of semantic differentials and have a subject rate each of a set of stimuli on each of the semantic differential scales. For a given subject the stimuli-by-scales matrix of ratings can be used to compute interstimulus association measures. These might range from simple matching coefficients to correlation or Euclidean distance measures. The *derived* measures of stimulus pair association could then serve as input to a multidimensional scaling program.

A number of problems are encountered with this approach. First, the experimenter may not have picked all of the relevant constructs (scales) that people might evoke in making overall similarity responses. Second, there is a question of what weights to assign to each scale in computing overall association measures. Usually, equal (manifest) weight is applied to each of the scales for lack of any better procedure. In other instances, however, the interstimulus association measures may be computed on the basis of factor scores obtained after a preliminary component analysis of the correlation matrix of scale pairs across stimuli.

In our own research we have frequently employed the monadic scale procedure in *conjunction* with direct judgments of overall similarity. This approach not only provides an intermethod comparison but is useful in interpreting the results of scaling the overall similarity measures (as will be described later). Mention should also be made of the possibility of developing a configuration of *both* objects and scales as obtained by the implied ordering of each object on each scale. Guttman and Lingoes' SSAP-II program [21] has been designed with this objective in mind. Metric or nonmetric factor analyses are also relevant to this objective but involve a point-vector representation.

There are some areas of application where derived measures can be quite useful. For example, if the researcher has objective data on the properties of a set of stimuli, association measures can be computed over these "performance" profiles. This approach is covered in more detail in Chapter 5.

As a second illustration, the researcher may wish to develop derived measures of *intersubject* association, as obtained from a subjects-by-similarities matrix. In this case the columns of the matrix would consist of the $\frac{1}{2} n(n-1)$ pairs of stimuli. This approach can be useful in developing individual differences in points of view, a topic discussed in a subsequent section of this chapter.

Future Research Needs

It should be clear by this point that the variety of procedures available for collecting similarities data may represent a mixed blessing. The choice of which procedure to use depends at least upon the number of stimuli and the amount of data "upgrading" which the experimenter is willing to perform. Relatively little research has been conducted on the invariance of proximity measures over alternative data gathering procedures. Such research is surely needed if we are ever to be able to evaluate the suitability of specific techniques for various data gathering objectives.

In addition to field-level comparisons, the study of data collection alternatives can be profitably undertaken by Monte Carlo analysis of synthetic data. This type of study is relatively inexpensive to conduct and should provide complementary results to empirical studies dealing with inter-technique comparisons.

SOLUTION INTERPRETATION IN MULTIDIMENSIONAL SCALING

In Chapter 2 it was indicated that multidimensional scaling solutions involving any type of Minkowski p-metric are invariant over translation, reflection, and uniform stretching (or compression) of the axes. Moreover, in the case of the Euclidean distance measure—the metric most often used in empirical applications— the solution is invariant over rotation of the axes as well. Thus, interpretation of the axes, even when uniquely oriented, still presents a problem in all Minkowski p-metrics, while in Euclidean space (the metric on which we concentrate here) one needs to orient the configuration as well.

Some of the scaling programs conventionally orient the configuration to principal components axes [31] while others orient it to "simple structure" by means of a Varimax sub-routine [32]. For purposes of this section's discussion we shall assume that the scaling solution has been rotated to principal components; clearly, this orientation might *not* be the best from the standpoint of axis interpretation.

Several methods have been used to assist the researcher in the task of axis identification. They include: (a) research expertise aided by respondents' listings of criteria which they believed they used in making their similarities judgments; (b) "property fitting" procedures; and (c) experimental design methods. Each approach is discussed in turn.

Researcher Expertise

Probably the most usual approach to axis interpretation is based on the more or less *ad hoc* judgments of the researcher, as formed by examining the configuration itself. Candidate axes may be suggested by having respondents list— at the completion of the similarities task—the main criteria which they believe they used in making their similarity judgments. Sometimes the researcher's judgment may be augmented by enlisting the interpretive aid of the subject himself after the data have been scaled.

Any of the above procedures entail a large element of subjectivity and perhaps can most appropriately be considered as bases for hypothesis formation, to be examined by subsequent experiments in which new subjects are asked to give similarities judgments according to these prespecified constructs. The one-dimensional solutions obtained by this means may be tested as possible dimension "labels" by procedures described in the next section.

Property Fitting Procedures

If the researcher obtains unidimensional construct ratings on prespecified attribute scales (in addition to the subject's unstructured similarities judgments), a variety of techniques are possible for axis interpretation. For example, based on prior studies or experimenter judgment, a set of preselected constructs can be chosen and the respondent asked to rate each stimulus on each construct according to, say, a 9-point scale. (The constructs themselves might be developed from a preliminary study using Kelly's repertory grid [17].

In any event, the researcher would have two sets of data for each subject. The first set consists of the stimulus configuration obtained from scaling the subject's overall similarities data; the second consists of the respondent's ratings of each stimulus on each prespecified construct. The objective then, would be to "fit" the outside property vectors representing the unidimensional ratings. Such fitting entails finding, for each property vector separately, a direction (vector) in the stimulus space whose stimulus projections are maximally correlated with the candidate property vector's scale values.

The three procedures most appropriate for this task are: (a) the *max "r" procedure* [24]; (b) *monotone multiple regression* [4]; and (c) Carroll and Chang's *nonlinear correlation* [3]. The max "r" procedure assumes the regression to be linear, while the other two procedures do not require linearity; the third procedure requires "smoothness" (but not monotonicity, necessarily). Thus, the procedures make successively weaker assumptions about the form of the "psychophysical" transform relating the projection sought in the similarities space to the property vector being fitted.

The above approaches fit the property vectors one at a time. In parallel the researcher may wish to run a canonical correlation between the coordinate values of the stimulus configuration and the *whole* set of candidate constructs. The canonical weights, so obtained, may then be used to find those linear compounds of the original constructs that are maximally associated with linear compounds of the coordinate values. Successive sets of linear compounds would be uncorrelated with those previously extracted. Examination of construct "loadings" could then suggest candidate labels for describing the new orientation of the transformed coordinates.

An illustration of property fitting by means of the max "r" procedure is shown in **Figure 3-8**. In this application overall similarities judgments were obtained on eleven brands of automobiles [10]. This was followed by having the same subject rate each of the eleven cars on each of twelve semantic differential scales. Figure 3-8 shows the two-space stimulus configuration obtained from scaling the average subject's overall similarities data.

We note from Figure 3-8 that the vertical axis appears to be best labeled "sportiness." The horizontal axis has several property vectors which are almost collinear with it—elegant, sophisticated, husky, and complex. If we wish to keep the axes orthogonal, a $30°$ rotation from the original orientation appears to provide a reasonable axis interpretation. Note that many of the scales are not even close to being collinear with either component axis. This suggests that they could be considered as composites of the "basic" dimensions or, alternatively, that an oblique representation of the axis is most appropriate for interpretive purposes.

Experimental Design Procedures

In some studies the experimenter may wish to vary the attribute levels of the stimuli themselves, e.g., sweetness and degree of carbonation of soft drinks, strongness of cigarette tobacco, and so on. If the stimuli are designed by the experimenter, a set of objective property vectors is obtained. Any of the above methods could be used to find appropriate projections in the similarities space, using the *objective* scales as property vectors. In addition, one could obtain subjective ratings or, possibly, similarities judgments as well, according to the prespecified (objective) constructs.

The authors used this type of approach in a pilot study of how Canadian housewives perceived lingerie which varied according to type of fabric, style, color, and price. The objective price vector was found to be poorly correlated with its best fitting projection in virtually all of the similarities configurations, suggesting that it was *not* a highly salient dimension in the women's overall similarities judgments of lingerie.

Experimental design procedures might also be used in a sequence of studies by varying the composition of the stimulus set. For example, if a preliminary experiment suggests that price and style are the two most salient dimensions, additional studies could be run in which the respondents were given stimuli of similar style but varied price or, alternatively, similar price but varied style. The scales found here could then be checked for congruency with those found in the original study.

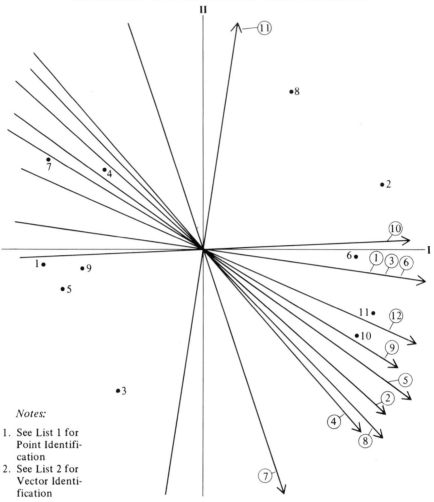

FIGURE 3-8

AVERAGE-SUBJECT CONFIGURATION AND VECTORS MOST HIGHLY
CORRELATED WITH SEMANTIC DIFFERENTIAL SCALES

Notes:

1. See List 1 for
   Point Identifi-
   cation
2. See List 2 for
   Vector Identifi-
   cation

List 1: Automobile Brands Used as Stimuli

1. Volkswagen 1300 Sedan
2. Lincoln Continental V8
3. Ford Mustang 6
4. Dodge Dart V8
5. Chevrolet Camaro V8
6. Jaguar XKE Coupe

7. Ford Galaxie V8
8. Buick Le Sabre V8
9. Buick Opel Sedan
10. Chevrolet Corvette V8
11. Porsche Sports Coupe

List 2: Semantic Differential Adjective Pairs

1. Sophisticated - Unsophisticated
2. Exciting - Dull
3. Husky - Weak
4. Eccentric - Conventional
5. Bold - Shy
6. Simple - Complex

7. Sporty - Businesslike
8. Stale - Fresh
9. Swift - Slow
10. Elegant - Plain
11. Reliable - Unreliable
12. Masculine - Feminine

While the problem of interpreting scaling solutions is still far from resolved, it seems to us that the approaches described above—property vector fitting and experimental design—provide helpful adjuncts to the subjective expertise of the researcher. Our discussion also underscores the value of running a sequential set of experiments in order to examine the relevance of hypothesized constructs as well as to provide checks on inter-occasion or inter-person reliability.

Another problem encountered in the interpretation of similarities configurations concerns the appropriateness of a *dimensional* interpretation itself as opposed, say, to a class-like or categorical interpretation [28] of the configuration. We discuss this problem and some proposed solutions at some length in Chapter 5.

SPECIAL ISSUES IN THE ANALYSIS OF SIMILARITIES DATA

A number of interesting topics of a rather specialized nature are associated with the analysis of similarities data. These include: (a) methods for dealing with individual differences in similarity judgments and their relationship to market segmentation; (b) the dependence of similarity judgments on scenario and changes in the composition of the stimulus set; and (c) extension of scaling methods to deal with multi-way data matrices. Each of these topics is discussed in turn.

Individual Differences in Similarity Judgments

In a fairly large size sample it would be rare indeed if all respondents "perceived" the stimuli in exactly the same way or, on the other hand, used no dimensions in common. In our judgment it is dangerous to assume homogeneity of similarities judgments across people and then, by simple aggregation, find one configuration which purportedly is representative of the group. The other extreme would be to develop each individual's configuration separately, not only an unwieldy task in itself, but an approach which militates against generalization.

Our own position on the matter is that it is usually best to follow a middle course, namely, to search for "points of view" in which each point of view may be shared by a number of subjects, but, in turn, is presumed to be different from other points of view. If homogeneity is found by analysis—not ordained by assumption—then aggregation over subjects can be done in a more reasonable manner. Moreover, there is a second advantage to be gained through the study of individual differences and that is the possible identification of market segments, as developed from the analysis of similarities data. These segments may, in turn, be related to identifiable characteristics (demographic, socioeconomic) of the respondents.

Two major approaches (and a hybrid of the two) are available for the systematic study of individual differences in similarities data: (a) Tucker and Messick's *factor analytic model* [30] and (b) Carroll and Chang's *"shared space" model* [5]. We discuss each of these briefly and then comment on a dual approach which we have considered. Still other procedures have been proposed by Kruskal [19] and McGee [23].

The Tucker-Messick Model. Tucker and Messick's approach is quite simple. It is a metric procedure—although nonmetric analogues can be employed as well—and it is based on a Q-type component analysis of the subjects by similarities matrix. Association measures (cross-products, covariances, correlations) are obtained for each pair of subjects across the whole vector of similarities judgments and the resulting matrix is then factored by principal components. A subject configuration is obtained in component space and clustering techniques—to be described in Chapter 5—can then be used to group subjects. Various procedures can be employed to choose representative subjects for each cluster (or "point of view") and separate scalings of each representative subject's data are obtained.

Figure 3-9 shows, illustratively, a subject configuration associated with the car brand stimuli whose stimulus configuration (for the average subject) has already been shown in Figure 3-8. In this instance we were interested in whether subjects who were shown a color photograph of each car model, in addition to the brand name, would give different similarities responses than those subjects who received brand names only as stimuli.

FIGURE 3-9
PLOT OF FIRST TWO COMPONENTS—TUCKER AND MESSICK
POINTS OF VIEW ANALYSIS

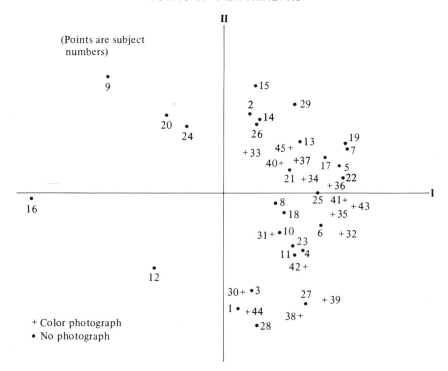

Figure 3-9 shows that this was not the case. A two-group discriminant analysis (based on the three-space coordinates for each subject) confirmed the visual evidence. We do note, however, that some subjects (numbers 9, 12, 16, 20, and 24) plot at some distance from the major cluster. As would be expected, their stimulus configurations differed from that obtained from the representative subject closest to the centroid of the major cluster.

After the stimulus configuration associated with each point of view is found, these can be rotated [6] for maximal congruence with each other, in order to get some idea of the degree of correspondence. Moreover, if other characteristics (demographic, socioeconomic) of the subjects are available one can run canonical correlations between the subject coordinates (see Figure 3-9) and the matrix of subject property vectors. In this way, correlates of points of view may be found which could be useful for market segmentation strategy.

The Carroll and Chang Model. Carroll and Chang's "shared space" model represents a more recent development in the study of individual differences. Carroll and Chang raise a fundamental issue concerning the Tucker-Messick approach, namely, that subsequent scalings of the similarities data associated with each point of view do not show *directly* how each point of view is related to the others, i.e., the dimensions which they may have in common.

Carroll and Chang's approach—also metric but capable of being made quasi-nonmetric—assumes that all subjects share a common, or group, space but are allowed to *weight* the dimensions of this space idiosyncratically. Moreover, some subjects may assign zero weights to one or more of the axes. Their model develops both the group space and a set of subject weights which represent the different saliences which each subject places on each dimension. In this way an estimate of each subject's stimulus configuration can be obtained by transformation of the group configuration through differential stretching of its axes.[4]

A goodness of fit on each *individual* stimulus configuration, as estimated by the model, is also obtained. This measure can be used to set aside, for separate analyses, those subjects whose similarities data are not well represented by the shared space model. **Figure 3-10** shows a three-space stimulus configuration obtained from Carroll and Chang's model and **Figure 3-11** shows the three two-space projections of the subject weights [12].

Looking first at Figure 3-10 it appears as though appropriate labels for the axes are:

> Axis   I   "Classical . . . Popular"
> Axis II "Serious . . . Commercial"
> Axis III "Groups . . . Individuals"

As noted from Figure 3-11, however, individual subject weights differ markedly among subjects. Subject A, for example, gives highest weight to axis I, low

[4]Another feature of the Carroll-Chang model is the fact that the group stimulus space, found in the analysis, is *uniquely oriented* (i.e., not subject to orthogonal rotation). Thus, if the model adequately describes the data, the *specific* dimensions found in the analysis should be capable of interpretation.

FIGURE 3-10
THREE-DIMENSIONAL STIMULUS CONFIGURATION FROM CARROLL-CHANG
INDIVIDUAL DIFFERENCES MODEL

Groups B and M

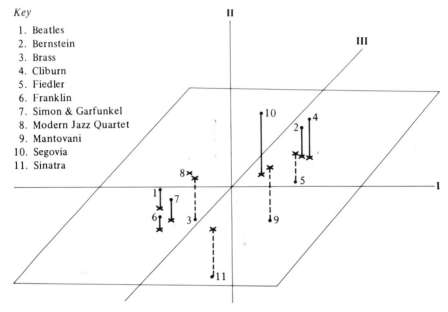

Key

1. Beatles
2. Bernstein
3. Brass
4. Cliburn
5. Fiedler
6. Franklin
7. Simon & Garfunkel
8. Modern Jazz Quartet
9. Mantovani
10. Segovia
11. Sinatra

FIGURE 3-11
THREE-DIMENSIONAL SALIENCE CONFIGURATION

Dimensions I and II

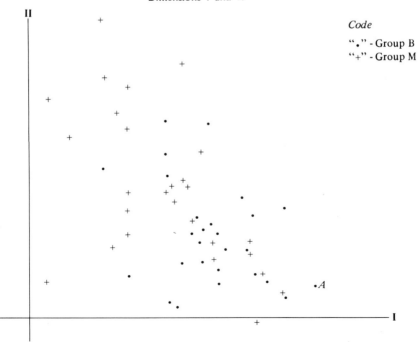

Code

"•" - Group B
"+" - Group M

Dimensions I and III

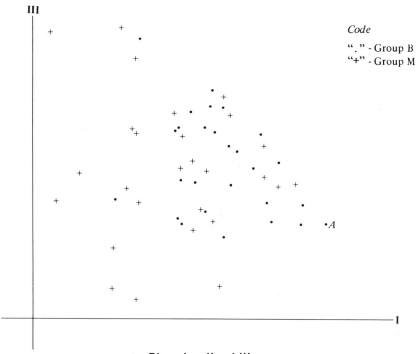

Code
".” - Group B
“+” - Group M

Dimensions II and III

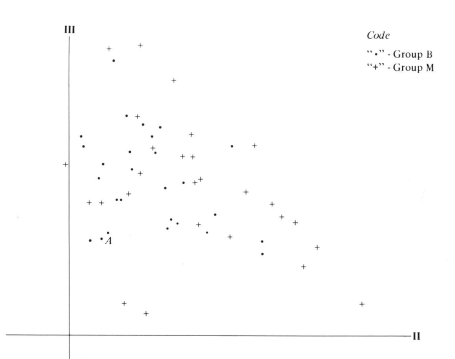

Code
".•” - Group B
“+” - Group M

weight to axis II, and moderate weight to axis III. Generally speaking, business students gave more weight to axis I than did music majors. Moreover, greater heterogeneity (and higher dimensionality of solution) were noted for the music majors.

A Hybrid Approach. The authors are currently experimenting with a hybrid approach which combines features of both the Tucker-Messick and Carroll-Chang models. A difficulty with the Carroll-Chang model is the large number of rather unimportant dimensions that might conceivably occur. Scores on these axes would be treated as error variance if not enough subjects were to share the dimensions to make their effect felt in the group stimulus space. In the hybrid approach the subject by similarities matrix would first be "factored" by a non-metric analogue of the Tucker-Messick procedure. Subject clusters would then be obtained and representative subjects selected from each cluster.

The Carroll-Chang model would then be applied both *within* each cluster and across clusters, using data for the representative subjects as the appropriate set of similarities vectors in the latter case. In this way the fine structure of each cluster would be obtained as well as shared dimensions across clusters for the representative subject of each point of view. So far our experience with this hybrid approach is too meager for useful evaluation, but its rationale appears to be appropriate for the kinds of empirical problems in which we are interested.

Configuration Invariance Over Changes in
Scenario and Composition of Stimulus Set

Another special topic of interest to applied researchers concerns the invariance of stimulus configurations over changes in: (a) scenarios under which the similarities judgments are obtained and (b) changes in the composition of the stimulus set. As discussed in Chapter 2, in the Euclidean distance model we mean invariance up to a similarity transformation—translation, uniform stretching of the axes, reflection, and rotation. None of these transformations will affect the rank order of the derived interpoint distances.

Scenario Influences. Most similarities judgments are obtained on an unstructured basis where the subject is asked to give responses regarding "overall" similarity for pairs of stimuli. Indeed, the rationale for this approach is to find out what dimensions are evoked by the subject when he is *not* constrained to make comparisons along any preselected set of scales. It seems reasonable to suppose, however, that the dimensions which are evoked are context bound.

As an example, take the case of brands of soft drinks; if no scenario is specified, it is possible that dimensions like "caloricness" or "lightness of taste" may be evoked. However, if the scenario "appropriateness for serving as mixers for alcoholic beverages" is used, other attributes, e.g., "degree of carbonation," "cola versus non-cola" might be evoked.

To the authors' knowledge no extensive study of the effect of conditions of product or service use on similarity judgments has been made as yet. From an operational standpoint it is quite feasible to develop second-order configurations (a "mapping of maps") where the points are scenarios and where scenario similarity is based on the correspondence of stimulus configurations under each scenario.

Such work could lead to a more extensive investigation of consumers' cognitions in which a "basic" configuration—or "superspace"—is related to a set of context-bound sub-configurations. The authors have explored this notion in the preference domain (see Chapter 4) but much more research remains to be done on the question of scenario influence on similarities and preference judgments.

Changes in Stimulus Set Composition

A companion problem associated with the scaling of similarities judgments concerns the effect of changes in the composition of the stimulus set on interpoint distances of core set items. Do these interpoint distances "stay put" as other items are added to or deleted from the set? We have explored this question in two studies involving automobile brands [11] and T.V. shows [13] with encouraging results regarding configuration invariance. However, in both of these studies the changes did not involve marked disparities in the composition of the stimulus set in which the core items were embedded.

It seems to us that serious study of similarities judgments will have to consider interrelationships among stimulus domains, including those stimulus domains which appear to form nested sets—for example, cola drinks, soft drinks, all beverages. Here one would be interested in the dimensions evoked for within-class discrimination when cola drinks are embedded, say, in the class of all soft drinks.

Multi-Way Matrices

Up to this point our discussion has emphasized the traditional two-way matrix form, e.g., stimuli by stimuli or persons by similarities vectors, in the case of points of view analysis. Many instances arise in the analysis of similarities data where the data entail multi-way matrices, e.g., persons by concepts by scale ratings or even persons by concepts by scale ratings by occasions.

Two models—both metric—have been proposed recently for dealing with multi-way matrices. Tucker has advanced a procedure, *multi-mode factor analysis* [29] which is capable of dealing with such multi-way matrices. A feature of this procedure is the development of a central or "core" matrix which is operated upon by transformation matrices that summarize data by various components of the multi-way matrix.

Carroll and Chang's shared space model (named INDSCAL for *In*dividual *D*ifferences *Scal*ing) described earlier is similar in spirit to the Tucker model and can be generalized to quasi-nonmetric form.[5] At this stage in the state of the art neither model has been applied extensively. We speculate, however, that extensions of scaling methods to multi-way matrices will engage the attention of many researchers in the future. This kind of extension appears needed for a more complete understanding of the interconnections among the many facets [15] by which similarities data can be described.

SUMMARY

Our objective in this chapter has been to discuss the analysis of similarities data from both a conceptual and empirical point of view. The earlier sections of the chapter emphasized the assumptions underlying distance models of proximity data, the types of proximity matrices that can be represented by distance models and the computational features of various algorithms. Some of these algorithms were demonstrated in the analysis of artificial data.

We then turned to empirical matters concerning the analysis of proximities— mainly, methods of data collection and procedures for interpreting the scaling solutions. As was described, both of these substantive areas provide extensive opportunities for additional research since little is known about the correspondence of various data collection procedures and alternative methods of configuration interpretation.

The last major section of the chapter dealt with a variety of special issues—individual difference models, scenario dependence, and extension of scaling techniques to multi-way matrices. These topics reveal both the potential power of scaling methods and, at the same time, the many problems that remain for further study, if the potential of this methodology is to be realized in marketing research.

REFERENCES

1. R. W. Beals, D. H. Krantz, and Amos Tversky, "The Foundations of Multidimensional Scaling," MMPP 67-2, Michigan Mathematical Psychology Program, University of Michigan, April 1967.

2. F. J. Carmone, P. E. Green, and P. J. Robinson, "TRICON—An IBM 360/65 FORTRAN IV Program for the Triangularization of Conjoint Data," *Journal of Marketing Research,* Vol. 5 (May 1968), pp. 219–20.

3. J. D. Carroll and J. J. Chang, "A General Index of Nonlinear Correlation and Its Application to the Interpretation of Multidimensional Scaling Solutions," *American Psychologist,* Vol. 19 (1964), p. 540.

4. J. D. Carroll and J. J. Chang, "Relating Preference Data to Multidimensional Scaling Solutions via a Generalization of Coombs' Unfolding Model," mimeographed, Bell Telephone Laboratories, Murray Hill, N.J., 1967. Also, see

[5]It should also be mentioned that Carroll and Chang's canonical decomposition procedure, used in their INDSCAL model [5], can be generalized to nonmetric (not merely quasi-nonmetric) form if used as a multi-mode factoring procedure.

J. D. Carroll, "Individual Differences and Multidimensional Scaling," mimeographed, Bell Telephone Laboratories, Murray Hill, N.J., 1969.

5. J. D. Carroll and J. J. Chang, "A New Method for Dealing with Individual Differences in Multidimensional Scaling," mimeographed, Bell Telephone Laboratories, Murrary Hill, N.J., 1969.

6. Norman Cliff, "Orthogonal Rotation to Congruence," *Psychometrika*, Vol. 31 (1966), pp. 33-42.

7. C. H. Coombs, *A Theory of Data* (New York: John Wiley & Sons, 1964).

8. P. E. Green, F. J. Carmone, and P. J. Robinson, "A Comparison of Perceptual Mapping Via Confusions Data and Direct Similarity Judgments," in R. L. King (ed.), Proceedings of the Denver Conference of the American Marketing Association (Chicago: American Marketing Association, 1968), pp. 323-34.

9. P. E. Green and Arun Maheshwari, "A Note on the Multidimensional Scaling of Conditional Proximity Data," *Journal of Marketing Research*, Vol. 7 (February 1970), pp. 106-110.

10. P. E. Green, Arun Maheshwari, and V. R. Rao, "Self Concept and Brand Preferences: An Empirical Application of Multidimensional Scaling," *Journal of the Market Research Society*, Vol. 11 (1969), pp. 343-60.

11. P. E. Green, Arun Maheshwari, and V. R. Rao, "Dimensional Interpretation and Configuration Invariance in Multidimensional Scaling: An Empirical Study," *Multivariate Behavioral Research*, Vol. 6 (April 1969), pp. 159-80.

12. P. E. Green and T. W. Morris, "Individual Differences Models in Multidimensional Scaling: An Empirical Comparison," working paper, University of Pennsylvania, April 1969.

13. P. E. Green and V. R. Rao, "Configuration Invariance in Multidimensional Scaling: An Empirical Study," Proceedings of the Cincinnati Conference of the American Marketing Association, Cincinnati, Ohio (Chicago: American Marketing Association, 1969).

14. Marshall Greenberg, "A Variety of Approaches to Nonmetric Multidimensional Scaling," paper presented at the 16th International Meeting of The Institute of Management Sciences, New York, March 1969.

15. Louis Guttman, "A General Nonmetric Technique for Finding the Smallest Coordinate Space for a Configuration of Points," *Psychometrika*, Vol. 33 (1968), pp. 469-506.

16. R. M. Johnson, "Market Segmentation—A Comparison of Techniques," paper presented at the 16th International Meeting of The Institute of Management Sciences, New York, March 27, 1969.

17. G. A. Kelly, *Psychology of Personal Constructs* (New York: Norton Publishing Co., 1955).

18. J. B. Kruskal, "Multidimensional Scaling by Optimizing Goodness of Fit to a Nonmetric Hypothesis," *Psychometrika*, Vol. 29 (1964), pp. 1-27.

19. J. B. Kruskal, "How to Use M-D-SCAL, a Program to do Multidimensional Scaling and Multidimensional Unfolding," Version 4 and 4M of M-D-SCAL (all in FORTRAN IV), mimeographed, Bell Telephone Laboratories, Murray Hill, N.J., 1968.

20. J. C. Lingoes, "An IBM 7090 Program for Guttman-Lingoes Smallest Space Analysis":
SSA-I, *Behavioral Science*, Vol. 10 (1965), pp. 183-4
SSA-II, *Behavioral Science*, Vol. 10 (1965), p. 487

SSA-III, *Behavioral Science*, Vol. 11 (1966), pp. 75–6
SSA-IV, *Behavioral Science*, Vol. 11 (1966), p. 407

21. J. C. Lingoes, "A General Nonparametric Model for Representing Objects and Attributes in a Joint Metric Space," in J. C. Gardin (ed.), *Les Compte-rendus de Colloque International sur L'emploi des Calculateurs en Archeologie: Problemes Semiologiques et Mathematiques* (Marseilles: Centre National de la Recherche Scientifique, 1969); J. C. Lingoes, "An IBM 360/67 Program for Guttman-Lingoes Smallest Space Analysis–PI," *Behavioral Science*, Vol. 14 (1969), in press.

22. V. E. McGee, "The Multidimensional Analysis of 'Elastic' Distances," *British Journal of Mathematical and Statistical Psychology*, Vol. 9 (1966), pp. 181-96.

23. V. E. McGee, "Multidimensional Scaling of N Sets of Similarity Measures: A Nonmetric Individual Differences Approach," *Multivariate Behavioral Research*, Vol. 3 (April 1968), pp. 233-48.

24. J. E. Miller, R. N. Shepard, and J. J. Chang, "An Analytical Approach to the Interpretation of Multidimensional Scaling Solutions," *American Psychologist*, Vol. 19 (1964), pp. 579-80.

25. J. P. N. Phillips, "A Procedure for Determining Slater's *i* and All Nearest Adjoining Orders," *British Journal of Mathematical and Statistical Psychology*, Vol. 20 (November 1967), pp. 217-25.

26. R. N. Shepard and J. D. Carroll, "Parametric Representation of Nonlinear Data Structures," in P. R. Krishnaiah (ed.), *Multivariate Analysis* (New York: Academic Press, 1966), pp. 561-92.

27. W. S. Torgerson, *Theory and Methods of Scaling* (New York: John Wiley & Sons, Inc., 1958).

28. W. S. Torgerson, "Multidimensional Scaling of Similarity," *Psychometrika*, Vol. 30 (1965), pp. 379-93.

29. L. R. Tucker, "The Extension of Factor Analysis to Three-Dimensional Matrices," in N. Frederiksen and H. Gulliksen (eds.), *Contributions to Mathematical Psychology* (New York: Holt, Rinehart & Winston, 1964), pp. 109-27.

30. L. R. Tucker and Samuel Messick, "An Individual Differences Model for Multidimensional Scaling," *Psychometrika*, Vol. 28 (1963), pp. 333-67.

31. F. W. Young and W. S. Torgerson, "TORSCA, A FORTRAN IV Program for Shepard-Kruskal Multidimensional Scaling Analysis," *Behavioral Science*, Vol. 12 (1967), p. 498.

32. F. W. Young, "TORSCA, An IBM Program for Nonmetric Multidimensional Scaling," *Journal of Marketing Research*, Vol. 5 (August 1968), pp. 319-21.

CHAPTER FOUR

Analysis of
Preference Data

This chapter is concerned with the analysis of preference data, the second major application area for multidimensional scaling methods. The format will be similar to that of the preceding chapter and the following main topics will be discussed: (a) conceptual structure and models for portraying preference judgments; (b) computational procedures and results; (c) empirical problems, including data collection and solution interpretation; (d) special issues, including evaluation function problems and the analysis of preferences for stimulus "bundles."

First the concept of preference is described and is related to various types of models—the distance model, the vector model, and the compensatory distance model. This introduction involves a discussion of preference matrices and the types of algorithms appropriate for analyzing either preference data alone or a combination of similarities and preference data (covering the same group of stimuli and respondents). We show the behavior of some of these algorithms in the analysis of synthetic data of known characteristics.

The next section of the chapter discusses the major empirical problems associated with the analysis of preferences, including alternative data gathering methods and procedures for the interpretation of joint space configurations.

The concluding section discusses a variety of special topics in preference analysis, including the relationship of choice probability to ideal point and vector models, the problem of indifference relations, and decision rules used to choose among multi-attribute alternatives.

MODELS OF PREFERENCE JUDGMENTS

A variety of models have been proposed for the analysis of preference judgments. For our purposes they can first be divided into those utilizing preference judgments only versus those which are appropriate for analyzing both similarities data and preference data, collected from the same respondents on the same set of stimuli. Each class is discussed in turn.

Models Based on Preference Data Only

By far the most attention by psychometricians has been paid to models using preference data only. The key objective in these models is: given a set of preference data of N subjects for n stimuli, develop a joint space of subjects and stimuli that permits additional inferences to be drawn about the subjects, stimuli, or both. In the case of either metric or nonmetric approaches, nothing further can be done if each subject gives exactly the same preference order to the same set of stimuli. Constraints enter only when *disparate* scale values or orderings of the same stimuli are observed across subjects.

All models based on preference data alone must assume homogeneity of perception if differences in preference are not to be confounded with differences in perception.[1] The models also assume that the (implied) perceived dimensions constitute the arguments of the value (or utility) function and that preferences differ across subjects. Given these common assumptions, we may then classify the major models by the descriptors: (a) type of representation—distance models, vector models, or compensatory distance models; and (b) type of algorithm—metric versus nonmetric. Our discussion is organized according to the first descriptor.

Distance Models. Distance models have already been encountered in our discussion of similarities data. The conceptual notion underlying the distance model in the context of preference is the ideal point [8], a hypothetical stimulus possessing a specific combination of "scores" on the underlying (perceptual) dimensions. For the moment we assume that preference is maximum at the ideal point and declines symmetrically in all directions as one moves away from the ideal. This conceptualization is pictured in **Figure 4-1** for the case of a single subject. The right-hand panel of the figure illustrates the associated isopreference curves, in this case a series of concentric circles of increasing radius. All stimulus points on a given isopreference curve are assumed to be equally preferred.

In either the metric or nonmetric case the assumption here is that the dimensions of the joint space are multidimensional interval scaled and the interpoint distance between any pair of points—ideal to ideal, ideal to stimulus, stimulus to stimulus—is ratio scaled. The joint space configuration is assumed to be unique up to a similarity transform (assuming a Euclidean metric).

---

[1]It is relevant to point out that various types of "weighted" unfolding models (using only preferences as input data) could be constructed in which differential weights (including the possibility of zero weights) are assumed to be due to intersubject differences in perception. If so, however, these perceptual differences would be confounded with differences in dimension salience for preference alone.

FIGURE 4-1

ILLUSTRATIVE UTILITY FUNCTION AND ISOPREFERENCE CONTOURS

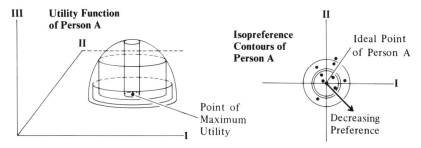

In short, the assumption structure of the distance model applied to preferences is quite similar to that already noted in our discussion of similarities data. The principal distinction is that we deal with an off-diagonal matrix of input data, consisting of relations on points drawn from two different sets.

Types of input data may again be conditional or unconditional, as shown in panels (a) and (b), respectively, of **Figure 4-2**. In the case of conditional proximities we do not assume that data values are comparable across rows. In the case of unconditional data we assume that all cell values in the off-diagonal matrix are comparable, a rather strong assumption. Another way of putting this is to say that the parameter values of the utility function linking manifest preferences to distance can be idiosyncratic in the first case, while in the second case all individuals share the same parameterized utility function. (We do assume in both cases, however, that all individuals share the same functional *form* of utility function, e.g., that it is monotonic.)

Distinctions among algorithms for scaling preference data rest on the questions of: (a) conditional versus unconditional input data; and (b) metric versus ordinal assumptions regarding the preference values. In the case of conditional proximities the Kruskal M-D-SCAL IV program [12] and the Guttman-Lingoes SSAR-II program [13] can be used for ranked data. In addition, the M-D-SCAL IV program can be used for prespecified preference functions (linear, quadratic, etc.) and, as such, can perform a metric scaling of the data. Finally we should mention that Carroll and Chang's parametric mapping program [16] can also be used for "unfolding" purposes [8], using the "smoothness" criterion discussed in Chapter 3. In this case the subjects' preference functions need not be either monotonic or of the same functional form.

If we allow comparisons *across* rows, panel (b) of Figure 4-2, a variety of programs, including Guttman and Lingoes' SSAR-I [13] and Young's TORSCA 9 [22] programs can be used in the nonmetric case, as well as M-D-SCAL IV. Moreover, the factor analytic portion of TORSCA 9 can be used for preference data in which a linear relation is assumed between preference values and, say, distances from ideal point, as can M-D-SCAL IV (using linear or other specified functional forms).

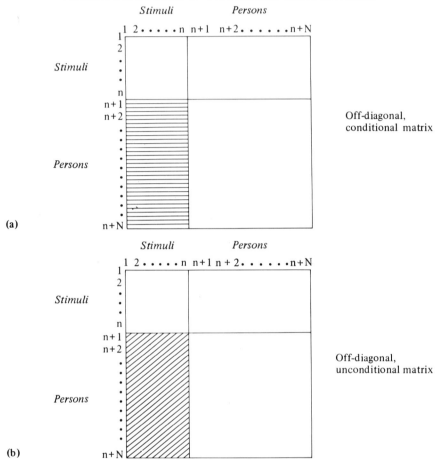

FIGURE 4-2
ALTERNATIVE FORMS OF PREFERENCE DATA MATRICES

The objective of using any of these methods is the development of a joint space of $N + n$ points from manifest relations on only a subset of those points, namely, the off-diagonal input data matrix, conditional or unconditional, as the case may be. If the model holds, *all* distances are assumed to be comparable, including ideal-ideal and stimulus-stimulus, even though no relations on these pairs of pairs are observed.

The principal danger in working with so few inequality constraints, in the case of the nonmetric approaches, is that the configuration might not be well determined. We return to this point when we later demonstrate the use of some of the above programs in the context of synthetic data.

Vector Models. The traditional factor analytic model is the (metric) prototype of this class. The first model of this type was proposed by Tucker [20] for dealing with metrically scaled preferences. Tucker assumed that all respondents shared the same perceptual space. However, their preferences were assumed to be linearly related to the projections of the stimulus points on each respondent's specific (undimensional) vector, which is interpreted as the set of weights he applied to each of the basic dimensions in arriving at a unidimensional scale of preference values.

In terms of Figure 4-2 we first deal with the off-diagonal, conditional proximity matrix—panel (a)—where we assume that scale comparisons are maintained within rows only. The metric version of the vector model makes the major assumption that preference changes linearly with the "saturation" of a stimulus j on dimension k. As consequences of this assumption: (a) one can have "mediocre" stimuli which are not preferred by any subject; and (b) all "ideal" points lie outside the range of stimuli (as a matter of fact, are infinitely distant in directions defined by the vectors).

Figure 4-3 shows the effect of these assumptions graphically. We note that different preference values are accounted for by different vector directions (the

FIGURE 4-3
ILLUSTRATIVE VECTOR MODEL AND ISOPREFERENCE CURVES

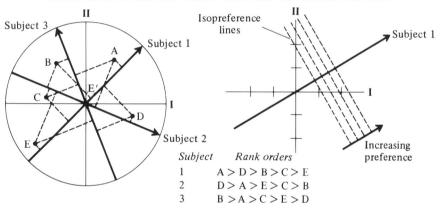

Subject	Rank orders
1	A > D > B > C > E
2	D > A > E > C > B
3	B > A > C > E > D

vectors being conventionally scaled to unit length). We see that stimulus C, for example, is neither most nor least preferred by any of the three subjects.[2] Finally, the scale values for each subject are read off by projecting each stimulus point on to each vector, in turn.

In this version of the metric vector model we are free to choose a unit and zero point independently on each coordinate axis. The coordinate axes are independent interval scales and we can compare stimulus points *only on each axis separately*. The projections of stimulus points on each subject's preference vector are defined only up to an interval scale transformation.

---

[2] A less ambiguous illustration of a mediocre stimulus is point E', shown near the origin in the left panel of Figure 4-3. In this case *no* vector could be found in which point E' projects higher than all of the other points.

On the other hand, if we assume that all preference values are comparable across subjects (Figure 4-2b), the subject weights on each axis are interval scaled with *fixed* zero point and so are the stimulus values on each preference vector. This is because we assume that all preference scales are comparable across rows. Even here, however, we can compare stimulus points only on each axis separately, since we are allowed free choice of unit.[3]

Since the development of Tucker's model,[4] Shepard and Kruskal [17] and Roskam [15] have proposed nonmetric versions of the vector model.[5] In these formulations one finds a space of stimulus points and a set of vector directions (in a space of low dimensionality) such that the *order* of the stimulus point projections on each vector agrees as closely as possible to the orders observed in the off-diagonal, conditional proximity matrix. Moreover, Roskam [15] has formulated his model to handle both of the cases shown in Figure 4-2.

Carroll and Chang's MDPREF model [6] also uses a vector formulation which can handle, metrically, the case of either rank-ordered data or paired comparisons, utilizing the form of data relations shown in panel (a) of Figure 4-2.

All vector model formulations can be viewed as special cases of the distance model in which the ideal points are assumed to extend to infinity. Under this assumption the rank order of a set of stimulus points from the "ideal" would agree with the rank order of projections on the vector. Analogously, the isopreference "contours" in the two-dimensional case are then represented by a series of parallel lines, each line perpendicular to the subject's vector; this is demonstrated for subject 1 in the right-hand panel of Figure 4-3.

[3]By way of summary, we can say that in any vector model the solution is defined, at most, up to a linear transformation of the stimulus space and the "spaces" defined by the subject vectors. In the case where comparability across subjects' stated preference values is assumed, we still allow the possibilities of: (a) rotation; (b) magnification; and (c) reflection. Each axis of the stimulus space is defined as a separate interval scale with fixed zero point, and the subject weights are also defined up to this same form of scale. As such, we can compare stimulus points only on each axis separately; moreover, stimulus projections on subject vectors are defined only up to an interval scale transformation.

In the "conditional" case (Figure 4-2a) we allow all of the above transformation possibilities plus the possibility of shifting the origin of the space, amounting to free choice of an additive constant for each axis. Transformations of subject weights which merely preserved the sign pattern (or precisely reversed it) would be admissible since each dimension is considered to allow free choice of unit and origin (an affine transformation).

[4]Tucker's model originally solved for stimulus dimensions, only, via a multidimensional generalization of Thurstonian paired comparisons scaling. Probably the first model dealing with an off-diagonal, unconditional proximity matrix was proposed by Slater (see Patrick Slater, "The Analysis of Personal Preferences," *The British Journal of Statistical Psychology*, Vol. 13 (1960), pp. 119–35).

In this same context, mention should also be made of a more recent metric model proposed by Bechtel (see Gordon Bechtel, "Individual Differences in the Linear Scaling of Choice," paper presented at the meeting of the Psychometric Society in Princeton, New Jersey, April 1969).

[5]A related nonmetric (or "non-parametric") procedure, based on paired comparisons data, has also been formulated by Carroll and Chang (see J. D. Carroll and J. J. Chang, "Nonparametric Multidimensional Analysis of Paired-Comparisons Data," paper presented at the joint meeting of the Psychometric and Psychonomic Societies in Niagara Falls, October 1964).

Compensatory Distance Models. The compensatory distance model is a type of hybrid model, mentioned by Coombs [8] and formulated for the nonmetric case by Roskam [15]. In the case of preference data the model assumes that each subject "collapses" the multidimensional space to a unidimensional vector (similar in spirit to the vector model) but that an ideal point exists on his vector such that his observed ranking reflects increasing distance of stimulus projections on either side of the ideal point along the compensatory vector; thus, ideal points do *not* extend to infinity in this case. **Figure 4-4** illustrates this type of model.

FIGURE 4-4
COMPENSATORY DISTANCE MODEL

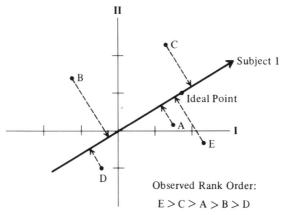

Observed Rank Order:

E > C > A > B > D

In the compensatory distance model an independent choice of unit on each coordinate axis is permitted as well as translation of the origin. Also the unit of each subject's scale is independent but is ratio scaled with an origin located at the ideal point. While coordinates of the stimuli are interval scaled they are not of common unit; hence interstimulus comparisons are confined to each dimension separately (unlike the distance model described earlier). If, however, data of the variety noted in panel (b) are obtained, one can compare the interpoint distances between pairs of stimulus points.

Because the compensatory distance model has been developed only recently, little experience has been accumulated on its behavior, with regard to either synthetic or real data. We mention it here only for the sake of completeness and refer the reader to a much more extensive account in Roskam [15].

Models Utilizing Similarities or Similarities-Preference Data

Basically there are two approaches for dealing with a joint space representation of stimuli and ideal points, using either similarities or similarities plus preference data. The one to be described first makes use of the "explicit ideal" concept. We then describe models which develop joint spaces from a combination of similarities and preference data.

Explicit Ideal Point Formulation. The notion of an explicit ideal is a simple one and requires no new analytical concepts. Essentially the approach involves including an $n + 1$ stimulus which is described as an *ideal* brand, service, company, or whatever. The respondent is asked to imagine what his ideal brand would be like. Operationally, similarities data are collected for all pairs of $n + 1$ stimuli. When these data are scaled by the usual distance model for describing similarities data, the distances of real stimuli from the hypothetical ideal are assumed to reflect decreasing preference, assuming the basic conditions surrounding the ideal point concept (maximal preference at the ideal and a utility function that declines monotonically with distance from the ideal point).

A metric version of the approach would consist of having N subjects rate an explicit ideal on the same set of prespecified attributes with which they rate the real stimuli. Derived measures of interpoint distance could then be scaled along the lines discussed in Chapter 3. In any event, the stimulus space would consist again of $n + N$ points with distances from the ideal given the same interpretation as above.

While the use of an explicit ideal is certainly economical of time and effort, there are some conceptual and empirical problems associated with this approach. First, it is not clear that respondents can conceptualize the notion of an explicit ideal; one may prefer to *infer* its position from their simple preference judgments. Second, when subjects move from a similarities to preference context they may weight the (perceptual) axes differentially; this effect would *not* show up clearly if the similarities comparisons involving the explicit ideal are merely mixed in with those involving real stimulus pairs. Finally, some evidence [14] exists to the effect that use of the explicit ideal does not predict (independently obtained) preference orderings for the same group of subjects covering the same set of real stimuli.

Although we do not want to reject out of hand the concept of explicit ideal, we believe there are more defensible models which exhibit greater flexibility in relating preferences to geometric representations obtained from similarities data. We comment next on those generalizations of the ideal point concept that have been proposed by Carroll and Chang.

Ideal Point Generalization. Carroll and Chang [5] have proposed two models for generalizing the Coombsian concept of ideal point. The models use *both* similarities and preference data for the same group of subjects and stimuli. Also, both models permit the development of a joint space for a single subject if desired. The models are distinguished on the basis of being metric versus nonmetric.

The metric version of the model assumes that an individual's utility function is *linearly* related to the weighted squared distance of each of the real stimuli from his ideal. The model is applied in the following way:

1. The similarities data of each of the N persons for all pairs of n stimuli are first scaled by one of the metric or nonmetric multidimensional scaling programs. This step may be preceded by a points of view analysis (Chapter 3) so as to

partition individuals by commonality of perception. The similarities configuration for those who exhibit commonality of perception represents one input to the Carroll-Chang model.

2. The second set of input data consists of the preference data (covering the same stimuli) of those persons presumed to exhibit homogeneity with respect to their similarities judgments, as obtained from the preceding step.

3. The approach then entails finding ideal point positions (or, in one case, vectors) of each subject, according to each of four models.

   (a) The simplest model is a vector model in which a direction is found for each person (in the common similarities space) whose stimulus point projections are maximally correlated with the scale values of the manifest preference data.

   (b) The second model is a straightforward Coombsian ideal point model in which all subjects are assumed to share the same "evaluative" space (possibly rotated and differentially stretched from the original similarities configuration).

   (c) The third (ideal-point) model subsumes the above and also permits idiosyncratic stretching of the axes, using as a reference the evaluative space of the average subject.

   (d) The fourth (ideal-point) model is completely individualistic and includes rotation *and* differential axis stretching for each subject (though within the framework of a common space).

4. In addition, the model allows for the possibility of positive ideal points, negative (anti-ideal) points or combinations whose "signs" vary by dimensions.

5. A goodness of fit measure (multiple correlation) is computed for each subject with regard to each model and F-ratios are also printed out. These can be used for running statistical significance tests on the contribution of more complex models in accounting for variance in the preference data.

In order to illustrate the above description somewhat less starkly, several of the features of the Carroll-Chang PREF-MAP model are shown in Figures 4-5 and 4-6. **Figure 4-5** shows the shapes and orientation of isopreference contours (illustrated for the positive ideal point case) while **Figure 4-6** shows various ideal point classes.

Let us examine Figure 4-5 first. Model 1, the simple vector model, merely assumes that preferences are linearly related to the projections of the points in the similarities space on the subject's compensatory vector (assumed to extend to infinity). Isopreference "contours" are a series of parallel lines perpendicular to the subject's "trade-off" vector. The direction cosines of the vector indicate the relative weights given to changes in each dimension.

Model 2 shows the case where the similarities space has first been differentially stretched (*after* possible rotation) to best accommodate the preference data of the average subject.[6] Then it is assumed that *all* subjects share this evaluative space. Individual differences are permitted in ideal point location,

---

[6]Note the *order* of the operations—rotation followed by differential stretching. If differential stretching preceded rotation, the combined effect would be tantamount to differential stretching alone.

FIGURE 4-5
TYPES OF POSSIBLE REPRESENTATIONS IN THE CARROLL-CHANG GENERALIZATION OF THE UNFOLDING MODEL

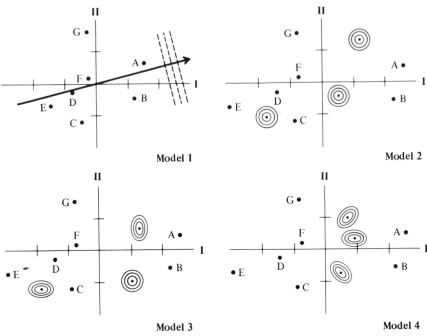

Model 1   Model 2

Model 3   Model 4

FIGURE 4-6
TYPES OF ISOPREFERENCE CONTOURS, ILLUSTRATED IN TWO DIMENSIONS FOR MODEL 2

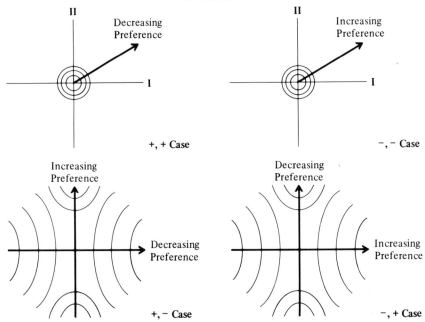

+, + Case   -, - Case

+, - Case   -, + Case

however. In two dimensions the isopreference contours are circles, *after* the space has been rotated (if necessary) and differentially stretched.

Model 3 allows individual subject weighting in the (possibly) rotated and differentially stretched space of the average subject. In this case the weights are represented (inversely) by the lengths of axes of the isopreference contours (ellipses) that are parallel to the coordinate axes.

Model 4 shows the completely general case where the individual subject can not only weight differentially the axes of the average subject's configuration (already differentially stretched and rotated), but is allowed his own rotation as well. Thus, the isopreference ellipses need not be parallel to the coordinate axes.

Figure 4-6 shows the variety of ideal points possible with models 2 through 4, illustrated for the case of two dimensions and model 2. (The origin has been translated to the ideal point for illustrative purposes.) In the typical (Coombsian) [+, +] case, preference declines with increasing distance from the ideal along each dimension. In the anti-ideal or [-, -] case, preference increases with increasing distance from the ideal. In the [+, -] or [-, +] cases the preference function takes the form of a saddle point with rectangular hyperbolas as isopreference contours.

As can be surmised from the above description, the Carroll-Chang model is quite flexible and provides a variety of ways of characterizing preference data in the (evaluatively transformed) similarities space. In our own research we have found that the simpler models (models 1 and 2) are often good representations of the data. From a psychological standpoint, however, the possibility of an *anti-ideal* point is of interest. This formulation allows respondents to prefer highly dissimilar stimuli—only dispreferred items need be seen as similar to each other. It is reasonable to suppose that a number of real world situations could be represented by this type of model.

The *nonmetric* version of the Carroll-Chang PREF-MAP model proceeds along quite similar lines. In this case, however, utility is assumed to be only monotonically related to weighted squared distance from the ideal (in models 2 through 4). Operationally, the program finds metric solutions for all models and then, by a series of monotone regressions, adjusts the solutions to obey the nonmetric constraints. The model is then parameterized on the basis of the regression weights obtained from the monotone regression.

A Comparison of Models

A number of approaches to the scaling of preferences or preference and/or similarities data have now been presented. As the reader may surmise, the authors display a predilection for the Carroll-Chang models, both from the standpoint of their ability to avoid problems of local minima and degeneracy (to be discussed in Chapter 6) and from the viewpoint of their completeness of representation. By "completeness" we mean, in part, the imputed weights applied to the dimensions of the similarities configuration as one moves from a perceptual to an evaluative frame of reference.

The models that develop joint-space configurations from preference data alone, of course, obviate the need for collecting similarities judgments. The trade-off consists of a loss of information regarding the transformation associated with "moving" from a similarities to a preference context, plus the strong assumption that all respondents "see" the stimuli in the same way. Later in this chapter we compare, empirically, the "unfolding" of preference data alone with an approach using one of the Carroll-Chang models.

SYNTHETIC DATA ANALYSES

So the reader can better judge the behavior of various approaches to the analysis of preference data, we return to an analysis of synthetic data of the type first shown in Figure 3-2 in the preceding chapter. This time, however, we employ *two* sets of points, tracing out the initials "AM." **Figure 4-7** shows the two-space configuration, consisting of 35 points in total.

FIGURE 4-7
SYNTHETIC DATA UTILIZED IN JOINT SPACE SCALING COMPUTATIONS

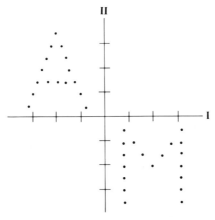

If one were to compute interpoint distances of *all* pairs of points, a total of 595 distances results. For reference purposes, **Figure 4-8** shows the effect of scaling the ranks of all 595 interpoint distances by means of two illustrative programs, TORSCA 9 and M-D-SCAL IV. As such, this step is similar to the synthetic data analyses already shown in the preceding chapter (Figures 3-3 through 3-6).

Now, however, suppose we pretend that the points representing letter "A" are stimuli and those representing letter "M" are ideal points in a common Euclidean space. In preparation for the TORSCA 9 unfolding run we computed the interpoint distances of each of the points in "A" from each of the points in "M." These 304 interpoint distances were ranked and then submitted

FIGURE 4-8
RESULTS OF MULTIDIMENSIONAL SCALING OF RANKED DISTANCE DATA—
ALL INTERPOINT COMPARISONS

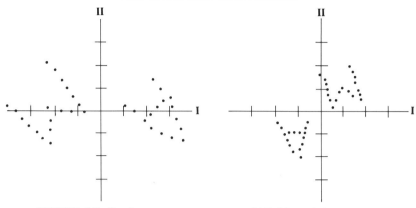

TORSCA 9 Scaling Program   M-D-SCAL-IV Scaling Program

to the program. In the M-D-SCAL IV unfolding run, however, input ranks of the 16 points comprising the letter "A" were compared only *within* each of the 19 rows comprising the letter "M." Thus, in the TORSCA 9 run we assumed that an off-diagonal, unconditional matrix was appropriate while in the M-D-SCAL IV run we assumed an off-diagonal, conditional matrix.[7]

The left-hand portion of **Figure 4-9**, summarizing the TORSCA 9 results, shows the effect on recovery of fewer constraints available for fixing the configuration (see the left-hand portion of Figure 4-8 for contrast). For ease of interpretation, the points comprising the letter "A" have been connected by a light line, while those comprising the letter "M" have been joined by a heavy line. We note some distortion in both letters, indicating that a reduction in rank information involving 595 distances to 304 distances provides less determinancy in the solution.

The effect is even more pronounced in the right-hand portion of Figure 4-9. While the letter "A" appears to be recovered quite well, the letter "M" (representing the 19 ideal points) is quite distorted, compared to the recovery achieved in the right-hand panel of Figure 4-8. This is not surprising in view of the fact that no *direct* constraints are placed on ideal point location in the M-D-SCAL IV application. However, the assumption of inter-utility comparisons is not required in this model either, which seems more realistic in applied research. In this case, then, ideal "points" might more appropriately be construed as regions insofar as the model's ability to portray their positions accurately is concerned.

[7]It is important to point out here that we are *not* comparing the relative effectiveness of the two programs—TORSCA 9 versus M-D-SCAL IV. Rather we are comparing the effect on solution "recovery" using unconditional versus conditional data. The M-D-SCAL IV program *could* have been used for both scalings (since it can handle either conditional or unconditional proximities) but it should be reiterated that the TORSCA 9 program is (currently) limited to the scaling of unconditional proximities.

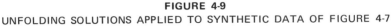

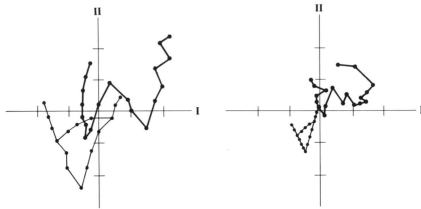

In summary, unfolding approaches—like those illustrated here—can be used to construct joint-space configurations from preference data alone. As was demonstrated, however, the reduction in the number of nonmetric constraints takes its toll in our ability to recover synthetic data configurations by means of these procedures. Similar limitations would apply to applications involving real data.

DATA COLLECTION METHODS

In Chapter 3 we discussed at some length the various procedures that can be used to obtain similarities data. In the case of preferences we are dealing in the Coombsian sense with the problem of ordering k out of n stimuli. This task subsumes common data collection methods like paired comparisons, triad ordering, and so on, up through a full rank order (where $k = n - 1$).

A second major approach to data collection is to use rating scales in which each stimulus is assigned a numerical value on, say, an 11-point scale. In the nonmetric approaches we assume that only the ordinal information provided by such data is relevant, while in the metric models we assume interval scale properties.

A third principal approach (associated with the notion of an explicit ideal point) involves the rating of both actual stimuli and the subject's explicit ideal on each of a series of attribute scales or constructs prespecified by the researcher. Preferences (or perhaps their obverse) can then be derived by computing some type of distance measure (across attributes) between the explicit ideal and the actual stimuli as positioned in attribute space. We examine, in turn, each of three approaches briefly.

Ordering Methods

Ordering methods—ranging from paired comparisons to full rank orders—appear to be one of the most popular procedures for obtaining preference data. Methods can be distinguished on the basis of the redundancy level [8] which the experimenter wishes to include in the data collection task. For example, if all $\frac{1}{2} n(n - 1)$ paired comparisons of n stimuli are presented to the subject, checks on the subject's transitivity of preference judgments are provided. In contrast, in the method of simple rank ordering, transitivity must be assumed; the subject is "not allowed" to be intransitive. On the other hand, the chances of respondent fatigue and decrease in motivation are reduced in the case of rank order tasks.

If redundant procedures like paired comparisons are used, two problems arise: (a) when should a subject's responses be rejected as being "too inconsistent"; and (b) how can some "best" complete rank order be obtained from data which turn out to display some inconsistency? The first problem can be approached by use of Kendall's coefficient of agreement [11] while the second problem can be handled in a variety of ways. In our own work we have favored the use of Slater's i [18] as a procedure for transforming intransitive data into some "best" complete order; the TRICON II program [4] provides a computational procedure for doing this, for either similarities or preference data.

The problem of respondent fatigue developing, if a highly redundant data collection procedure is used, can be mitigated by the use of various balanced incomplete block designs [3]. These designs still permit various consistency checks to be carried out but reduce considerably the number of independent pairwise comparisons which the subject is forced to make.

Rating Methods

Rating procedures of various types permit tied data and interval-scaled information (if the experimenter is willing to assume the latter). A variety of such approaches can be used: (a) two-category assignment, e.g., "like" versus "dislike"; (b) numerical "thermometer" scales; (c) degree of liking (or disliking) relative to a prespecified standard stimulus, and so on. Also, mention should be made of hybrid approaches in which, for example, paired comparisons are presented and the subject is asked not only to choose which member of the pair he prefers but also his "intensity" of preference.

Rating scales assume a kind of subjective anchoring on the part of the subject so that the same scale is applied to all stimuli throughout the task. Clearly, it is a prudent procedure to obtain at least a subset of replicated judgments in order to provide a check on the stability of the scale. Another problem associated with rating procedures is the tendency for some subjects to use only a small part of the scale. Such response bias tendencies may often be handled by standardizing each subject's ratings to, say, zero mean and unit standard deviation.

Rating scales can be appropriate when a large number of stimuli are involved and ordering methods—even ranking procedures—would place heavy judgmental demands on the subject. Here again, however, a hybrid approach can be used involving, first, the assignment of stimuli to a small set of ordered categories, and, second, a ranking of stimuli within each ordered category.

Rating scales also can be useful in establishing a respondent's neutral or indifference point by the inclusion of such categories as "neither like nor dislike." Here again this approach can be used in combination with ordering procedures.

Explicit Ideal Ratings

Under this method the actual stimuli and a hypothetical ideal are rated individually on a series of attribute scales, e.g., "saltiness of taste," "crunchiness," and so on. Preferences (or their obverse) are derived by the computation of distance of each real stimulus from the ideal. If the dimensions are all "evaluative" in the sense of "the more the better" for each attribute, then the method is not particularly revealing since the explicit ideal would always be presumed to score at the top of the scale for each attribute. In this case a vector model appears most appropriate.

We have already discussed some of the general limitations of explicit ideal point rating procedures and there is no need to repeat them here. These procedures represent a very popular data collection technique in marketing research and, in parallel with some of the procedures already described in this and the preceding chapter, may be useful in the interpretation of joint space configurations.

Other Methods

A number of other procedures are available for obtaining "value" data, including standard gamble methods [21], indifference mapping, the Churchman-Ackoff value measure [1], Thurstonian Case V scaling [19], and the like. Usually these approaches attempt to develop metric data, interval-scaled or stronger. Since our emphasis here is primarily on nonmetric methods, we do not explore these alternative approaches further. Such omissions are a matter of point of view, however, rather than a reflection of any criticism of the feasibility or usefulness of these procedures.

SOLUTION INTERPRETATION IN JOINT SPACE CONFIGURATIONS

Much of what we have to say on the problem of configuration interpretation has already been said in Chapter 3 in the context of similarities data. Since the interpretation of joint space configurations of stimuli and ideal points (or vectors) assumes that the perceptual dimensions—possibly transformed in an evaluative context—*also* underlie the preference judgments, our previous discussion is relevant here as well.

Two problems, however, are germane to a discussion of the interpretability of joint space configurations. The first problem concerns the interpretation of configurations as obtained from preference data alone and their correspondence to inter-stimulus distances obtained from similarities data. The second problem relates to scenario influences, a topic already discussed in Chapter 3 in the context of similarities data. Both problems are described from an empirical standpoint and are illustrated with data obtained from past pilot applications of multidimensional scaling.

The Unfolding Problem

As noted in previous chapters, the name "unfolding" is originally attributed to Coombs [8] as applying to procedures used to develop configurations from off-diagonal proximity matrices. In its original formulation the matrix was of the off-diagonal, conditional variety, the type of data usually obtained when N persons each rank n stimuli in terms of preference. In the unidimensional case the persons and stimuli were assumed to be positioned along a common attribute continuum. Each person's rank order was assumed to reflect the common scale "folded" at his ideal; the objective of the method was to unfold such data so as to reveal the joint scale of stimuli and persons. As was noted earlier, the concept was generalized to the multidimensional case by Bennett and Hays [2]. (Currently "unfolding" is a rather ambiguous label, presumably applicable to both intact proximities and off-diagonal proximities.)

Nonmetric programs like Kruskal's M-D-SCAL IV program, Torgerson and Young's TORSCA 9 program, and Guttman and Lingoes' SSAR II program represent nonmetric analogues of fully nonmetric methods. As discussed previously, their use in joint space scaling of off-diagonal proximity matrices assumes that all respondents share a common perceptual space but are allowed idiosyncratic ideal point positions. The empirical question explored here is: does one obtain a *derived* stimulus configuration from the analysis of preference data alone which agrees with that obtained by the independent scaling of similarities data collected from the same group of respondents?

This question was examined empirically by obtaining *both* similarities and preference data from each of four respondent groups with regard to seven graduate schools of business [9]. The stimuli were the graduate business schools of: (a) Carnegie-Mellon, (b) Chicago, (c) Columbia, (d) Harvard, (e) Massachusetts Institute of Technology, (f) Stanford, and (g) Wharton. The four respondent groups consisted of MIT students, Stanford students, Wharton students, and corporate recruiters. (See Chapter 1, Figure 1-2 for contrast; this earlier study involved only Wharton respondents.)

Figure 4-10 shows, for comparison purposes, each respondent group's two-space map as obtained independently from scaling their similarities data. The

FIGURE 4-10
STIMULUS CONFIGURATIONS FROM ANALYSIS OF DIRECT SIMILARITIES
DATA BY RESPONSE GROUP

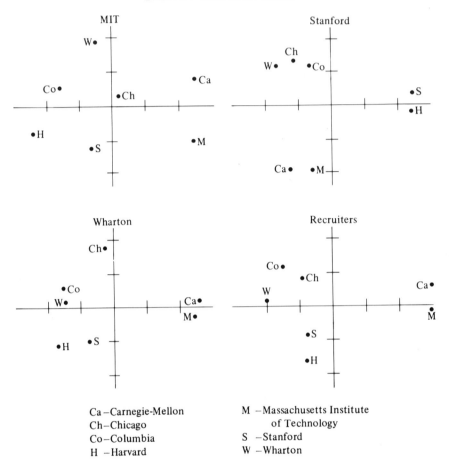

Ca – Carnegie-Mellon   M – Massachusetts Institute
Ch – Chicago   of Technology
Co – Columbia   S – Stanford
H – Harvard   W – Wharton

data were pooled over 15 respondents, in each case after a preliminary points of view analysis had established homogeneity in each group's subjects-by-similarities matrix. Preference data also were obtained from each of the four respondent groups and were submitted to the following programs: (1) TORSCA 9, (2) M-D-SCAL IV, and (3) Parametric Mapping, for the purpose of "unfolding" the off-diagonal, conditional proximities matrices.[8]

The *stimulus* interpoint distances derived from the unfolding procedures

[8] In the case of the TORSCA 9 Program, we are continuing to assume that the matrix is off-diagonal, unconditional; this assumption was made to compare the results with M-D-SCAL IV and parametric mapping which can scale conditional proximity matrices.

were then correlated with their counterparts obtained in the standard (calibration) phase, based on direct similarities judgments (Figure 4-10).

The almost universally poor "recovery" of the "standard" configurations (based on direct similarities data) is summarized in Table 4-1. The table shows the interpoint distance correlations for each program and each respondent group. The "recovery" is seen to be uniformly poor.

TABLE 4-1

CORRELATIONS OF INTERPOINT DISTANCES OF STANDARD VERSUS
"UNFOLDED" STIMULUS CONFIGURATIONS BY RESPONSE
GROUP AND METHOD

	Respondent Groups			
	MIT	*Stanford*	*Wharton*	*Recruiters*
TORSCA 9	−0.10	0.47	0.72	0.07
M-D-SCAL IV	−0.13	−0.26	0.24	0.43
Parametric Mapping. . . .	0.19	0.56	0.41	0.19

When the same unfolding solutions were *canonically correlated* (permitting rotation and differential stretching of the perceptual dimensions) with their counterpart coordinate values of Figure 4-10, the results were, with virtually no exceptions, uniformly excellent, i.e., canonical correlations of 0.9 or higher for the first linear compound.

In effect, then, the unfolding solutions were providing not the "perceptual" configurations (obtained from the similarities data) but rather a configuration which was rotated and differentially stretched so as to reflect the saliences of the perceptual dimensions in the context of preference. This type of transformation is seen graphically in **Figure 4-11** which shows an application of the Carroll-Chang ideal point generalization (metric version) to the *combined* similarities and preference data.

As will be recalled, the Carroll-Chang model permits vectors or ideal points to be positioned in the (possibly rotated and differentially stretched) similarities space so as to accommodate best the preference data.[9] Figure 4-11 shows that the dimensions did indeed receive different saliences as subjects "moved" from perceived to evaluative spaces.

The above example shows rather forcibly the distinction that can exist between "perceived" and "evaluative" stimulus spaces. This distinction is one of the reasons why we believe the Carroll-Chang approach provides a more

[9]The comment applies most appropriately to the ideal point—rather than vector—model. As mentioned earlier, a vector (as opposed to ideal point) model will fit as well to a linearly transformed configuration as the configuration itself, assuming the transformation is non-singular. What *can* be said, however, is that a configuration obtained by application of unfolding or vector models to preference data *alone* will not, in general, be related to (an independently obtained) perceptual configuration by a similarity transform but, at most, by the weaker class of linear transforms. This latter transform permits rotation of the configuration followed by differential axis stretching. As such, the rank order of interpoint distances is *not* preserved.

FIGURE 4-11

JOINT SPACE CONFIGURATIONS OBTAINED FROM A COMBINED ANALYSIS OF
SIMILARITY AND PREFERENCE DATA (CARROLL-CHANG METRIC MODEL)

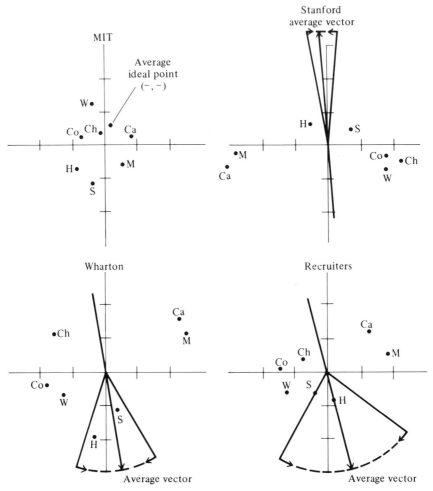

complete and flexible procedure for dealing with preferences, albeit at the expense of requiring the collection of similarities as well as preference data.

Scenario Influence on Preference Judgments

In Chapter 3 we pointed out a general belief that both similarities and preferences are context bound. In the case of preferences it seems reasonable to suppose that a variety of ideal points could exist, conditional upon the use situation or, perhaps, the general problem solving context confronting the respondent. For example, dessert preferences could easily be conditional upon such scenarios as: (a) "after a full meal;" (b) "late evening snack;" or (c) "appropriateness for a bridge club meeting," and so on.

If the specific scenario can be described rather precisely, it seems to us that the notion of a single ideal point or vector makes sense. On the other hand, the experimenter may be interested in the movement of either ideal point or vector in the evaluative space (or spaces) as the scenario changes. We illustrate this phenomenon by showing the results of some pilot research on this problem [10].

In this case the stimuli consisted of ten print advertisements and the respondents were either professional advertising people or graduate students (control group). Each respondent was asked to rank the ten advertisements according to his judgment of their relative ability to draw coupon responses, magazine unspecified. Next, the respondent was shown copies of six magazines: (a) *True*, (b) *Sport*, (c) *Popular Mechanics*, (d) *Guy*, (e) *Women's World*, and (f) *Men Today*, as candidate vehicles for the advertisements. After getting some idea of the general appearance and editorial format of the magazines, the respondent was asked to rank the same ten ads with regard to their relative ability to draw coupon responses for each magazine in turn.

Again, the Carroll-Chang generalization of the unfolding model was used, since similarities data were available for the same subjects. **Figure 4-12** shows the effect of vehicle on the joint space configurations of the average subject in each of four sub-groups (two clusters of experts and two clusters of students) who had first been partitioned into clusters on the basis of homogeneity of similarities data. We note from the chart that in most cases a vector model was adequate for representing the preference data.

In this study, with the exception of *Women's World*, the preference judgments did *not* appear to be highly sensitive to vehicle. To these subjects a "good ad" appeared to be a "good ad" independent of vehicle insofar as the five male-audience magazines were concerned. In other stimulus classes, however, it is quite possible that preferences might be highly conditioned upon scenario. If so, the Carroll-Chang approach appears to provide a useful way to portray such ideal point, or vector, "movements" as scenarios are altered.

SPECIAL ISSUES IN PREFERENCE ANALYSIS

A number of special topics arise in the analysis of preferences which have involved little substantive research to date. We comment on some of them briefly, more from the standpoint of posing them as areas for future investigation than reporting past research results; such research, for the most part, does not exist.

Segmentation Based on Joint Space Configurations

In the preceding chapter we discussed the possibility of relating individual differences in perceptual point of view to other respondent characteristics (socioeconomic, demographic, etc.). The same approach could be used in the

FIGURE 4-12

JOINT SPACE CONFIGURATIONS OF STIMULI AND EVALUATIONS—
CONTROL VERSUS EXPERT GROUP

C_1, C_2—Control Group Clusters
E_1, E_2—Expert Group Clusters

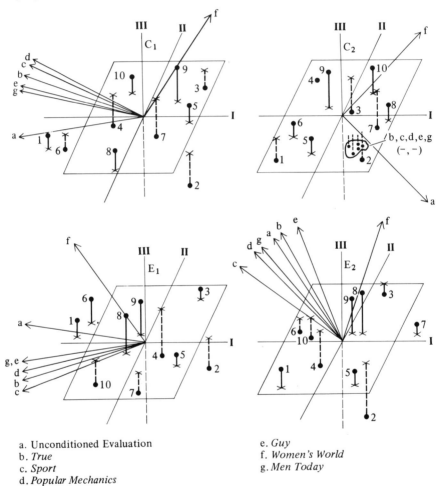

a. Unconditioned Evaluation   e. *Guy*
b. *True*   f. *Women's World*
c. *Sport*   g. *Men Today*
d. *Popular Mechanics*

case of joint space configurations of subjects' ideal point locations in evaluative space. Thus, in line with our discussion in the Introduction and Problem Setting, subjects could first be partitioned into reasonably homogeneous groups based on commonality of similarities data. These groups could then be further partitioned on the basis of commonality of transforms which lead to evaluative spaces (using the Carroll-Chang PREF-MAP models). Finally, subjects could be further partitioned on the basis of commonality of ideal point position or vector direction, as the case may be.

Various clustering methods (to be discussed in Chapter 5) could be used to assist in the partitioning task. One might then attempt to describe clusters in terms of *other* subject characteristics. Since the clusters would be formed on the basis of "independent" criteria (perceptions and preferences), multiple discriminant analyses might be employed in order to see which components of a vector of "external" characteristics contribute most highly to cluster discrimination. If such "predictor" variables *are* found, knowledge of them, in principle, could be useful in the formation of policy based on market segmentation objectives.

Probability of Choice Models

As also discussed in the Introduction and Problem Setting, research needs to be carried out on the relationship of probability of choice, in a purchase situation, to distance from ideal point (or in the case of a vector model, relative magnitude of projections on the vector). It is reasonable to assume, in the typical positive ideal point case, that probability of choice would decrease with increasing distance from ideal point.

One way to estimate the parameter values of the probability function would be to obtain brand switching data from members of a consumer panel, in addition to their similarities and preference data. Empirical fitting procedures could be used to estimate the probability choice function if stability can be assumed over the data collection period.

Another type of modeling approach would be to assume that the stimulus closest to the ideal is always chosen and that observed differences in choice are dependent upon the frequency with which various product uses (scenarios) appear. This approach would require a rather extensive collection of preference data, conditional upon various use situations and, of course, would also assume stability in the use-generating "mechanism."

A third possibility would be to develop a simulation in which various probability functions are tried out with a view toward "predicting" aggregate shares of market for each brand. Additional variables—availability, in-store dealing activity, etc.—might well have to be included for reasonably accurate predictions. Ultimately, of course, one would like to see if the market share of some new brand (or modification of an existing one) could be predicted by the output of the preceding sequence; this type of problem is being considered by Cook and Herniter [7]. Research on this class of problems is only just beginning. Such investigations are expected to be both expensive and time-consuming but are clearly vital to the prescriptive use of multidimensional scaling models in marketing.

Stimulus "Bundles"

Another topic of substantive interest concerns the prediction of preference for stimulus "bundles"—season tickets, investment portfolios, cereal combination packs, fringe benefit packages, etc.—from the values of their components.

Related to this question is the utility for "variety" and the question of "second choice" preferences, given that the respondent can obtain his first choice [8].

Again it seems reasonable to suppose that preferences for items are conditional upon the assortment already owned by the potential buyer. Little is known, however, concerning the decision procedures used in evaluating bundles as some function of the value of their components. The problem is quite a difficult one, and one that we are examining in our current research.

Evaluation Functions

Closely allied to the "bundles" problem are ones concerning the procedures that people use to evaluate multi-attribute items—vendors, houses, schools, automobiles. As discussed already in this chapter, most stimuli are perceived as multi-attribute items where one item can be better than another on one characteristic and worse on some other characteristic.

The study of people's evaluation functions, that is, the processes used to "collapse" partially ordered alternatives into a complete order, is fascinating in its own right. The breadth of application is considerable, ranging all the way from governmental and corporate decision-making to decisions made at the household level.

Aside from a few pilot level studies, research in this area is just beginning. We expect, however, that it will assume increasing importance in future research activity, not only by marketing researchers but by operations research analysts, political scientists, and economists as well.

SUMMARY

This chapter has covered a broad range of topics related to the joint space representation of preference or similarities-preference data. We started with a discussion of the conceptual basis and assumption structure underlying the major scaling models—the distance model, the vector model, and the compensatory distance model. This led to a demonstration of two of the major joint space scaling programs in the context of "recovering" known synthetic data configurations.

We then discussed a variety of empirical problems, including various data collection procedures for gathering preference data and some of the limitations associated with attempting to develop joint space representations from preferences alone. The influence of scenario was also described and illustrated by some pilot study results.

We concluded the chapter with brief discussions of special topics and areas for future research. These topics included issues arising in market segmentation, probability of choice models, and decision procedures utilized in choosing among multi-attribute alternatives.

REFERENCES

1. R. L. Ackoff, *Scientific Method: Optimizing Applied Research Decisions* (New York: John Wiley & Sons, Inc., 1962).

2. J. F. Bennett and W. L. Hays, "Multidimensional Unfolding: Determining the Dimensionality of Ranked Preference Data," *Psychometrika*, Vol. 25 (1960), pp. 27–43.

3. R. A Bradley and M. E. Terry, "Rank Analysis of Incomplete Block Designs," *Biometrika*, Vol. 39 (1952), pp. 324–45.

4. F. J. Carmone, P. E. Green, and P. J. Robinson, "TRICON–An IBM 360/65 FORTRAN IV Program for the Triangularization of Conjoint Data," *Journal of Marketing Research*, Vol. 5 (May 1968), pp. 219–20.

5. J. D. Carroll and J. J. Chang, "Relating Preference Data to Multidimensional Scaling Solutions via a Generalization of Coombs' Unfolding Model," mimeographed, Bell Telephone Laboratories, Murray Hill, N. J., 1967. Also see J. D. Carroll, "Individual Differences and Multidimensional Scaling," mimeographed, Bell Telephone Laboratories, Murray Hill, N. J., 1969.

6. J. J. Chang and J. D. Carroll, "How to Use MDPREF, A Computer Program for Multidimensional Analysis of Preference Data," mimeographed, Bell Telephone Laboratories, Murray Hill, N. J., 1969.

7. V. J. Cook and J. D. Herniter, "Preference Measurement in a New Product Demand Situation," in R. L. King (ed.), Proceedings of the Denver Conference of the American Marketing Association (Chicago: American Marketing Association, 1968), pp. 316–22.

8. C. H. Coombs, *A Theory of Data* (New York: John Wiley & Sons, 1964).

9. P. E. Green and F. J. Carmone, "Multidimensional Scaling: an Introduction and Comparison of Nonmetric Unfolding Techniques," *Journal of Marketing Research*, Vol. 6 (August 1969), pp. 330–41.

10. P. E. Green and F. J. Carmone, "Advertisement Perception and Evaluation: An Application of Multidimensional Scaling," working paper, University of Pennsylvania, May 1968.

11. M. G. Kendall, *Rank Correlation Methods* (London: Griffen Publishing Co., 1948).

12. J. B. Kruskal, "How to Use M-D-SCAL IV, a Program to Do Multidimensional Scaling and Multidimensional Unfolding," (Version 4 and 4M of M-D-SCAL, all in FORTRAN IV) mimeographed, Bell Telephone Laboratories, Murray Hill, N. J. 1968.

13. J. C. Lingoes, "An IBM 7090 Program for Guttman-Lingoes Smallest Space Analysis":

    SSAR I *Behavioral Science*, Vol. 11 (1966), p. 322
    SSAR II *Behavioral Science*, Vol. 11 (1966), p. 323
    SSAR III *Behavioral Science*, Vol. 11 (1966), p. 323
    SSAR IV *Behavioral Science*, Vol. 12 (1967), pp. 74–5

14. L. A. Neidell, "Physicians' Perception and Evaluation of Selected Ethical Drugs: An Application of Nonmetric Multidimensional Scaling to Pharmaceutical Marketing," unpublished doctoral dissertation, University of Pennsylvania, 1968.

15. E. E. Roskam, *Metric Analysis of Ordinal Data in Psychology* (Voorschoten, Holland: University of Leiden Press, 1968).

16. R. N. Shepard and J. D. Carroll, "Parametric Representation of Nonlinear Data Structures," in P. R. Krishnaiah (ed.), *Multivariate Analysis* (New York: Academic Press, 1966), pp. 561–92.

17. R. N. Shepard and J. B. Kruskal, "Nonmetric Methods for Scaling and for Factor Analysis," *American Psychologist*, Vol. 19 (1964), pp. 557–58.

18. Patrick Slater, "Inconsistencies in a Schedule of Paired Comparisons," *Biometrika*, Vol. 48, Nos. 3 and 4 (1961), pp. 303–12.

19. L. L. Thurstone, *The Measurement of Values* (Chicago: The University of Chicago Press, 1959).

20. L. R. Tucker, "Dimensions of Preference," E.T.S. Memo RM-60-7, Educational Testing Service, Princeton, N. J., 1960.

21. Amos Tversky, "Additivity Analysis of Choice Behavior: A Test of Utility Theory," MMPP 62-2, Michigan Mathematical Psychology Program, University of Michigan, May 1965.

22. F. W. Young, "TORSCA, an IBM Program for Nonmetric Multidimensional Scaling," *Journal of Marketing Research*, Vol. 5 (August 1968), pp. 319–21.

23. F. W. Young and W. S. Torgerson, "TORSCA, a FORTRAN IV Program for Shepard-Kruskal Multidimensional Scaling Analysis," *Behavioral Science*, Vol. 12 (1967), p. 498.

CHAPTER FIVE

Dimension-Reducing Methods and Cluster Analysis

In preceding chapters we have frequently mentioned the terms "objective space" and "cluster analysis." While our previous discussion emphasized the use of multidimensional scaling methods in the representation of psychological responses—namely, similarities and preferences—we also indicated from time to time that the methodology can be viewed as a means of data reduction and summarization. In this latter role the input need not be subjective response data at all. Our interest here is on reducing manifest data, portrayed as objects in variable space, into a space of fewer dimensions, with little loss in information.

We can, of course, turn the problem around and consider the dual question of reducing the number of objects by partitioning them into homogeneous groups, based on their "closeness" to one another in variable space. The first approach may be called reduced space analysis and the second, cluster analysis. We shall often consider the use of both approaches in tandem.

This chapter first discusses these dual problems in the context of nonpsychological data. After describing some of the basic characteristics of the data or "score" matrix we discuss both metric and nonmetric approaches to reduced space representation. We then turn to the topic of cluster analysis and describe the major characteristics of clustering procedures, including the choice of association coefficient, types of grouping algorithms, cluster description, and problems of statistical inference.

The concluding section discusses some recent developments in reduced space and cluster analysis, particularly a hybrid clustering, dimensional technique that appears useful in describing special classes of data structures.

THE DATA MATRIX

The key concept underlying the utilization of reduced space and cluster analysis is that in most real world situations multiple measurements on a set of objects

97

are partly redundant, i.e., associated in some way. (The dual of this assertion is that some pairs of objects, when considered across variables, are usually associated with each other; that is, if N objects were plotted in N-1 space we would generally not find all points equidistant from each other.)

While one can often take advantage of natural association to make predictions—as, for example, in regression analysis or discriminant analysis—situations occur in which no variable can be singled out as a dependent or criterion variable whose values are to be predicted by some function of another set of variables. We may still wish, however, to summarize the information provided by the whole set of objects-by-variables' "scores" into some more parsimonious structure which removes redundancy in the original set of data and/or attempts to preserve most of the information contained in the original data matrix.

In either case, the "raw input" to any such analysis consists of the data matrix. By this is meant a rectangular array of numerical entries whose informational content is to be summarized and portrayed in some way. For example, the computation of the mean and standard deviation of a unidimensional array is often done simply because we are unable to comprehend the meaning of the entire column of values. In so doing we often (willingly) forgo the full information provided by the data in order to understand some of its basic characteristics, e.g., central tendency and dispersion. The problem becomes even more complex when we have multiple measurements on a set of objects.

Table 5-1 shows a conceptual illustration of a data matrix. We note that the array consists of a set of objects (the N rows) and a set of variables (the n columns). The (i,j) th cell entry represents the value of object i on variable j. The objects may be people, things, concepts or events. The variables are characteristics, properties or attributes of the objects.

Cell values may consist of nominal, ordinal, interval, or ratio-scaled measurements or various combinations of these as we go across columns. The complete (row) *vector* of values is often called an object's *profile*.

In many cases the investigator is able to partition the data matrix into subsets of columns (or rows) on the basis of prior information. For example, suppose the first column of Table 5-1 is average weekly consumption of coffee by household and the other columns consist of various demographic and socioeconomic measurements of the N households. The analyst may wish to predict average weekly consumption of coffee from some linear combination of the n-1 remaining variables. If so, he has used prior judgment regarding how the dependence is to be described and, in this instance, would probably use multiple regression to establish the hypothesized functional relationship.

Quite frequently, however, we may have no reasonable basis for prior partitioning of the data matrix into criterion or predictor variables. Our purpose here may merely be to group objects into "similar" subsets (based on their correspondence over the whole profile of variables) or to portray the columns of the data matrix in terms of a smaller number of new variables (e.g., linear combinations of the original set) which retain most of the information in the

TABLE 5-1
ILLUSTRATIVE DATA MATRIX

Objects	1	2	3	Variables	j		n
1	X_{11}	X_{12}	X_{13}	...	X_{1j}	...	X_{1n}
2	X_{21}	X_{22}	X_{23}	...	X_{2j}	...	X_{2n}
3	X_{31}	X_{32}	X_{33}	...	X_{3j}	...	X_{3n}
.	.	.	.		.		.
.	.	.	.		.		.
.	.	.	.		.		.
i	X_{i1}	X_{i2}	X_{i3}	...	X_{ij}	...	X_{in}
.	.	.	.		.		.
.	.	.	.		.		.
.	.	.	.		.		.
N	X_{N1}	X_{N2}	X_{N3}	...	X_{Nj}	...	X_{Nn}

original data matrix. These are the cases with which this chapter is concerned. Both classes of procedures start with the data matrix or some set of measures derived from it.

REDUCED SPACE ANALYSIS

In earlier chapters we saw how a set of association measures (similarities data, for example) could be "dimensionalized" by multidimensional scaling techniques. We also saw how a set of stimuli in variable space could be converted into a set of "association" measures (e.g., distances) between each stimulus pair. In general, we can go from an association matrix to a dimensional representation and vice versa.

In reduced space analysis we usually, though not necessarily, start off with a data matrix like that conceptualized in Table 5-1. The objective here is to transform this matrix into one having the same number of rows but fewer columns, without serious loss in information. In finding this reduced space representation, however, we may go through the seemingly roundabout process of: (a) finding inter-object association measures; and, then, (b) transforming these measures back to a dimensional representation of the same number of objects (rows) but fewer columns.

Historically, the methods of factor analysis were used to perform this role. We shall briefly discuss one type of factoring—principal components factor analysis—as the major *metric* technique for reducing the variable space.

Metric Reduction—Principal Components Analysis

A factor in factor analysis is merely a linear combination of the original scores—assumed here to be at least interval scaled. Any set of weights, same or different over each column, plus or minus, might suffice. As a matter of fact, the various types of factoring methods are differentiated in terms of the bases upon which the weights are selected. Factor *scores* are obtained by merely finding for each object the numerical value of the linear combination obtained by substituting its original score values in the linear equation of the factor:

$$F = a_1 X_1 + a_2 X_2 + \cdots + a_n X_n$$

where the a_j are the factor weights.

If we then correlate each of these new columns of factor scores with the original variables, we obtain a set of factor *loadings*. A factor loading is defined simply as the correlation (across objects) of an original variable with a factor.

If the method of *principal components* is used, the weights are chosen in such a way that the successive factors (more specifically the successive components) will:

1. Account for a maximal portion of total variability in the data, subject to
2. Being mutually orthogonal to all previously obtained linear combinations.

That is, the first set of weights will lead to a set of component scores which account for maximum variance. The second set of weights will lead to a set of component scores, orthogonal to the first set, which maximally account for residual variance in the original variables. In general, each successive component will account for a decreasing portion of total variance in the original set of data.

A geometric demonstration of principal components analysis is shown in **Figure 5-1**. We assume that the original data matrix consists of the measurements of N objects on two variables. We note from the chart that the positions of the objects are portrayed as an elliptical "swarm" of points. The principal components are represented by a new set of axes drawn through the major and minor axes of the ellipse.

If we project the points onto the new axes and compute the variances of these projections, such variances are sequentially maximal, subject to each set of component scores being mutually orthogonal with previously extracted components. The first component displays the larger variance in component scores and the second (orthogonal) component accounts for all residual variance (in the case of two variables). The direction cosines of the angle of rotation can be viewed as the weights described earlier. Each component axis thus represents a linear combination of object scores on the original variables.

Factoring the Association Matrix. In practice one usually factors not the data matrix itself, but a set of association measures—cross products, covariances, correlations—that are *derived* from the data matrix.

If as many components are extracted as there are variables, the original association matrix (e.g., matrix of correlation coefficients) can be perfectly reproduced by a matrix product of the factor loadings.[1] Of course, in this case no

---

[1] This assumes a data matrix of full rank where $N > n$. The matrix product consists of the component loading matrix post-multiplied by its transpose.

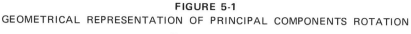

FIGURE 5-1

GEOMETRICAL REPRESENTATION OF PRINCIPAL COMPONENTS ROTATION

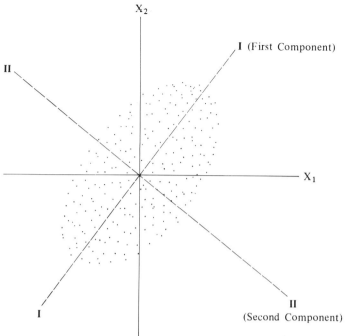

parsimony would be obtained, since one would have as many linear combinations (components) of the variables as there were variables to begin with. If "lesser" components are ignored, however, a close approximation to the original correlation matrix often can be obtained by using only the first few component loadings.

Metric Approach to Reduced Space Analysis. In terms of our emphasis on reduced space techniques, principal components analysis represents the major metric procedure for reducing the manifest variables space. In the usual case of R-technique (involving a variables' correlation matrix as the starting point for the component analysis) one can compute unit-variance scores for each object on each component. If weighted squared distances in component space are computed between object pairs, using component eigenvalues as weights, such measures will be proportional to squared interpoint distance in the original variables space if all components are extracted.[2]

If only the first m out of n components are extracted, the resulting interpoint distances will only approximate the squared interpoint distances between object pairs in the original variables space. The "information lost" is represented by the contribution to squared interpoint distance made by the $n - m$ compo-

[2] The "weights" in this case are the eigenvalues (sums of squares of the component loadings).

nents not extracted. By the nature of the principal components technique we are assured that each of the lesser components accounts for less variance in the original set of data than each of those which are extracted.

Gower [9] has shown that for any symmetric association matrix with elements $-\frac{1}{2} d_{ij}^2$ which can be put in the following form:

$$f_{ij} = e_{ij} - \overline{e}_i - \overline{e}_j + \overline{e},$$

(where $\overline{e}_i$ denotes row mean; $\overline{e}_j$ denotes column mean; and $\overline{e}$ denotes grand mean) such that F is positive semi-definite, the squared distance between points i and j is given by:

$$d_{ij}^2 = f_{ii} + f_{jj} - 2f_{ij}$$

As an illustration of this approach, suppose we started out with an interobjects' correlation matrix. Such Q-type correlations are related to interobject squared distances by

$$d_{ij}^2 = 2(1 - Q_{ij})$$

where: Q_{ij} is the product moment correlation between objects i and j.

If we were to use Gower's approach we would:

1. Convert the Q-type correlation matrix entries to squared distances, d_{ij}^2.
2. Form the matrix whose general entry is $e_{ij} = -\frac{1}{2} d_{ij}^2$.
3. Form the matrix F by double centering E.
4. Factor F by principal components.

If the above steps are taken, the k-th eigenvector of F (whose sums of squares are normalized to equal the k-th eigenvalue) yields coordinate values of the objects on the k-th principal component dimension.

Since a large variety of association measures—matching coefficients, correlations, covariances, etc.—can be expressed through suitable transformations as squared interpoint distances, the preceding approach is an extremely general one. We emphasize, however, that the approach is metric; we attempt to reproduce (up to a positive proportionality transformation) the numerical values of the input matrix F.

Nonmetric Reduced Space Analysis

In general, if the function relating interpoint distance between pairs of points to input data is nonlinear but monotonic, application of a metric procedure like principal components analysis will lead to a larger number of dimensions in which to portray the point locations in terms of orthogonal axes than would be the case with linear functions. However, what if we replace the objective of attempting to reconstruct the actual values of the input matrix by the objective of trying to reproduce only their *rank order*?

This "milder" objective will, in general, lead to a space of fewer dimensions. Moreover, it turns out that multidimensional scaling techniques—e.g., M-D-SCAL IV, TORSCA, the SSA series, parametric mapping—can be used as types of nonmetric factoring procedures. The input data can consist of a symmetric matrix of any type of association measure whose values can be weakly ordered and obey the metric axioms discussed in Chapter 2.

In addition to nonmetric programs that find a dimensional representation of a single set of points (e.g., objects) whose ranks of interpoint distances are monotonic with the original input data, other approaches leading to joint spaces can be employed. For example, Guttman and Lingoes' SSAR series [15] and their SSAP-I and SSAP-II programs [17] find *two* sets of points which obey certain between-set (or within and between-set) constraints. The vector models described in Chapter 4, as well as unfolding procedures, can also be used for the same general objective, depending upon the type of representation desired.

CLUSTER ANALYSIS

Cluster analysis, like reduced space analysis, is concerned with data matrices in which the variables have *not* been partitioned beforehand into criterion versus predictor subsets. In reduced space analysis our interest centered on reducing the variable space to a smaller number of orthogonal dimensions which maintained most of the information—metric or ordinal—contained in the original data matrix. Emphasis was placed on the variables rather than on the objects (rows) of the data matrix.

In cluster analysis our concern is with the *similarity of the objects*, that is the resemblance of their profiles over the whole set of variables. These variables may be the original set or may consist of a representation of them in reduced space. In either case the objective of cluster analysis is to find similar groups of objects, where "similarity" between each pair of objects is usually construed to mean some global measure over the whole set of characteristics—either original variables or derived coordinates, if preceded by a reduced space analysis.

In this section we discuss various methods of clustering and the key role that distance functions play as measures of the proximity of pairs of points. We first discuss the fundamentals of cluster analysis in terms of major questions concerning choice of proximity measure, choice of clustering technique, and descriptive measures by which the resultant clusters can be defined. We show that clustering results can be sensitive to the type of distance function used to summarize proximity between pairs of profiles.

We next discuss the characteristics of various computer programs that have been proposed for grouping profiles, i.e., for partitioning the rows (objects) of the data matrix. This is followed by brief discussions of statistics for defining clusters and the problems associated with statistical inference in this area.

Basic Questions in Cluster Analysis

The usual objective of cluster analysis is to separate objects into groups such that each object is more like other objects in its group than it is to objects outside the group. Cluster analysis is thus concerned ultimately with classification and represents a set of techniques which are part of the field of numerical taxonomy [7].

The typical clustering procedure that we shall discuss results in the assignment of each object to one and only one class. Objects within a class are usually assumed to be indistinguishable from one another. Thus we assume that the underlying structure of the data involves an unordered set of discrete classes. In some cases we may also view these classes as hierarchial in nature, with some classes divided into subclasses.

Clustering procedures can be viewed as "preclassificatory" in the sense that the analyst has not used prior judgment to partition the objects (rows of the data matrix). However, he is assuming that some of the objectives are heterogeneous, that is, that "clusters" exist. This type of presupposition is different from the case in discriminant analysis where *a priori* groups of objects have been formed on the basis of criteria *not* based on profile resemblance in the data matrix itself. Given no information on group definition in advance, the major problems of cluster analysis can be stated as:

1. What measure of interobject similarity is to be used and how is each variable to be "weighted" in the construction of such a summary measure?
2. After interobject similarities are obtained, how are the classes to be formed?
3. After the classes have been formed, what summary measures of each cluster are appropriate in a descriptive sense; that is, how are the clusters to be defined?
4. Assuming that adequate descriptions of the clusters can be obtained, what inferences can be drawn regarding their statistical significance?

The above questions constitute the main points of our discussion in this section of the chapter.

Choice of Proximity Measure

The choice of proximity, similarity, association, or resemblance measure (all four terms will be used synonymously here) is an interesting problem in cluster analysis. The concept of similarity always connotes the question: similarity with respect to what? Proximity measures are usually viewed in relative terms—two objects are similar, relative to the group, if their profiles across variables are "close" or they share "many" aspects in common, relative to those which other pairs share in common.

Most clustering procedures use pairwise measures of proximity. The choice of which objects and variables to use in the first place is largely a matter for the researcher's judgment. While these (prior) choices are important ones, they are beyond our scope of coverage. Even assuming that such choices have been made, however, the possible measures of pairwise proximity are many. Generally speaking, these measures fall into two classes: (a) distance-type measures (including correlation coefficients); and (b) matching-type measures.[3] The characteristics of each class are discussed in turn.

---

[3] Even this latter group of measures, under certain circumstances, can be viewed as a type of distance measure [9].

Distance-Type Measures. A surprisingly large number of proximity measures—including correlation measures—can be viewed as distances in some type of metric space. In Chapter 2 we introduced the notion of Euclidean distance between two points in a space of r dimensions. We recall that the formula was:

$$d_{ij} = \left[\sum_{k=1}^{r} (x_{ik} - x_{jk})^2 \right]^{1/2}$$

where x_{ik}, x_{jk} are the projections of points i and j on dimension k; ($k = 1, 2, \ldots, r$).

Inasmuch as the variables are often measured in different units, the above formula is usually applied *after* each variable has been standardized to mean zero and unit standard deviation. Our subsequent discussion will assume that this preliminary step has been taken.

The Euclidean distance measure assumes that the space of (standardized) variables is orthogonal, i.e., that the variables are uncorrelated. While the Euclidean measure can still be used with correlated variables, it is useful to point out the (implicit) weighting of the components underlying the associated variables which occurs with the use of the Euclidean measure in this case:

1. Squared Euclidean distance in the original variable space has the effect of weighting each underlying principal component by that component's eigenvalue.
2. Squared Euclidean distance in the component space (where all components are first standardized to *unit* variance) has the effect of assigning equal weights to all components.
3. In terms of the geometry of the configuration, in the first case all points are rotated to orthogonal axes with no change in squared interpoint distance. The general effect is to portray the original configuration as a hyperellipsoid with principal components serving as axes of that figure. Equating all axes to equal length has the effect of transforming the hyperellipsoid into a hypersphere where all "axes" are of equal length.

The above considerations can be represented in terms of the following squared distance model:

$$\overset{*}{d}{}_{ij}^{2} = \sum_{k=1}^{r} (y_{ik} - y_{jk})^2$$

where: y_{ik}, y_{jk} denote unit variance components of profiles i and j on component axis k ($k = 1, 2, \ldots, r$). If one weights the component scores according to the variances of the components (before standardization) the expression is:

$$d_{ij}^{2} = \sum_{k=1}^{r} \lambda_k (y_{ik} - y_{jk})^2$$

where λ_k is the k-th component variance, or eigenvalue. *This expression is equivalent to d_{ij}^2 expressed in original variable space.*

The above relationships assume that *all* principal components are extracted. As described earlier, if such is not the case, squared interpoint distances will be affected by the fact that they are computed in a component space of lower dimensionality than the original variable space.

In summary, both the Euclidean distance measure in original variable space and the Euclidean distance in component space (assuming all components have been extracted) preserve all of the information in the original data matrix.[4] Finally it should be pointed out that if (in addition to being standardized to mean zero and unit variance) the original variables are uncorrelated, both d_{ij}^2 and $\overset{*}{d}_{ij}^2$ will be equivalent.

Other Euclidean Distance Measures. Two other measures have often been proposed as proximity measures. Both of these measures derive from historical clustering methods which used Q-type factor analysis to cluster objects. In Q-type factor analysis—as described briefly in our discussion of reduced space analysis—the correlation (or covariance) matrix to be factored consists of *inter-object* rather than intervariable proximities. In these methods the weights λ_k are left intact.

The effect of Q-type component analysis of either covariance or correlation matrices, as shown by Cronbach and Gleser [5], is to reduce the dimensionality of the space underlying the computation of proximity measures. Both procedures reduce the dimensionality of the original space to one less dimension by equating all profiles to *zero* mean. As such, profile differences in elevation are removed. In addition, a Q-type analysis applied to the interobject correlation matrix will remove interprofile variation due to differences in dispersion. The result in this case is to project the point representing each profile into *two* fewer dimensions.[5]

Figures 5-2 and 5-3 show these effects geometrically. In the case of either covariance or correlation matrices the profile mean is subtracted from each vector component which, in the 2-component case of Figure 5-2, results in a centroid with (new) origin located at point X on the figure.

Figure 5-3 shows the effect of removing profile dispersion. If we assume that the profiles were originally positioned in three-space, removal of each profile's mean reduces their dimensionality to two-space. By using a correlation matrix we *further* reduce dimensionality by projecting all points on to the unit circle, since the standard deviation of a profile can be represented by the distance of the

---

[4]Although not discussed here, another measure of interpoint distance, Mahalanobis D^2, can be utilized; this measure is equivalent to d_{ij}^2 under the conditions described here [11].

[5]Some care should be taken in interpreting this statement. Centering the configuration at the centroid will reduce its dimensionality by one (unless, of course, it has already been so centered). Effecting a reduction of two dimensions (by equating profile dispersions) depends upon the range of variation in the points. If this range is small, the points will fall essentially on a hyperplane, of one less dimension, a total reduction of two dimensions. If their range of variation is large, only the "local" dimensionality is reduced. Their global dimensionality will still be $r - 1$ dimensions (assuming still that the configuration has been centered at its centroid).

FIGURE 5-2
EFFECT OF Q-TYPE COMPONENT ANALYSIS OF COVARIANCE OR
CORRELATION MATRIX ON PROFILE MEANS

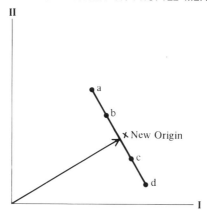

FIGURE 5-3
EFFECT OF Q-TYPE COMPONENT ANALYSIS OF CORRELATION MATRIX
ON PROFILE DISPERSION

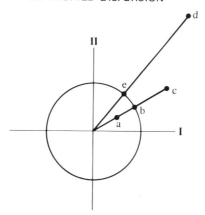

profile point from the origin (the centroid of the points first having been translated to the origin). Thus profiles a, b, and c would all be identical after the
transformation, as would profiles d and e. The cosine of the angle separating the
two vectors represents the Q-correlation between them.

Of course, there may be cases where the analyst is not interested in profile
differences due to either mean and/or dispersion. If so, a Q-type analysis applied
to covariance or correlation matrices, as the case may be, is perfectly sensible
even though information is (willingly) discarded.[6]   In general, however, we

_____

[6]Interestingly enough, a Q-type component analysis of interprofile "raw" cross products
(and computation of squared distances in component space) will produce results that are
equivalent to the Euclidean distance measure in the original variables space [9].

should expect differences in the derived squared distance measure computed from these procedures—both between themselves and between those computed by the techniques previously discussed.

While the authors have a predilection for the information-preserving measure d_{ij}^2 and $\overset{*}{d}_{ij}^2$, it is well to point out that no universally applicable distance measure exists. The choice of which measure to use depends upon what aspects of the data are worth "preserving." A wide variety of distance-type measures are available for cluster analysis; several of these are compared in a paper by Green and Rao [11].

Matching-Type Measures. Quite often the analyst wishing to cluster profiles must contend with data that are only nominal scaled, in whole or in part. While dichotomous data, after suitable transformation, can often be expressed in terms of interpoint distances, the usual approach to nominal-scaled data uses attribute matching coefficients. Intuitively speaking, two profiles are viewed as similar to the extent to which they share common attributes.

As an illustration of this approach, consider the two profiles appearing below:

	ATTRIBUTE					
Object	1	2	3	4	5	6
1	1	0	0	1	1	0
2	0	1	0	1	0	1

Each of the above objects is characterized by possession or non-possession of each of six attributes, where a "1" denotes possession and a "0" denotes non-possession. Suppose we just count up the total number of matches—either 1, 1 or 0, 0—and divide by the total number of attributes. A simple matching measure could then be stated as:

$$S_{12} = \frac{M}{N} = \frac{2}{6} = \frac{1}{3}$$

where M denotes the number of attributes held in common (matching 1's or 0's) and N denotes the total number of attributes. We notice that this measure varies between zero and one.

If weak matches (non-possession of an attribute) are to be de-emphasized, the above measure can be modified to:

$$S'_{ij} = \frac{\text{No. of attributes which are 1 for both objects } i \text{ and } j}{\text{No. of attributes which are 1 for either } i \text{ or } j \text{ or both}}$$

In this case $S'_{ij} = \frac{1}{5}$. This measure is known as the Tanimoto coefficient. A variety of such matching type coefficients are described in the book by Sokal and Sneath [21].

Attributes need not be limited to dichotomies, however. In the case of un-ordered multichotomies, matching coefficients are often developed by means similar to the above by recoding the k-state variables into k-1 dummy (zero-one) variables. Naturally such coefficients will be sensitive to variation in the number of states in each multichotomy.

Finally mention should be made of the case in which the variables consist of mixed scales—nominal, ordinal, and interval. Interval-scaled variables may be handled in terms of similarity coefficients by the simple device of computing the range of the variable R_k and finding:

$$S_{ijk}^{*} = 1 - [\,|X_{ik} - X_{jk}|/R_k\,]$$

This measure has been suggested by Gower [8] as a device to handle both nominal- and interval-scaled data in a single similarity coefficient.

Mixed scales which include ordinal-scaled variables present greater difficulties. If ordinal and interval scales occur, one can downgrade the interval-scaled data to ordinal scales and use nonmetric procedures. If all three scales—nominal, ordinal, and interval—appear, one is more or less forced to downgrade all data to nominal measures and use matching type coefficients. An alternative approach would be to compute "distances" for each pair of objects according to each scale type separately, standardize the measures to zero mean and unit standard deviation, and then compute some type of weighted association measure. Such approaches are quite *ad hoc*, however.

Finally, some comments should be made about relating matching coefficients based on dichotomous attributes to distance interpretations. Gower [9] shows how this can be accomplished in the context of principal components analysis. Later in the chapter we shall describe an alternative (and nonmetric) approach in an empirical context.

Clustering Programs

Once the analyst has settled on some pairwise measure of profile similarity, he must still use some type of computational routine for clustering the profiles. A large variety of such computer programs already exist and more are being developed as interest in this field increases. Each clustering program tends to maintain a certain individuality, although certain common characteristics can be drawn out. Ball and Hall [2] have made a rather extensive survey of clustering methods. The following categories are based, in part, on their classification:

1. *Dimensionalizing the Proximity Matrix*—these approaches use principal components or other factor analytic methods to find a dimensional representation of points. Clusters are then developed visually or on the basis of grouping objects according to their highest component "loadings" as obtained by the Q-type analysis.

2. *Non-Hierarchical Methods*—these methods start right from the proximity matrix and can be characterized as:
   a. *Sequential Threshold*—in this case a cluster center is selected and all objects within a prespecified threshold value are grouped. Then a new

cluster center is selected and the process is completed. Once points enter a cluster they are removed from further processing.

    b. *Parallel Threshold*—this method is similar to the one immediately above except that several cluster centers are selected in advance and points within threshold level are assigned to the nearest center; threshold levels can then be adjusted to admit fewer or more points to clusters.

    c. *Parallel Partitioning*—this method is similar to the one immediately above except that once several cluster centers are chosen, the whole set of data is partitioned into disjoint sets based on nearest distance to cluster centers.

    d. *Optimizing Partitioning*—this method differs from (a), (b), and (c) in that points can be reassigned to clusters on the basis of optimizing some overall criterion measure, e.g., average within-cluster distance for a given number of clusters.

3. *Hierarchical Methods*—these procedures are characterized by the construction of a hierarchy or tree-like structure. In some methods each point starts out as a unit (single-point) cluster. At the next level the two closest points are placed in a cluster. At the next level a third point joins the first two or else a second two-point cluster is formed, based on various criterion functions for assignment. Eventually all points are grouped into one large cluster. Variations on this procedure involve the development of a hierarchy from the top down. At the beginning the points are partitioned into two subsets based on some criterion measure related to average within-cluster distance. The subset with the highest within-cluster distances is next partitioned into two subsets, and so on, until all points eventually become unit clusters.

4. *Connectivity Methods*—these measures are characterized by the development of linkages based on whether an object's nearness (interpoint distance) to one member of a cluster is less than some threshold. In this case, however, the object need only *connect* with a single member of the group. This concept views similarity as meaning "relatedness" where similar objects are those connected to other objects through being within threshold distance of still other objects.

While the above classes of programs are not exhaustive of the field, most of the currently available routines can be typed as falling into one (or a combination) of the above categories. Criteria for grouping include such measures as average within-cluster distance and threshold cut-off values. The fact remains, however, that even the "optimizing" approaches generally achieve only *conditional* optima, since an unsettled question in this field is *how many* clusters to form in the first place.

    At this state in the development of cluster analysis, the authors are of the opinion that clustering might best be approached in terms of a combination of dimensional representation of the points (reduced space analysis) and techniques which group points in the reduced space (obtained from principal components or nonmetric scaling techniques). This tandem approach, if the dimensionality is small, enables the analyst to stay "close to his data" and to augment the clustering results with visual inspection of the configuration.

Describing the Clusters

Once clusters are developed, the analyst still faces the task of describing the clusters. One measure which is used frequently is the *centroid*, that is, the average value of the objects contained in the cluster on each of the variables making up each object's profile. If the data are interval scaled and clustering is performed in original variable space, this measure appears quite natural as a summary description. If the space consists of principal components' dimensions obtained from nonmetric scaling methods, the axes usually are not capable of being described simply. Often in this case the analyst will want to go back to the original variables and compute average profile measures in these terms.

If matching type coefficients are used, the analyst may describe a cluster in terms of the group's modal profile on each of the attributes; in other cases arithmetic averages may be computed.

In addition to central tendency, the researcher may compute some measure of the cluster's variability, e.g., average interpoint distance of all members of the cluster from their centroid or average interpoint distance between all pairs of points within the cluster.

Statistical Significance

Despite attempts made to construct various tests of statistical significance of clusters, in the authors' view no defensible procedures are currently available [7]. The lack of appropriate tests stems from the difficulty of specifying realistic null hypotheses. First, it is not clear just what the universe of content is. Quite often the researcher arbitrarily selects objects and variables and is often interested in confining his attention to only this sample. Second, the analyst is usually assuming that heterogeneity exists in the first place—otherwise why bother to cluster? Moreover, the clusters are formed *from the data* and not on the basis of outside criteria. Thus one would be placed in the uncomfortable statistical position of "testing" the significance between groups formed on the basis of the data itself. Third, the distributions of objects are largely unknown, and it would be dangerous to assume that they conformed to some tractable model like a multivariate normal distribution.

We continue to believe that, at least in the present state of cluster analysis, this class of techniques should be viewed as *preclassification* where the object is to *formulate* rather than test categorizations of data. After a classification has been developed and supported by *theoretical research* and subsequent reformulation of classes, other techniques like discriminant analysis might prove useful in the assignment of new members to groups identified on grounds which are *not* solely restricted to the original cluster analysis.[7]

---

[7] Discriminant analysis, as an *ad hoc* device, may be used to find "optimal" weights for variables after performing the cluster analysis. In this case, however, its use would be limited to description.

While the above caveats are not to be taken lightly, it seems to us that clustering techniques can still be quite useful—in ways comparable to the objectives of factor analysis—as systematic procedures for the orderly preclassification of multivariate data. The results of using these approaches can be helpful and meaningful (after the fact) as will be illustrated in the next section of this chapter.

AN APPLICATION OF REDUCED SPACE AND CLUSTER ANALYSIS

Thus far, our descriptions of reduced space and clustering methods have largely remained at the conceptual level. In this section of the chapter we describe their application to a realistically sized problem—one dealing with the similarities and differences among 102 different computer models whose dates of first installation range from 1955 to 1968 [10]. In this abridged version of the study we illustrate the use of reduced space and cluster analysis in tandem. We first describe the motivation for the study. This is followed by a description of the techniques and a brief report of findings.

In the Introduction and Problem Setting of this monograph, we suggested that computers—like many industrial products such as electric motors, machine tools, and gas turbines—can be characterized by a set of performance characteristics. If we assume that each computer model can be represented as a point in performance space, some models will probably be "closer" to others in this performance space, i.e., more competitive in terms of performance similarities. Moreover, the "scores" (projections on each axis of the space) of each computer model and the relationships among models may be changing over time—a reflection of technological change and inter-model competition.

A major problem is to describe these interrelationships, among entities and over time, in a compact and interpretable way. The problem is complicated by the fact that some of the performance characteristics of a computer model are represented by "features"—attribute data expressed dichotomously such as possession or nonpossession of a table look-up device. The methodology to be discussed provides a way to "metricize" such data so that the closeness of any two entities in the derived space reflects the extent to which entities share the same features.

The Data Base

The data for this study consisted of selected performance measures on 102 different computer models [1]. Each machine was represented by a vector of scores on 22 characteristics. Table 5-2 shows the characteristics by which each computer model was described. The first 12 of these characteristics are measured variables, while the last 10 are dichotomous "features."

In order to obtain a comparison between two different time periods, the computer models were divided into two classes, based on date of first installation.

TABLE 5-2
PERFORMANCE CHARACTERISTICS OF 102 COMPUTER MODELS

Measured Variables	Features Data
1. Word length in binary bits	13. Floating point representation
2. Likely fixed point execution time: a + b in microseconds	14. Binary arithmetic radix
	15. Checking of data transfers
3. Likely fixed point execution time: ab in microseconds	16. Program interrupt facility
	17. Indirect addressing
4. Likely fixed point execution time: a/b in microseconds	18. Special editing capabilities
	19. Boolean operations
5. Maximum number of index registers	20. Table look-up
6. Maximum number of input/output channels	21. Storage checking
	22. Storage protect
7. Minimum number of words in storage	
8. Maximum number of words in storage	
9. Maximum total storage in digits	
10. Maximum total storage in characters	
11. Cycle time in microseconds	
12. Effective transfer rate in characters per second	

Class 1 was composed of 55 machines whose date of first installation was between 1955 and 1963. Class 2 was made up of 47 machines whose date of first installation was between 1964 and 1968. Separate analyses were made for each class.

Several computer programs were used throughout the analysis. The program which was used for most of the clustering work was a hierarchical grouping technique [12]. This clustering routine partitions the computer models first into 2 groups, then 3, and so on, down to 20 groups; the criterion at any given level of partitioning is to find clusters whose within-sums of squares, summed over all clusters, is minimal. The algorithm used for the reduced space analysis was Kruskal's M-D-SCAL (version III) program [13].

An Association Measure for Combined Variables

The development of useful clusters of computer models required some means of combining the features and measured data. As discussed earlier in the chapter, one way to put both sets of variables on a common basis is to "downgrade" the measured variables, in this case by dichotomizing at the median of each variable, considered singly.[8] A "one" would indicate that the machine had a value above the median and a "zero" would indicate a value below the median. If this is done, each machine can be characterized by a 22-component vector of ones and zeroes. A rough measure of similarity would involve merely counting up the number of times a 1, 1 or 0, 0 match occurred for each pair of machines. One

---

[8] An alternative approach would be to treat the dichotomous data as "continuous" data which just happen to take on one of only two possible values. Distance measures (either weighted or unweighted) could then be computed after all variables are standardized to mean zero and unit standard deviation.

could then divide that total by 22 and obtain a matching coefficient, S_{ij}, as discussed previously.

However, a major problem associated with this approach is that the columns of 1's and 0's are, themselves, intercorrelated. A way to handle this problem is first to compute a series of inter-column likenesses, L_{ij} ($0 \leqslant L_{ij} = L_{ji} \leqslant 1$) and then a series of column coefficients w_i, where the

$$w_i = \frac{1}{\sum\limits_{j=1}^{n} L_{ij}} ; \left[\sum_{j=1}^{n} L_{ij} \right] > 0$$

provides a set of weights that reflect each column's pairwise association with every other column [14]. The w_i will be smaller the more alike that column is to every other column. Thus, "redundant" columns receive low weight while "informative" columns receive higher weight. The rationale for this procedure is based on the commonsense notion that two objects should be more similar if they match on a characteristic that object pairs do not normally share than if they happen to match on a characteristic that virtually all object pairs display.

Several association measures may be used to obtain values for L_{ij}. The particular measure used here was Guttman's lambda measure,[9] defined as:

$$\lambda_G = \frac{\Sigma f_r + \Sigma f_c - (F_r + F_c)}{2N - (F_r + F_c)}$$

where:

    f_r = sum of maximum frequencies of each within-class row
    f_c = sum of maximum frequencies of each within-class column
    F_r = maximum frequency of marginal totals—rows
    F_c = maximum frequency of marginal totals—columns
    N = total frequency

For example, if we considered only two columns (performance variables) the contingency matrix for 55 computers might be:

		Column j		
		0	1	Sum
Column i	0	25	20	45
	1	2	8	10
	Sum	27	28	55

Substitution in the above formula yields:

$$\lambda_G = \frac{(25+8) + (25+20) - (45+28)}{2(55) - (45+28)} = 0.135$$

[9] A discussion of this statistic may be found in L. C. Freeman, *Elementary Applied Statistics* (New York: John Wiley & Sons, 1965).

After each $\lambda_{G(ij)}$ value (the specific value of L_{ij}) is obtained, the program then computes the w_i values for each column i. If two computers match on column i (either on a 1, 1 or 0, 0 basis) the w_i value is accumulated for each such match [3].

Results of the Analysis

Application of the above procedure yielded *weighted* agreement scores, consisting of two matrices—a 55×55 matrix of entries for class 1 machines and a 47×47 matrix of entries for class 2 machines. These matrices constituted proximity measures for each pair of computers. As indicated at the beginning of this chapter, only their rank order is needed for nonmetric reduced space analysis.

The Kruskal algorithm was then applied and solutions in four to two dimensions were sought. As might be surmised, the two-space fits were rather poor but excellent results were found in the four-space representations.

Clustering of the computer models was therefore based on the *computation of interpoint distances in the derived (orthogonal) space of four dimen-*

FIGURE 5-4
TWO-SPACE SCALING SOLUTION AND EIGHT-LEVEL CLUSTERING—
CLASS 1 MACHINES
(Combined Data)

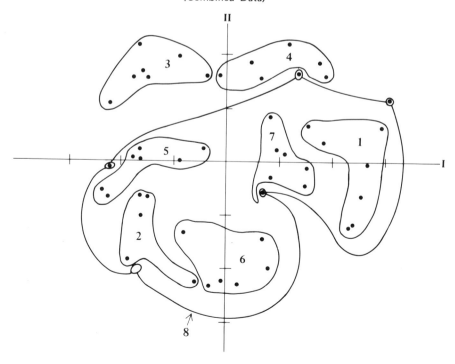

sions.[10]   For graphical purposes the two-space representations are shown, although the cluster boundaries are based on the (more accurate) four-space representations. **Figures 5-4** and 5-5 show the results for class 1 and class 2 machines, respectively.

In Figure 5-4, for example, we note that cluster membership is approximately evenly distributed over the eight clusters. Moreover, with the exception of cluster 8, the groups are rather compact (bearing in mind that the clustering was based on the four-space, not the two-space scaling solutions). Cluster 5 is characterized by small, fairly slow, business-oriented machines, while Cluster 7 is characterized by large, relatively fast, scientific machines.

Figure 5-5 also shows, with the exception of cluster 8, fairly compact groupings. Cluster 3, for example, is composed of large, relatively fast, scientific machines, while cluster 6 represents small, relatively slow, business-type orientations. Interpretation of the axes of both Figures 5-4 and 5-5 is difficult, however,

FIGURE 5-5
TWO-SPACE SCALING SOLUTION AND EIGHT-LEVEL CLUSTERING—
CLASS 2 MACHINES
(Combined Data)

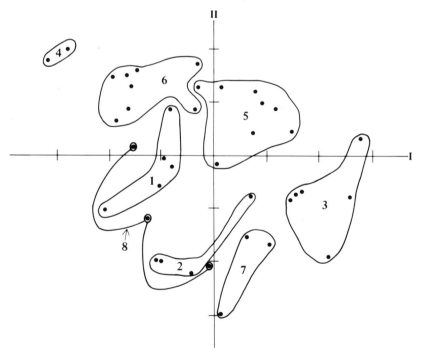

[10] By using various nonmetric clustering techniques (see Appendix A) one could have clustered on the basis of the original proximity measures (rather than on measures obtained from the four-space coordinates), thus arriving at a set of clusters which would be independent of the dimensionality of the scaling solution.

inasmuch as one is attempting to represent order relations based originally on a 22-component vector in only two dimensions.

From Tables 5-3 and 5-4 one can get some idea of early and current inter-manufacturer competition. For example, cluster 5 of Table 5-4 shows rather clearly that segments of the IBM 360 computer series compete directly with segments of the RCA Spectra series. Cluster 3 in Table 5-4 brings out the competition among CDC, GE, Honeywell, IBM, and Univac. One notes, not surprisingly, that IBM has models in five out of the eight clusters. But Honeywell shows models in six of the eight clusters, a result which was not anticipated by us. On the other hand, the depth of concentration of CDC is shown by its membership in only two of the eight clusters.

TABLE 5-3
CLUSTER COMPOSITION—CLASS 1 MACHINES
(Combined Data)

Cluster #1	*Cluster #5*
IBM 1401	Burroughs B100/200
IBM 1440	Burroughs B200/300
IBM 1460	GE 215
IBM 1620-I	GE 225
IBM 1620-II	Honeywell 400
RCA 301/303, 304, 305	Univac SS 80/90 I
RCA 301/354, 355	Univac SS 80/90 II
Cluster #2	Univac 418-I
Burroughs B5500-B460	
Burroughs B5500-B461	*Cluster #6*
CDC 3600	IBM 1410
IBM 7040	IbM 7010
IBM 7044	IBM 7070
Univac 494	IBM 7072
Univac 1107	IBM 7074
Cluster #3	IBM 7080
CDC 160	NCR 315 & 315-100
CDC 160-A	
LPG 30	*Cluster #7*
Monrobot XI	CDC 1604 & 1604-A
Recomp II	Honeywell 800
Recomp III	Philco 2000/211-2100
RPC 4000	Philco 2000/212-2100
Univac 1004-I	Philco 2000/212-2000
Univac 1004-II, III	Univac III
Cluster #4	
IBM 704	*Cluster #8*
IBM 709	Univac 418-II
IBM 7090	Univac 1050-III
IBM 7094-I	Univac 1050-IV
Philco 2000/210	Univac 490
Philco 2000/211-2200	Univac 491/492

TABLE 5-4
CLUSTER COMPOSITION—CLASS 2 MACHINES
(Combined Data)

Cluster #1	*Cluster #5*
Burroughs B2500	IBM 360/30
GE 415	IBM 360/40
GE 425	IBM 360/50
GE 435	IBM 360/65
Honeywell 1400	IBM 360/75
IBM 1130	IBM 360/44
	IBM 360/67
Cluster #2	RCA Spectra 70/35
CDC 3100	RCA Spectra 70/45
CDC 3200	RCA Spectra 70/55
CDC 3300	RCA 3301/3304
CDC 3400	*Cluster #6*
Honeywell 1800	GE 235
	Honeywell 200/120
Cluster #3	Honeywell 200/200
CDC 6400	IBM 360/20
CDC 6600	RCA Spectra 70/15
CDC 6800	RCA Spectra 70/25
GE 625	Univac 9200
GE 635	Univac 9300
Honeywell 200/8200	*Cluster #7*
IBM 7092-II	Honeywell 200/2200
Univac 1108	Honeywell 200/4200
	NCR 315 RMC
Cluster #4	*Cluster #8*
Burroughs B300	Burroughs B3500
GE 115	Honeywell 200/1200
IBM 1401-G	RCA 3301/3303

Summary of Study

The foregoing results constituted only one facet of the overall study. Additional steps involved: (a) the development of clusters based only on the nominal-scaled (features) data: (b) the development of clusters based only on the interval-scaled data; and (c) clustering (involving both features and measured data) on a combined time period basis.

In terms of substantive results, we found that four "factors" explained most of the similarities and differences among the computer models—total number of different features, the pattern of the features, speed, and machine capacity. The resulting clusters indicated which manufacturers competed with which other manufacturers in terms of similarity in the performance profiles of their machines.

For purposes of this chapter, suffice it to say that clustering techniques can be used in marketing studies involving large-scale data banks. Moreover, the combination of reduced space—using principal components analysis or, as in the case described here, a nonmetric scaling of profile similarities that can be viewed as a type of nonmetric factor analysis—and cluster analysis can provide a useful dual treatment of the data. The reduced space phase provides help in summarizing the original variables in terms of a smaller number of dimensions, e.g., speed or capacity. The clustering phase permits one to group machines according to their coordinates in this reduced space.

RECENT DEVELOPMENTS IN CLUSTERING TECHNIQUES

Our previous discussion of clustering analysis has tended to emphasize the tandem approach of dimensional and nominal (class-like) representation of data structures. For example, the performance structure study of the computer market employed both nonmetric reduced space analysis and a subsequent cluster routine to group objects (computer models) into discrete classes; proximity measures for the clustering were developed from the coordinates of the objects in the reduced space while "agreement" scores provided proximity measures for the original scaling.

In addition to using multidimensional scaling techniques for reduced space analysis, a number of other nonlinear approaches have been proposed. McDonald [18] has considered the problem of nonlinear factor analysis and has presented some techniques for implementing his approach. Carroll [4] has developed a very flexible approach to polynomial factor analysis. On a somewhat different tack, Lazarsfeld has pioneered in the development of latent structure analysis, a useful approach for "decomposing" nominal scaled data.[11]

On the nonmetric level of factor analysis, the SSAR-II program of Guttman and Lingoes [15] deserves mention. Lingoes has also proposed CM-III [16] which performs a type of nonmetric scaling of the data matrix prior to using a metric (or nonmetric) factoring method. His SSAP-I and SSAP-II programs, mentioned earlier, are explicitly designed as nonmetric analogues to metric factor analysis.[12]

Space does not permit anything but brief mention of this interesting work. We do consider in some detail, however, a combination qualitative-quantitative approach to an important problem in reduced space analysis—the interpretation of data structures.

Nominal Versus Dimensional Structures

As mentioned earlier, even a pure class structure—where class membership accounts for all of the information in the data—can be represented spatially. More commonly, however, we consider cluster analysis as a more appropriate tech-

[11]A useful overview of this work may be found in Lazarsfeld and Henry's *Latent Structure Analysis* (New York: Houghton-Mifflin Co., 1968).

[12]Mention should also be made of the Shepard-Kruskal nonmetric factor analysis algorithm which finds a point-vector representation of the data. Thus, stimuli could be characterized as point projections on individual subjects' vectors in, say, the analysis of preference data. See R. N. Shepard and J. B. Kruskal, "Nonmetric Methods for Scaling and for Factor Analysis," *American Psychologist*, Vol. 19 (1964), pp. 557-58.

nique for characterizing such data. On the other hand, other data structures are inherently dimensional, so that measures of proximity are assumed to be able to vary rather continuously throughout the whole matrix of proximities.

Pure typal and pure dimensional structures represent only two extremes. Since all proximity matrices (that obey certain properties [9]) can be represented spatially, it would seem of interest to consider data structures in terms of the restrictions placed on the points as they are arranged in that space. This motivation underlies many of the most recent developments in cluster analysis.

Torgerson [22] was one of the first researchers to become interested in the problem of characterizing data as "mixtures" of discrete class and quantitative variables. Several varieties of such structures can be obtained:

1. Data consisting of pure and unordered class structure. Dimensional representation of such data would consist of points at the n vertices of an $n - 1$ dimensional simplex where interpoint distances are all equal. For example, three classes could be represented by an equilateral triangle in two-space, four classes by a regular tetrahedron in three-space, and so on.

2. Data consisting of concentrated masses of points, corresponding to classes, where interclass distances are unequal, thus implying the existence of latent dimensions underlying *class* descriptions.

3. Data consisting of hierarchical sets of attributes where some classes are nested within other classes, e.g., cola and non-cola drinks within the diet-drink class.

4. Data consisting of dimensional variables nested within discrete classes, e.g., sweet to non-sweet cereals within the class of "processed" shape (as opposed to "natural" shape) cereals.

5. Data consisting of *mixtures* of ideal (mutually exclusive) classes so that one may find, for example, points in the interior of an equilateral triangle whose vertices represent three unordered classes.

6. Data consisting of pure dimensional structure in which, theoretically, all of the space can be filled up by points.

While the above categorizations are neither exclusive nor exhaustive, they are illustrative of the variety of data structures that could be obtained in the analysis of "objective" data or subjective (similarities) data of the sort described in the preceding chapters. From the viewpoint of cluster analysis, some of the above structures could produce elongated, parallel clusters in which average intracluster distance need not be smaller than intercluster distances. Moreover, one could have structures in which the clusters curve or twist around one another along some manifold embedded in a higher dimensional space [19].

Figure 5-6 shows three types of data structures as related to the above categories [22]. The first panel illustrates the case of three unordered discrete classes. The second panel illustrates the case of discrete class structure where class descriptors are assumed to be orderable. The third panel shows the case of three discrete classes and an orthogonal variable which is quantitative. Points occur only along the solid lines of the prism. The fourth panel illustrates the case where objects are made up of mixtures of discrete classes plus an orthogonal quantitative dimension. In this case all objects lie on or within

FIGURE 5-6
DIMENSIONAL PORTRAYAL OF ALTERNATIVE DATA STRUCTURES

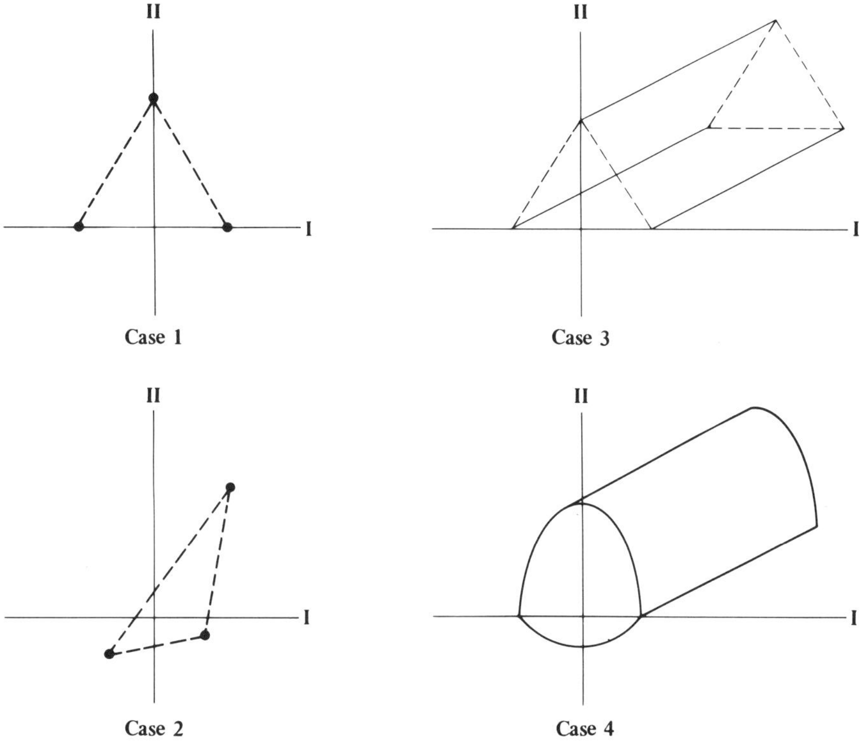

Case 1

Case 3

Case 2

Case 4

the boundaries of the curve prism while "pure" cases would lie at one of the three edges with location dependent upon the degree of the quantitative variable which each possesses.

Approaches to Data Structure Analysis

Quite recent developments in the analysis of complex data structures suggest that some of these problems may yield to a combination of dimensional and cluster analysis. Richard Degerman [6] has developed a computer-based approach that shows high promise for revealing data structures that represent a combination of discrete classes (ordered or unordered) and one or more orthogonal quantitative variables.

Input data consist of a multidimensional scaling configuration. Typically, of course, the configuration would *not* be in the most appropriate orientation for revealing the combination of class-like and dimensional structure.

Degerman's program first develops coefficients which reflect the extent to which sets of points deviate from the user's hypothesized number of classes. A clustering program is then used to group points and the space is rotated so that the class-like structure is revealed by a subspace projection—in the case of three classes, a plane. The dimensional portion is then revealed by an additional rotation which makes its axis (or axes) orthogonal to the subspace characterizing the class structure.

Figure 5-7 shows the results of an experiment in which 16 subjects were asked to rate stimulus pairs in terms of a 10-point dissimilarity scale. The stimuli consisted of geometric figures (triangle, circle, square) varying also according to 5 shades of gray. Results of his program reveal the combination of class and dimensional structure quite nicely, as shown in Figure 5-7.

Other researchers are experimenting with other approaches to revealing structure in data. For example, researchers at the Stanford Research Institute [2] have constructed display systems which enable the analyst to view subsets of data from any perspective desired in a three-space data plot. In addition, data in four dimensions are handled by coding devices in which the length of a line is made proportional to the third variable and its tilt angle is made proportional to the fourth variable. The system thus enables one to "visualize" relationships by observing only two-space representations.

Other variations of the routine allow displays of cluster centroid links which lie within a threshold distance selected by the user. Moreover, profile plots can be made to show intercluster variation along individual variables. Polaroid pictures can be obtained from the visual display and hard copy can also be gathered from an off-line plotting table.

Still other researchers, notably Shepard and Carroll [19], have been concerned with characterizing nonlinear data structures where points may lie on curved manifolds embedded in higher dimensional space. Carroll's approach of parametric mapping appears highly provocative for characterizing data struc-

FIGURE 5-7

PLOTS OF SELECTED DIMENSIONS OF SHAPE AND COLOR EXPERIMENT

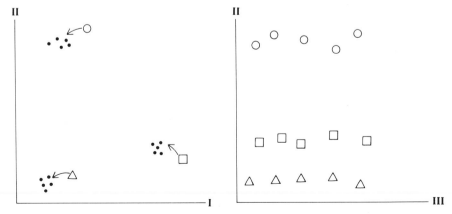

Source: Richard Degerman, "Multidimensional Analysis of Complex Structure: Mixtures of Class and Quantitative Variation," unpublished dissertation, Johns Hopkins University, Baltimore, Maryland, 1968, p. 24.

tures in the lowest dimensionality in which the original data can still be (parametrically) represented.

In short, research in cluster analysis and related techniques is proceeding in new directions for dealing with heretofore intractable data structures. The continued development and refinement of interactive display devices should further these efforts by enabling the researcher to "visualize" various characteristics of the data array as a guide to the selection of appropriate grouping methods.

SUMMARY

This chapter has dealt with a companion objective to the scaling of similarities and preference data—use of metric and nonmetric approaches in data reduction and taxonomy. As we tried to point out, many of the multidimensional scaling programs can serve useful functions as types of nonmetric factoring procedures. Moreover, clustering procedures are often a helpful adjunct in data analysis when one desires to group objects (or variables) according to their relative similarity.

We first discussed metric approaches to reduced space analysis, more specifically, principal components. This was followed by brief descriptions of nonmetric analogues to factor analysis, including several of the algorithms originally discussed in the context of similarities and preference data.

We then turned to a description of clustering methods and described the basic questions—association measure, grouping algorithm, cluster description and statistical inference—associated with their use. This led to presentation of some pilot research utilizing reduced space and cluster analysis, in tandem, in examining the performance structure of the computer market.

We concluded the chapter with a description of the general problem of portraying data structures that consist of mixtures of categorical and dimensional variables. Some recent advances in this field were mentioned and implications for interpreting scaling configurations were also pointed out.

REFERENCES

1. Auerbach Corporation, *Standard EDP Reports*, Philadelphia, Pa.

2. G. H. Ball and D. J. Hall, "Background Information and Clustering Techniques," working paper, Stanford Research Institute, Menlo Park, Cal., July 1968.

3. F. J. Carmone, P. E. Green, and P. J. Robinson, "WAGS: An IBM 360/65 FORTRAN IV Computer Program for Obtaining Weighted Agreement Scores for Multidimensional Scaling," *Journal of Marketing Research*, Vol. 5 (February 1968), pp. 95–98.

4. J. D. Carroll, "Polynomial Factor Analysis," mimeographed, Bell Telephone Laboratories, Murray Hill, N. J., 1969.

5. L. J. Cronbach and G. C. Gleser, "Assessing Similarity Between Profiles," *Psychological Bulletin*, Vol. 50 (1953), pp. 456–73.

6. Richard Degerman, "Multidimensional Analysis of Complex Structure: Mixtures of Class and Quantitative Variation," unpublished Ph.D. thesis, Johns Hopkins University, 1968.

7. R. E. Frank and P. E. Green, "Numerical Taxonomy in Marketing Analysis: A Review Article," *Journal of Marketing Research*, Vol. 5 (February 1968), pp. 83–94.

8. J. C. Gower, "Multivariate Analysis and Multidimensional Geometry," *The Statistician*, Vol. 17 (1967), pp. 13–28.

9. J. C. Gower, "Some Distance Properties of Latent Root and Vector Methods in Multivariate Analysis," *Biometrika*, Vol. 53 (1966), pp. 315–28.

10. P. E. Green and F. J. Carmone, "Structural Characteristics of the Computer Market: An Application of Reduced Space and Cluster Analysis," working paper, University of Pennsylvania, July 1967 (revised).

11. P. E. Green and V. R. Rao, "A Note on Proximity Measures and Cluster Analysis," *Journal of Marketing Research*, Vol. 6 (August 1969), pp. 359–64.

12. Nigel Howard and Britt Harris, "A Hierarchical Grouping Routine, IBM 360/65 FORTRAN IV Program," University of Pennsylvania Computer Center, Philadelphia, Pa., October 1966.

13. J. B. Kruskal, "Multidimensional Scaling by Optimizing Goodness of Fit to a Nonmetric Hypothesis," *Psychometrika*, Vol. 29 (1964), pp. 1–27.

14. J. B. Kruskal and R. E. Hart, "A Geometric Interpretation of Diagnostic Data from a Digital Machine: Based on a Study of the Morris, Illinois Electronic Central Office," *Bell System Technical Jounral* (October 1966) pp. 1299–1338.

15. J. C. Lingoes, "An IBM 7090 Program for Guttman-Lingoes Smallest Space Analysis":
        SSAR-I, *Behavioral Science*, Vol. 11 (1966), p. 322
        SSAR-II, *Behavioral Science*, Vol. 11 (1966), p. 322
        SSAR-III, *Behavioral Science*, Vol. 11 (1966), p. 323
        SSAR-IV, *Behavioral Science*, Vol. 12 (1967), pp. 74–5

16. J. C. Lingoes, "An IBM 7090 Program for Guttman-Lingoes Conjoint Measurement-III," *Behavioral Science*, Vol. 13 (1968), pp. 85–86.

17. J. C. Lingoes, "A General Nonparametric Model for Representing Objects and Attributes in a Joint Metric Space," in J. C. Gardin (ed.), *Les Compte-rendus de Colloque International sur L'emploi des Calculateurs en Archeologie: Problems Semiologiques et Mathematiques* (Marseilles: Centre National de La Recherche Scientifique, 1969); J. C. Lingoes, "An IBM 360/67 Program for Guttman-Lingoes Smallest Space Analysis-PI," *Behavioral Science*, Vol. 14 (1969), in press.

18. R. P. McDonald, "A Unified Treatment of the Weighting Problem," *Psychometrika*, Vol. 33 (1968), pp. 351–81.

19. R. N. Shepard and J. D. Carroll, "Parametric Representation of Non-linear Data Structures," in P. R. Krishnaiah, ed., *Multivariate Analysis* (New York: Academic Press, 1966), pp. 561–92.

20. P. H. A. Sneath, "The Application of Computers to Taxonomy," *Journal of General Microbiology*, Vol. 17 (1957), pp. 201–26.

21. R. R. Sokal and P. H. A. Sneath, *Principles of Numerical Taxonomy* (San Francisco: W. H. Freeman and Co., 1963).

22. W. S. Torgerson, "Multidimensional Scaling of Similarity," *Psychometrika*, Vol. 30 (1965), pp. 379–93.

CHAPTER SIX

Limitations of the Methodology and Areas for Further Research

In preceding chapters describing multidimensional scaling and related procedures we have briefly and sporadically discussed limitations of the methodology and suggested topics for further research. In this concluding chapter we try to consolidate these earlier remarks as well as describe additional problems and research areas.

It is not surprising, given the short history of most of this methodology, that algorithm development has outstripped application and evaluation of the techniques. It is our feeling that such testing and evaluation will be necessary over the next several years if these procedures are to receive the extent of application that they currently appear to warrant.

Present limitations of the methodology and associated research possibilities can be classified as (a) computational, (b) empirical, and (c) conceptual. We discuss each category in turn.

COMPUTATIONAL PROBLEMS

Several problems, broadly classified as "computational," remain in the systematic investigation of multidimensional scaling and related techniques:

1. Uniqueness of solution as a function of the number of stimuli, the nature of the transformation function and the type and extent of "noise" in the input data.
2. Determinateness of solution as a function of the extent of missing input data and the pattern of nonmetric constraints.
3. Invariance of solution over different algorithms, including traditional metric techniques.
4. Statistical reliability of solutions over samples with correlated or non-correlated error terms.

Each problem gives rise to a series of future research investigations.

Uniqueness of Solution

While some empirical investigation has been reported by Shepard [24] on the characteristics of the Kruskal M-D-SCAL III program [14] and the Shepard-Kruskal nonmetric factor analysis model [28] in "recovering" known configurations, definitive studies are still lacking on how the various algorithms behave as a function of such properties of the input data as number of points, type of distance transformation, and extent of experimental error.

In general, as the number of points increase, the solution—for a specific dimensionality—will become more "unique." Using synthetic, error-free data from a known (two-space) configuration, Shepard processed rank orders for 120 sets of data, ranging from as few as 3 points to as many as 45 points. He then computed correlations between the interpoint distances of the derived configurations and the known configuration.

The results of his analysis of the error-free data indicated that, for all practical purposes, perfect recovery was obtained with as few as 8 points, e.g., the lowest correlation coefficient was 0.985. Even with as few as 4 points, the lowest correlation was 0.896.

Shepard then performed a similar analysis for the Shepard-Kruskal nonmetric factor analysis model. With as few as 5 stimuli and 10 persons, the lowest correlation between pairs of distances was 0.927. For 10 stimuli and 10 persons this value rose to 0.991—for all practical purposes, a perfect recovery. It should be mentioned, however, that such tests were based upon randomly selected coordinate positions of stimuli and person-vectors under error-free conditions.

More recently, researchers are starting to examine the uniqueness of solutions under noisy data conditions; Kruskal [14] was among the first to report results on this topic. One would speculate that even in the case of somewhat noisy data, as the number of points increase, the solution should tend to approximate the known configuration. So far, this speculation has been found to be correct.

One of the authors' earlier studies explored, via Monte Carlo techniques, the effect of noisy data on the recovery of synthetic data configurations for not only the M-D-SCAL III program, but Guttman and Lingoes' SSA-I program [19] and the TORSCA 8 program [35] as well. Our findings indicated that all three programs yielded quite similar results. For error-free data and arbitrary monotone transformations all three programs yielded essentially perfect recovery for 10, 20, and 30 points. Moreover, recoveries continued to be good under moderately noisy data conditions, particularly as the number of points increased.

Since that study was completed we, and others, have made a number of other Monte Carlo simulations. One study [11] dealt with conditional proximity data and compared the effect of "ties" in the data and random error on configuration recovery. Both a triangularization procedure [2] and Kruskal's M-D-SCAL IV program [15] were used in the "unfolding" process. For all practical purposes both approaches performed about equally well and the techniques seemed to be remarkably robust over moderate levels of "ties" in the data and added noise.

A second study [12] showed that several of the programs (TORSCA 8, M-D-SCAL IV, and parametric mapping [27]) reproduced synthetic data configurations quite well when the transformation departed moderately from monotonicity. Extreme departures from monotonicity, however, generally lead to poor recovery, as was observed by McCracken [20]. However, McCracken also found in another study [21] that the parametric mapping of "second order" distances was able to cope rather well with departures from monotonicity.

Recent work by Shepard [25] has shown that the techniques are robust over those bizarre types of "distance" functions which fail to obey even the triangle inequality. This suggests that configurations based on Minkowski "quasi-metrics" (where $0 < p < 1$) might still be approximated well by the traditional Euclidean distance function.

Sherman and Young [29] have performed some interesting simulations in which they noted that Kruskal's stress measure underestimates the goodness of fit for large numbers of points. They propose making adjustments to the formula when large numbers (e.g., $n > 20$) of points are involved. From a pragmatic standpoint, the researcher, other things being equal, can tolerate a larger (poorer) value of stress when he has a larger number of points.

Cliff, Pennell and Young [7] independently found that with a large number (e.g., $n > 20$) of points one does not need all data values to recover the configuration well. Finally, Kruskal [16] has accumulated a fairly extensive body of findings on various synthetic data runs by himself and other investigators.

Determinateness of Solution

Another problem associated with nonmetric scaling methods concerns the determinateness of solutions, independent of number of points, noise level, type of transformation, etc. For example, some nonmetric programs will yield meaningless solutions, with zero stress, under situations where the points can be arranged in two clusters such that all between-cluster dissimilarities exceed within-cluster dissimilarities. Similarly, nonmetric joint space programs can break down if, for example, all individuals prefer a particular stimulus to all other stimuli. Such "degenerate" solutions may sometimes be avoided by choice of a good starting configuration. However, this device does not always work, and in cases where solution degeneracy shows up, the researcher is advised to fall back on metric methods.

In other cases the nonmetric programs will sometimes incur local minima, where the program appears to get trapped in a "valley" that does not represent a global minimum. In cases such as these one can change the step size (Chapter 2) or run the program again with a new starting configuration.

The companion problems of degeneracy and local optima underscore the value of using nonmetric methods in tandem with metric procedures. This approach usually insures the choice of a "good" initial (metric) configuration, to be modified nonmetrically. We have followed this strategy in much of our own research and have found it to be useful "insurance" as well as providing comparative information about the effect of metric versus nonmetric assumptions on the characteristics of the scaling solution.

Invariance of Solution Over Different Algorithms

We have already commented briefly on the problem of comparability of solutions across various nonmetric scaling techniques under noisy data conditions. We have also commented on a related problem, viz., the need for examining the robustness of the techniques to departures from monotonic transformation functions.

Gleason [10] has shown analytically that the major monotone programs all exhibit similar approaches to: (a) the measurement of monotone fit and (b) configuration improvement if the fit is unsatisfactory. Moreover, factor analytic (metric) methods often provide good approximations to the nonmetric solutions, a point made by Torgerson [30].

Choice of which program to use will depend on the interests of the researcher and the particular options which he desires to utilize. Kruskal's M-D-SCAL IV program probably represents the most versatile approach, particularly if the program is coupled with a metrically obtained starting configuration. We have tended to use this program (and TORSCA 8) in much of our work. What we have done—and what other users may also wish to do—is to modify one or more of the basic programs to provide features that are tailored to the types of applications that interest the user. Since all major programs are available in source language (e.g., FORTRAN IV) such modifications can be made quite straightforwardly.

Statistical Reliability of Solutions

A fourth problem in the use of multidimensional scaling programs concerns the statistical reliability of these approaches. For example, if one were to assume a "known" configuration, subject to certain specified sampling fluctuations, what are the distributional properties of the derived (sample) configurations?

This type of study can be examined by means of experimental sampling. An appropriate response measure would be the correlation between interpoint distances of the derived configurations and interpoint distances of the original configuration. Alternative, and possibly superior, "agreement" measures are also available [18].

Variations of the analysis could range from source configurations in which the error term is identically and independently distributed with equal variance to configurations whose error variance is dependent upon interpoint distance.

One could also explore the effect of: (a) number of points and (b) dimensionality of source configuration on the empirically derived sampling distributions of Kruskal's stress measure and interpoint distance correlations.

In summary, it seems to us that nonmetric scaling methods require considerably more detailed investigation of their "sampling" distribution properties as well as examination of their uniqueness and determinateness. This is not to say that such work will be easy or inexpensive, however.

EMPIRICAL PROBLEMS

From the marketing researcher's point of view, the chief concern with multidimensional scaling methods evolves around the question: do they yield useful results in the study of marketing behavior? Consideration of this question gives rise to several current problems and areas for continued research in the application of these methods.

1. Effect of stimulus set composition, context, and data collection method on scaling configurations.
2. Labeling and rotation of dimensions underlying scaling configurations and the relationship of perceived dimensions to objectively measured characteristics of the stimuli.
3. The relationship of overall judgments to individual attribute judgments, e.g., the composition function with regard to judged overall similarity or the evaluation function with regard to judged overall preference.
4. The relationship of probability of choice to perceived distance from ideal point (or vector projection) in the case of joint space models.
5. The amalgamation of similarities or preference maps over individuals.
6. The relationship of changes in policy variables to changes in similarities, preference, and choice behavior over time.

Each of these problems, in turn, suggests various studies for future research.

Stimulus Set Composition, Context and Data Collection Method

In previous chapters we discussed the effect of various "stimuli" on the data collection task. These include: (a) the stimulus set itself; (b) instructions to the respondent; (c) procedures by which the data are gathered; and (d) general background conditions. While our work so far has indicated a rather high within-subset stability of relationships between core items embedded in different stimulus sets, much additional work along these lines is required. The large number of alternative data collection methods also suggests the need to examine their correspondence. The effect of "scenario" and background conditions can, it seems to us, be quite pronounced.

The above problems would seem to heighten the need to run sequences of experiments with the same subjects for the purpose of examining response reliability and other general questions associated with verbal or behavioral responses of similarity and preference.

Associated with the above problems is the general question of quality of input data. If the stimuli are not highly discriminable or the respondent is unfamiliar with some of them, one could obtain a fair number of intransitivities in the data (if "redundant" methods like those described in Chapter 3 are used). The relationship of intransitivities to configuration "stress" has not been thoroughly explored as yet, nor has the general problem of data reliability.

Procedures [8] are available for "significance testing" of intransitivities if one wishes to examine the problem of individual subject reliability. A second approach is to allow the respondent to express "confidence judgments" regarding his ability to discriminate between various pairs of stimuli. Kruskal's M-D-SCAL IV program provides an option for supplying such "confidence weights" for each cell value. A third possibility is to employ a series of check replications and to use the intransitivities themselves to attach differential reliability to the responses. However, to the authors' knowledge, none of these approaches has been extensively investigated as yet.

Labeling and Rotation Problem

Multidimensional scaling (like traditional factor analysis) is a set of numerical procedures and provides no intrinsic basis for labeling the dimensions of the derived configuration.   Such content implications must be determined extrastatistically.   Several possibilities are suggested as *ad hoc* ways for dimension labeling:

1. The experimenter may design the stimuli so that only a few (physical) characteristics are varying in some known fashion. The dimensions obtained in the scaling solution would then be presumed to represent some function of the underlying physical characteristics.

2. The respondent, after making similarity or preference comparisons, may be asked to state the criteria used in forming these judgments.

3. The respondent may be asked to make a series of similarity or preference judgments only with respect to prespecified attributes. He is then asked to make *overall* similarity or preference judgments.   Some technique such as multiple regression may then be used to determine the relative importance of each attribute in the respondent's composite function.   The predictive efficacy of individual attribute scales may then be checked by giving the respondents a new set of overall comparisons to make in which the alternatives are also described according to individual characteristics.

4. "Known" stimuli (for which adequate descriptions of perceptual characteristics already exist) may be included in the presentation set so as to serve as reference points for describing other stimuli.

5. In a subsequent interview, respondents may be shown the derived map and asked to "interpret" it. Such *post hoc* verbalization might be checked against one or more of the preceding procedures.

While the above approaches are probably not exhaustive of the ways one might attempt to label the dimensions, they are suggestive of a series of experiments which could be conducted in the search for pragmatic techniques for coping with this problem.

A related problem of interpretation—in the case of Euclidean spaces—concerns the "correct" orientation of the derived configuration. As discussed in preceding chapters, multidimensional scaling solutions based on a Euclidean metric are unique only up to a similarity transformation—rotation, translation, reflection, and uniform stretching or compression of the axes. Procedures may be required to *reorient* the configuration in some more interpretable way.

Several ways of dealing with this problem are available. One may submit the initial similarities configuration to a factor rotation program, e.g., varimax, in order to obtain "simple structure" [36]. Carroll and Chang [4] and Miller, Shepard and Chang [22] have suggested other procedures for coping with this problem as related to proximities data. Carroll and Chang [5] have also proposed a procedure for dealing with preference data in a manner similar to the "simple structure" approach.[1] In previous chapters the authors have described some applications of outside "property" fitting, where the property scale values are independently obtained monadic scale judgments on preselected attributes; these attributes are selected by the researcher as candidate dimension labels. Clearly, however, more empirical work on this series of problems is required.

The Composition Function Problem

We have already commented briefly upon the composition function problem—the relationship of judged overall similarity to individual attribute similarity. In the context of preference, this problem has been studied by many psychometricians and is evinced in the various models discussed in Chapter 4.

From an experimental viewpoint, there are several ways to develop composition functions or, in the context of preference, evaluation functions. The subject may be presented with composite (and explicitly described) alternatives and asked to state overall similarities or preferences, as the case may be. Configural scoring [3] and conjoint measurement [17] models are available to determine the "inputed" weights; these could then be compared to directly obtained weights from the subject.[2] In this respect we have some evidence [34] to suggest that instances arise where the results do not agree—a reflection of the subject's difficulty in assigning "importance" weights to attributes in isolation.

A related problem concerns the behavior of the composition function as the alternatives increase in complexity, e.g., involve a greater number of attributes or wider range of attribute scores. We would speculate that as the complexity increases, the composition function will undergo changes. The subject may de-emphasize interaction terms among dimensions in favor of such models as simple "main effects" models or "lexicographic" models (in which some attributes may receive zero weights) as the stimuli become increasingly complex.

[1]Carroll and Chang's INDSCAL model [6] also provides a unique orientation of the axes in the context of similarities data. Finally, if one chooses the *correct* non-Euclidean metric, a unique orientation also results, since Minkowski p-metrics (other than for $p = 2$) do not allow for arbitrary axis rotation.

[2]The "weights" described here have historically been associated with either the Euclidean or city block metrics.

Again, little systematic exploration of the composition or evaluation function has been made. Yet empirical investigation of this problem would seem to be important to the study of such marketing problems as vendor selection, new product evaluation, store site selection—in short, a whole variety of problems that are characterized by multiple objectives and tradeoff possibilities among these objectives.

Probability of Choice Models

Previous chapters have described various joint space models which embody a spatial representation of both stimuli and ideal points or vectors, as determined from preferences or a combination of similarities and preference data. Ultimately, however, we would like to predict consumer or industrial buyer choices. Clearly, other factors—brand availability, time pressures in shopping, etc.—will affect actual choices. That is, it does not follow that the buyer will *always* select his "most preferred" brand. More realistically, we would propose a stochastic model and speculate that probability of choice would decrease as "distance" from the (positive) ideal point increases.

But what form should the probability function relating choice to distance from ideal point take? One could try a variety of functional forms and attempt to "fit" the data to actual distribution-of-choice data. Or the problem might be approached in a more laboratory-like manner in which the respondent is required to make choices under various controlled conditions, after similarities and preference data are obtained. Other possibilities come to mind, as were discussed in Chapter 4.

In any case, it is probable that realistic formulations of the similarities-preference-choice sequence will entail some form of a simulation or search routine for determining parameter values that are "best," in some sense, for describing share-of-choice data. It would seem prudent to construct such models first on a laboratory scale so as to get more insight into the interconnections among the various components of the overall model. Ultimately, however, one would like to have a full-scale simulation, keyed to field data, in which changes in actual market share could be predicted.

The Aggregation Problem

Attempts to build comprehensive simulation models using similarities and preference inputs must ultimately contend with the problem of aggregation over individuals and groups. Earlier chapters have discussed the notion of market segmentation as viewed within the context of similarities and preference mapping. The joint space configurations, encompassing common perceptual and evaluative spaces but permitting idiosyncratic ideal points or vector directions, must eventually be aggregated if one is to make predictions about total brand choice behavior.

Aggregation procedures entail several empirical problems, not the least of which concerns the distribution of final choices and the delineation of ideal regions, rather than points. Aggregation of perceptions and preferences involves the substitution of averages of some kind for individual maps. Tucker and Messick's [32] or Carroll and Chang's [6] models may be useful for determining alternative "points of view" but some difficult methodological problems still remain in the aggregation of similarities and preferences. How "close" should respondents' similarities and preference maps be before one can aggregate them? Little investigation has been made as yet of the many problems of aggregation. Again we anticipate that analytical and laboratory research will precede the use of larger scale models in examining the conditions under which aggregation is appropriate and the types of summary statistics which are most useful in such aggregation tasks.

Policy Variables

The preceding discussion of probability of choice models and aggregation is related to the major applied problem for future investigation—measuring the impact of policy changes regarding product, price, promotion, or distribution on perception, preference, choice, and, ultimately, market share. A major premise of this monograph is that this set of techniques can be useful ultimately in predicting the effect of policy changes on output variables of interest to the firm.

Research directed to the policy question might proceed in two ways. First, it is possible that the methodology could be employed as an audit device in order to establish how current brands or services are perceived and evaluated. The results of the audit could then suggest various changes. Second, new product candidates or changes in type of sales effort might then be "tested" within the same framework.

But at this stage in the state of the art, relatively little is known regarding the translation of physical changes in the product or messages about the product into changes in similarities and preference. While similarities and preference mapping may be used to establish attribute salience and composition or evaluation functions, the hope is that one may ultimately be able to measure (and predict) the impact of changes in policy variables on changes in similarities, preferences and choice over time. Such "dynamic" models have not been explored as yet.

CONCEPTUAL PROBLEMS

The preceding classes of problems—loosely grouped as computational and empirical—hardly exhaust the possibilities for continued research in the scaling of similarities and preference data. Perhaps even more important are some basic conceptual problems underlying the measurement of perception and evaluation. Illustrative of these problems are:

1. The still ill-defined concepts of "similarity" and "preference" and their sensitivity to instructions and context.

2. The exploration of distance functions relating input similarities to configuration mapping.

3. Nonstationary, intrasubject models in which judged similarity and preference interact with stimulus pairs.

4. Models exploiting the concept of "second" (or n-th) choice in preference mapping.

5. Models for describing time changes in perception and preference as a function of stimulus and environmental change.

Each of these topics is dicussed in turn.

Conceptual Basis of Similarity and Preference

The terms "similarity" and "preference" are still not precisely defined. Experiments by Attneave [1], Shepard [26], and Torgerson [30] have indicated that subjects may adopt various strategies and states of attention when asked to make judgments of overall similarity among stimuli that are composed of perceptually distinct attributes for which no combinatorial rule suggests itself naturally.

For example, suppose a subject were presented with a series of circles varying both with respect to size and shading of gray. How much change in shading is equivalent to a specified change in size? Some subjects will attempt to equate the two changes in some compensatory manner while others will focus on only one of the attributes—which attribute, however, may change over the course of the experiment. Moreover, there is some reason to suspect that the subject's modal attention set may be sensitive to instructions and environmental context.

Restle [23] and others have hypothesized that overall similarity judgments may depend on a kind of "matching" process in which the subject attempts to find a measure on the set union of attributes possessed by each separate member of the pair. Restle has indicated how a distance function may be derived from set theoretic measures. While this approach is provocative, many questions remain unanswered. Which attributes are evoked? What is the relative importance of each? What is the functional relationship between overall similarity judgments and the arguments of this function?

A related problem in grappling conceptually with the meaning of similarity concerns the teleology of the response situation. That is, the attributes evoked in similarities judgments might be expected to be dependent on the respondent's problem solving context. One set of attributes could be relevant if the product is for personal use and another set if the product is to serve as a gift. The dependence of similarity on situation would seem to underscore the need for developing similarities configurations under a variety of scenarios and attempting to find appropriate transformations that link the configurations together [7].

Similar knotty problems are associated with the basic concept of preference. For example, under what conditions is total utility additive over part worth utilities? Experimental work by Tversky [33] and others suggests that additive utility models may be descriptive of a wide variety of actual choice situations. But comprehensive studies are still lacking in this area.

Extensions of "riskless" models of perception and preference might be made to deal with choice situations under uncertainty and some interesting theoretical and empirical work, employing utility approaches, is already going on. In all probability, however, more theoretical attention will be given in the future to the basic concepts of "similarity" and "preference" and their sensitivity to environmental context.

Distance Functions in Similarities Mapping

Most of the applications of nonmetric scaling to date have utilized Euclidean distance measures. Insofar as computer algorithms are concerned, however, this restriction is not required. Recent versions of most of the programs incorporate generalized Minkowski distance functions.

Some experimenters like Attneave [1] have questioned traditional reliance on the Euclidean metric as being representative of the psychological process involved in similarity judgments. More recently, Krantz [13] has discussed the matter of "rational" distance functions. The upshot of these criticisms is that the use of a Euclidean metric may be inappropriate in some situations involving judged similarities. Unfortunately, it is not known what these situations are, although Torgerson [30] and Attneave believe that stimuli composed of perceptually distinct attributes may be better represented by the city block metric. While Shepard's Monte Carlo study [25] suggests that scaling results may be quite robust over departures from the Euclidean metric, research in this area is just beginning, both from a conceptual and empirical standpoint.

Nonstationary Models

Another area suggestive of further study concerns the stability of evoked criteria in making similarity or preference judgments over trials. Present similarities models assume that the subject has a "mental configuration" of the stimuli and his comparison of "distances"—subject to transformation by an arbitrary monotone function in the presence of noise—leads to the observed responses, involving a rank order of the pairwise proximities.

In one sense the psychological basis of the above model is surely naive. Some of our experiments, for example, have suggested that the criteria by which similarity judgments are made may change over trials within a single subject. Moreover, which criteria *are* evoked on a given trial may be a function of the stimulus pairs—at least several protocol studies in which subjects were asked to "think out loud" while making similarity judgments suggest that this phenomenon can occur. This is not to say that such judgments are not imbeddable geometrically, but the question is: How?

One interpretation is to assume the subject has a stable configuration over trials and a set of simplistic rules-of-thumb for reacting to the task. For example, for any triad comparison A, B and C involving the "distances" $\overline{AB}$, $\overline{AC}$ and $\overline{BC}$, a subject might pick out the two most similar stimuli on the basis of that single dimension projection which leads to the greatest "scale separation" between the most similar pair and the next most similar pair. The *dimension* chosen, then, may interact with the particular triad of stimuli being compared. Moreover, when asked to pick out the two most different stimuli, the subject may employ some *other* single dimension projection in order to effect maximal discrimination.

If such a model were employed, what type of configuration would be recovered? One of our current projects has as its objective the investigation (via Monte Carlo techniques) of such models. Clearly, the preceding model could be generalized by assuming several potential configurations or "points of view" in which some probability mechanism is assumed to govern the evocation of a particular point of view on a given trial.

A second class of nonstationary models might be termed *sequential*. In this case the subject may choose some dimension along which comparisons might be most easily made, on the average. Additional dimensions are evoked only if distance "differences" are less than some threshhold.

Such nonstationary extensions of the basic model might also embrace investigation of the attributes themselves. For example, suppose a subject were given a set of stimuli with which he was largely unfamiliar. Rather than being asked to make similarity judgments directly, he could be asked to state what additional information (concerning stimulus attributes) he would most desire—at some charge for obtaining it—before making similarity judgments. Presumably the classes of information requested would bear some relationship to his expectations about those dimensions that are most discriminatory and/or most important for (anticipated) preference judgments.

The above suggested areas for further research are, at best, speculative but do point out the need to examine various nonstationary extensions of current similarities and preference models.

Second Choice Models

As Coombs [8] has pointed out, current preference models assume that all candidate stimuli are potential first choices. Underlying the specification of rank order is, for example, the presumption that choice number two would be preferred if choice number one were not available. Suppose, however, that choice number one *were* available but, in addition, the subject could obtain a second item. Under this set of conditions some other item, perhaps less "redundant" with item one, might be chosen. Obviously one could extend this notion to three or more items.

One way to develop this more complex model would be to ascertain preferences for items taken one at a time, two at a time, and so on—preferences being expressed in terms of the "bundle" of items. Composition of the bundles becomes the major problem of interest. Some items may be found to be "highly preferred" in the sense of appearing in most first-choice bundles, even though they receive few first choice mentions when items are judged individually. It seems to us that such studies of preference bundles are quite germane to the marketing field in which multiple brand usage is common in many product classes. If similarity judgments are included in the study, some insight may be gotten into which brands cluster together in a "commodity bundles" sense.

Time Changes in Perception and Preference

Most of our discussion thus far has been concerned with a static picture of perception and preference. From the firm's point of view, interest centers on the possibility of changing perception and preference in some way or ways favorable to the firm's brand or service. Virtually no research, either small-scale or field-level, has been conducted on time shifts in perception and preference as related to buyer "learning."

At the laboratory level, one might wish to study the impact of informative or persuasive messages on perception and preference. In a calibration phase the experimenter would first elicit similarity and preference judgments. Subjects would then be exposed to a series of messages—the experimental treatments. Some messages could be designed in an attempt to change preferences; others might be directed at selected stimuli in an attempt to change respondent perceptions of them. It would be interesting to determine the effectiveness of various classes of appeals and forms of information transmission on inducing changes in similarities and preference maps.

Extensions of this approach might involve the introduction of new stimuli into the previous array. How are perceptions among the old stimuli changed, if at all, with the introduction of new stimuli? Can one predict "aggregate" maps of the whole stimulus set from knowledge of the perceptual structure of partially overlapping subsets of stimuli?

Research at the field level is no less needed. We still know virtually nothing about the stability of perceptions and preferences over time. Such research would necessitate repeated measurement, preferably on the same sample of individuals, of similarities and preferences in a manner similar to already extant panel services. Such longitudinal studies, coupled with actual choice data (from respondent diaries), could be useful in the investigation of attitude and behavioral change under field conditions.

SUMMARY

In this chapter we have tried to discuss a variety of current limitations in multidimensional scaling and related methodology. This has been done not only to alert the reader to the many unsolved problems associated with this field but also to suggest the kinds of research tasks that could lead to better understanding and evaluation of the methodology.

Problems were discussed from several viewpoints—computational, empirical and conceptual. It seems to us that marketing researchers can be of valuable help in resolving some of these problems, particularly those at the empirical level. The results of such pilot studies might be useful in suggesting various modifications to, and extensions of, the currently available algorithms.

Research related to any of the three viewpoints is bound to be time consuming but, it seems to us, vital to any reasonable evaluation of these techniques in marketing decision-making. The research commitment appears sizable but, if our limited experience is any guide, so does the potential.

REFERENCES

1. Fred Attneave, "Dimensions of Similarity," *American Journal of Psychology*, Vol. 63 (1950), pp. 516–56.

2. F. J. Carmone, P. E. Green, and P. J. Robinson, "TRICON—An IBM 360/65 FORTRAN IV Program for the Triangularization of Conjoint Data," *Journal of Marketing Research*, Vol. 5 (May 1968), pp. 219–20.

3. F. J. Carmone, P. E. Green, and P. J. Robinson, "COFIS—An IBM 360/65 FORTRAN IV Program for Configural Scoring," *Journal of Marketing Research*, Vol. 5 (August 1968), p. 319.

4. J. D. Carroll and J. J. Chang, "A General Index of Nonlinear Correlation and Its Application to the Interpretation of Multidimensional Scaling Solutions," *American Psychologist*, Vol. 19 (1964), p. 540.

5. J. D. Carroll and J. J. Chang, "Relating Preference Data to Multidimensional Scaling Solutions via a Generalization of Coombs' Unfolding Model," mimeographed, Bell Telephone Laboratories, Murray Hill, N.J., 1967.

6. J. C. Carroll and J. J. Chang, "A New Method for Dealing with Individual Differences in Multidimensional Scaling," mimeographed, Bell Telephone Laboratories, Murray Hill, N.J., 1969.

7. Norman Cliff, Roger Pennell, and F. W. Young, "Multidimensional Scaling and Cognition I—Relations Among Judgments Obtained Under Varying Conditions," Technical Report No. 1, University of Southern California, Los Angeles, California, February 1967.

8. C. H. Coombs, *A Theory of Data* (New York: John Wiley & Sons, 1964).

9. R. M. Dawes, "Social Selection Based on Multidimensional Criteria," *Journal of Abnormal and Social Psychology*, Vol. 68 (1964), pp. 104–9.

10. T. C. Gleason, "A General Model for Nonmetric Multidimensional Scaling," MMPP 67-3, Department of Psychology, University of Michigan, 1967, mimeographed.

11. P. E. Green and Arun Maheshwari, "A Note on the Multidimensional Scaling of Conditional Proximity Data," *Journal of Marketing Research*, Vol. 7, (February 1970), pp. 106–10.

12. P. E. Green and V. R. Rao, "A Note on the Sensitivity of Multidimensional Scaling Solutions to Departures in Monotonicity," working paper, University of Pennsylvania, March 1969.

13. D. H. Krantz, "Rational Distance Functions for Multidimensional Scaling," *Journal of Mathematical Psychology* (1967), Vol. 4, pp. 226–45.

14. J. B. Kruskal, "Multidimensional Scaling by Optimizing Goodness of Fit to a Nonmetric Hypothesis," *Psychometrika*, Vol. 29 (1964), pp. 1–27.

15. J. B. Kruskal, "How to Use M-D-SCAL, a Program to do Multidimensional Scaling and Multidimensional Unfolding," (Version 4 and 4M of M-D-SCAL, all in FORTRAN IV), Bell Telephone Laboratories, Murray Hill, N.J., 1968.

16. J. B. Kruskal, personal communication, April 1969.

17. J. B. Kruskal, "Analysis of Factorial Experiments by Estimating Monotone Transformations of the Data," *Journal of the Royal Statistical Society*, Series B, Vol. 27 (1965), pp. 251–63.

18. J. B. Kruskal and J. D. Carroll, "Geometrical Models and Badness of Fit Functions," paper presented at International Symposium on Multivariate Analysis, University of Dayton, June 1968.

19. J. C. Lingoes, "An IBM 7090 Program for Guttman-Lingoes Smallest Space Analysis," *Behavioral Science*, Vol. 10 (1965), pp. 183–84.

20. R. F. McCracken, "Multidimensional Scaling and the Measurement of Consumer Perception: A Description and Sensitivity Analysis," unpublished MBA thesis, University of Pennsylvania, 1968.

21. R. F. McCracken, "The Parametric Mapping of Second Order Distances," informal notes, University of Pennsylvania, 1968.

22. J. E. Miller, R. N. Shepard and J. J. Chang, "An Analytical Approach to the Interpretation of Multidimensional Scaling Solutions," *American Psychologist*, Vol. 19 (1964), pp. 579–80.

23. Frank Restle, *Psychology of Judgment and Choice* (New York: John Wiley and Sons, 1961).

24. R. N. Shepard, "Metric Structures in Ordinal Data," *Journal of Mathematical Psychology*, Vol. 3 (1966), pp. 287–315.

25. R. N. Shepard, personal communication, August 1968.

26. R. N. Shepard, "Attention and the Metric Structure of the Stimulus," *Journal of Mathematical Psychology*, Vol. 1 (1964), pp. 54–87.

27. R. N. Shepard and J. D. Carroll, "Parametric Representation of Nonlinear Data Structures," in P. R. Krishniah (ed.), *Multivariate Analysis* (New York: Academic Press, 1966), pp. 561–92.

28. R. N. Shepard and J. B. Kruskal, "Nonmetric Methods for Scaling and for Factor Analysis," *American Psychologist*, Vol. 19 (1964), pp. 557–58. (Abstract.)

29. C. R. Sherman and F. W. Young, "Nonmetric Multidimensional Scaling: A Monte Carlo Study," Proceedings of the 76th Annual Convention, APA, 1968, pp. 207–8.

30. W. S. Torgerson, "Multidimensional Scaling of Similarity," *Psychometrika*, Vol. 30 (1965), pp. 379–93.

31. W. S. Torgerson, *Theory and Methods of Scaling* (New York: John Wiley and Sons, 1960).

32. L. R. Tucker and S. M. Messick, "An Individual Differences Model for Multidimensional Scaling," *Psychometrika*, Vol. 28 (1963), pp. 333–67.

33. Amos Tversky, "Additivity, Utility & Subjective Probability," *Journal of Mathematical Psychology*, Vol. 4, No. 2 (June 1967), pp. 175–201.

34. Yoram Wind, P. E. Green, and P. J. Robinson, "The Determinants of Vendor Selection: The Evaluation Function Approach," *Journal of Purchasing*, Vol. 4 (August 1968), pp. 29–41.

35. F. W. Young and W. S.Torgerson, "TORSCA, a FORTRAN IV Program for Shepard-Kruskal Multidimensional Scaling Analysis," *Behavioral Science*, Vol. 12 (1967), p. 498.

36. F. W. Young, "TORSCA, an IBM Program for Nonmetric Multidimensional Scaling," *Journal of Marketing Research*, Vol. 5 (August 1968), pp. 319–21.

Capsule Descriptions of Computer Programs

In this section of the monograph we provide brief descriptions of the major computing programs that have been developed for multidimensional scaling and related tasks. In each case we also reference the program's developer so that interested researchers can secure more up-to-date information on the algorithm and perhaps the program itself from the original source. All programs listed are available in FORTRAN IV source language.

Somewhat arbitrarily the following categories have been set up for describing the various programs:

1. Traditional scaling procedures.
2. Preprocessing programs for multidimensional scaling.
3. Multidimensional scaling programs.
4. Programs for analyzing qualitative data.
5. Cluster analytic routines.
6. Conjoint measurement, configural scoring and miscellaneous programs.

No definitive statement of all such programs is attempted here. (This is particularly the case insofar as cluster analytic programs are concerned.) Perusal of current literature in the journals cited in the monograph should provide an opportunity to maintain a current knowledge of new program development.

TRADITIONAL SCALING PROCEDURES

Prior to the advent of nonmetric multidimensional scaling [36], most psychometricians concentrated their efforts on unidimensional scales. Their procedures included such techniques as Thurstonian Case V scaling of paired comparison data, cumulative rank total scaling, successive intervals scaling and Guttman's scalogram analysis.

The STAT-PREF Package

One utility package [16] has been developed in conjunction with our own research for performing the following:

1. Thurstonian Case V scaling of paired comparisons data.
2. Cumulative rank totals scaling.
3. Successive intervals scaling.
4. Ancillary programs for transforming ranked data to paired comparisons.
5. Statistical tests on paired comparisons data.
6. Kendall's coefficients of consistency and concordance.

The STAT-PREF package can accept raw data in paired comparison form, ranked data or the frequency matrix itself. The Thurstonian Case V segment can accept up to 99 stimuli. It calculates scale values and mean absolute discrepancies. The rank-order scaling program accepts either ranked data or paired comparisons (up to a maximum of 25 stimuli) and prints out a table of the differences between cumulative rank totals. The successive intervals program handles up to a maximum of 200 stimuli (categorized data only), up to a maximum of 11 categories. Scale values are computed and the stimuli are ranked from least preferred to most preferred. In addition, two programs are available for converting data originally appearing as ranks to paired comparisons.

Part of the STAT-PREF package includes five significance tests [10] which can be conducted on data assumed to have come from paired comparison tests.

1. Test of one particular stimulus versus average of all others.
2. Overall test of equality among stimuli.
3. Test of equality between two particular stimuli.
4. Multiple comparison range test.
5. Score contrasts between stimulus pairs or weighted averages of stimulus groups.

This part of the program will handle up to 25 stimuli, 99 analyses, and 4,000 judges. All tests are run at three significance levels: alpha of 0.1; 0.05; and 0.01.

The last part of the STAT-PREF package consists of the computation of Kendall's coefficient of consistency for intrajudge agreement and Kendall's coefficient of concordance for interjudge agreement. The program computes appropriate summary measures and various statistics for significance testing.

Guttman's Scalogram Analysis

From time to time we have also utilized Guttman's scalogram analysis [13]. This program originally appeared in the Biomedical Program Package of UCLA and has since appeared in several other places as well. Like the Thurstonian procedures, scalogram analysis also assumes unidimensionality and attempts to place objects and subjects on a linear continuum from categorical scores.

PREPROCESSING PROGRAMS FOR MULTIDIMENSIONAL SCALING

Two programs have been developed in conjunction with our own research for preprocessing data prior to submission to multidimensional scaling analysis.

TRICON—Triangularization of Conjoint Data

The TRICON program [1] has been designed to process rank order similarity data from "raw" responses. Up to 15 stimuli can be handled, yielding as output a vector of ranks and frequencies and a half-matrix of ranks and frequencies for submission to nonmetric scaling programs. The program utilizes the triangularization method of Coombs.

The response data are first arranged in a square dominance matrix consisting of rows and columns that encompass all stimulus pairs; a one is placed in the cell if row dominates column. Rows and columns are then permuted in an attempt to triangularize the matrix. The number and location of intransitivities are then printed out. Intransitivities are cut by one of two procedures. The "cleaned" matrix is then powered and all possible disjoint pairs of pairs are filled in. Finally, the "best" complete order of proximities is printed in both vector and half matrix form. Cards are also punched as input to multidimensional scaling programs.

Two modifications of the basic program have also been prepared. TRICON II provides a different, more defensible, procedure for cutting intransitivities. The procedure is based on a method due to Phillips [34] and Slater [38]. This version also accepts as input a directly obtained matrix of pair comparisons. As such it can be used for obtaining a "best" complete order of preferences from (possibly intransitive) pair comparisons data. In this latter case up to 105 stimuli can be handled.

TRICON III incorporates still another procedure for resolving intransitivities and is considerably faster than TRICON II. In practice, however, all three versions of the program yield quite similar results for the types of data typically encountered in empirical applications. Their differences are largely of a technical rather than pragmatic character.

WAGS—Weighted Agreement Scores for Multidimensional Scaling

The WAGS program [2] is specifically designed for dealing with zero-one data matrices. For example, subjects might be classified as heavy (coded one) or light (coded zero) buyers of each of a set of brands. However, the brand profile components may be intercorrelated. The objective of the WAGS program is to develop a set of weighted similarity scores (based on the number of one-one and zero-zero matches) after intercorrelation in profile variables has been accounted for. Five different association measures can be computed prior to the computation of weighted similarities.

The program will handle up to a 75 × 75 matrix of zeroes and ones. Association measures and pairwise similarities are printed out. Also, the program will provide punched output of weighted similarity scores for submission to multidimensional scaling programs.

Tucker and Messick's VIEWS Model

This model, programmed by Young and Pennell [43], is a metric program for determining the number of different points of view, with regard to the same set of stimuli that is exhibited by a group of subjects. Multidimensional scaling programs can then be applied to each separate point of view.

Input consists of a subject by proximities matrix and the program performs a Q-type principal component analysis on either the intersubject raw cross products matrix, covariance matrix, or correlation matrix. Up to 99 subjects and 999 proximity "rows" can be handled. In addition, hypothetical subjects' points of view can be inserted and component "loadings" and "scores" can be obtained for subsequent processing by other programs.

MULTIDIMENSIONAL SCALING PROGRAMS

The major multidimensional scaling programs available for applications researchers are the following:

1. Kruskal's M-D-SCAL multidimensional scaling programs, Versions III and IV.
2. Guttman and Lingoes' SSA, SSAR and SSAP series.
3. Torgerson and Young's TORSCA programs, Versions 8 and 9.
4. Carroll and Chang's parametric mapping program.
5. McGee's multidimensional scaling programs, Versions EMD and DEMD-CEMD.
6. Carroll and Chang's MDPREF pair comparisons program.
7. Carroll and Chang's generalization of the Coombsian unfolding model, metric and nonmetric versions.
8. Carroll and Chang's INDSCAL program for individual differences analysis of similarities data.

Each program is described briefly, in turn.

Kruskal's M-D-SCAL Multidimensional Scaling Programs

Kruskal's M-D-SCAL III program [19] will scale up to 75 stimuli in up to 10 dimensions. Input data may be in either half matrix or whole matrix form. Missing entries, tied data, and asymmetrical data can be handled. Weights can be assigned to reflect the differing importance of various data values.

Scaling can be done in traditional Euclidean distance or any other special case of the Minkowski p-metric. The program plots the best fitting configuration and also plots the scatter diagram of proximities against computed distances and proximities against best fitting distances. A fit measure—Kruskal's stress—is also computed. The best fitting configuration can also be punched out on cards for subsequent processing.

Kruskal's M-D-SCAL IV program [21] is a more recent version which is upward-compatible with the earlier one. In this version a number of quite versatile options have been included which permit: (a) simple (metric) scaling as well as nonmetric scaling; (b) metric and nonmetric unfolding—as described in Chapter 4; (c) sublist splitting and various approaches for treating individual differences; (d) a choice of three bases of obtaining starting configurations; and (e) two different procedures for computing stress (see Chapter 3). It is probably the most versatile single program available for multidimensional scaling.

Guttman and Lingoes' SSA, SSAR, and SSAP Series

The Guttman and Lingoes' SSA [23], SSAR [24], and SSAP series [25] consists, respectively, of four programs for intact matrix analysis, four programs for off-diagonal matrix analysis, and two programs for partitioned matrix analysis. Their SSA-I program is designed to handle unconditional, intact and symmetric proximity matrices up to 60 by 60. Both the Euclidean and city block metrics are permitted. The program can handle tied data (but not missing entries) and also computes a fit measure—Guttman and Lingoes' normalized phi measure (which can be related mathematically to Kruskal's stress measure).

Their SSA-II program is designed to handle symmetric or asymmetric matrices where monotonicity is constrained within rows (or columns) only. As such, the program appears suitable for analyzing intact, conditional data matrices via Coombsian unfolding theory.

Guttman and Lingoes' SSA-III program is a scalar product rather than distance model and maps the ranks of scalar products (of the derived configuration) into the ranks of the input proximities. It also solves for communalities and can be viewed as a nonmetric factor analytic program, applicable when the researcher cannot justify the linearity assumptions of standard factor analysis.[1]

Their SSA-IV program is similar to SSA-I in terms of its point representation; it is similar to SSA-III in the sense that communalities are computed. In this program the correlation or covariance matrix is modified so that these proximities are monotonic with the set of computed (squared) Euclidean distances.

The Guttman-Lingoes SSAR series also consists of four programs dealing, in this case, with off-diagonal or rectangular proximities matrices, either unconditional or conditional. Their SSAR-I program is a nonmetric algorithm for finding point representations of ideal points and stimuli, as based on unconditional proximities matrices. Input data consists of a rectangular matrix of, say, pref-

---

[1] Although not widely distributed, mention should also be made of the Shepard-Kruskal nonmetric factor analysis model, as described in Shepard, R. N. and Kruskal, J. B., "Non-metric Methods for Scaling and for Factor Analysis," *American Psychologist*, Vol. 19 (1964), pp. 557-58.

erence orders of N subjects for n stimuli. Output of the program consists of a joint space point configuration of subjects and stimuli.

Their SSAR-II program imposes constraints only within rows (columns) and, as such, is designed for conditional proximities matrices. Their SSAR-III program has a provision for weighting orders within rows or columns, thus achieving a simultaneous R and Q-analysis. Their SSAR-IV program solves for communalities in the sense that distance between a row point and corresponding column point is taken to be an estimate of communality.

The two programs in their SSAP series are designed for scaling partitioned matrices and provide nonmetric analogues to factor analytic approaches. SSAP-I uses a subjects-by-categories and SSAP-II uses a subjects-by-variables matrix. The programs are similar in objective to SSAR-I and SSAR-II, respectively, but provide more constraints for solution determination.

Young and Torgerson's TORSCA 8 and 9 Programs

The TORSCA 8 program [41] represents a quite flexible approach to multidimensional scaling. The program will handle input data in either whole matrix, half matrix, or vector form for up to 75 stimuli. The first part of the algorithm performs a series of factor analyses on the scalar products of successively "corrected" matrices whose elements are monotonic with the original proximities data. An agreement index between the derived distances and best monotone distances is computed at each stage. As such, the first iteration performs a metric scaling of the data and successive iterations can be viewed as "quasi-nonmetric."

The second stage of the program represents a modification of one of Shepard's algorithms. On each iteration points are moved so as to decrease the discrepancy between derived distances and "best distances"—those that are monotone with the original data. The first stage or second stage may be used either singly or in combination, although the second stage does require an initial factor analysis in order to obtain a starting configuration.

Version 9 [42] of the program extends its flexibility to deal with off-diagonal (but unconditional) matrices, as well as providing additional features: (a) rotation of solution to "simple structure" (via a Varimax routine) or to match some configuration supplied by the user; (b) inclusion of the Minkowski p-metrics; and (c) tabulation of triangle inequality violations.

McGee's Multidimensional Scaling
Programs, EMD and DEMD-CEMD

McGee's EMD scaling program [30] is quite similar to Kruskal's in terms of its mechanics. Conceptually, however, McGee views distances between pairs of points as "elastic springs" and uses a chi square (work) criterion as an effectiveness measure. Increases in dimensionality are attempted only if lower dimensional solutions fail to reach a satisfactory value for his "work" criterion.

The McGee program, like Kruskal's, uses a steepest descent algorithm but initial starting coordinates (in one dimension) are nonarbitrary. Its major difference concerns the goodness of fit measure and the fact that solutions are started in one-space; fits in higher dimensions are attempted only if lower dimensional solutions do not satisfy the cut-off criterion.

McGee's DEMD-CEMD program [31] provides a way to deal with individual differences in proximities data. In this approach he tries to establish a kind of "maximally congruent" stimulus configuration (a single configuration reflecting commonalities of similarities judgments among subjects) and a "maximally discrepant" stimulus configuration (a single configuration reflecting disparities of similarities judgments among subjects). Their difference is interpreted as a type of "confidence interval" although no statistical inference statements are associated with the concept.

Carroll and Chang's Parametric Mapping Program

This program [37] is least like the preceding set of scaling programs in that a "continuity" assumption replaces the monotonic assumption. As such, it may be used to scale data where the relationship of proximities to distances is not necessarily monotonic. Rather, the components of each observation vector are assumed to be "continuous" functions of a set of fewer variables. The dimensionality of the space represents the smallest number of underlying variables for which the function is reasonably smooth or continuous.

The Carroll-Chang parametric mapping program will scale up to 150 stimuli. A fit measure is computed which summarizes how well the data can be approximated by a smooth function of values of a smaller set of orthogonal variables. The program uses a steepest descent algorithm to adjust the derived configuration until the fit measure—Carroll's kappa—is sufficiently small. The program appears particularly useful for dealing with data structures in which the stimuli lie in some curved manifold of lower dimensionality than the Euclidean space required to "contain" the manifold.

Carroll and Chang's MDPREF Paired
Comparisons Program

This Carroll-Chang program [4] is designed for the multidimensional analysis of preference data where preferences are expressed in paired comparisons (or rank order) form. The program handles missing entries, indifference relations, and inconsistencies by means of a (metric) vector model in which the subjects are viewed as vectors and the stimuli as points in the same multidimensional space. The objective of the program is to maximize a measure of agreement between projections of points on subject vectors and the initial paired comparisons data for each individual.

In cases where a vector model appears appropriate, it is an extremely useful program inasmuch as both missing and indifference relations data can be analyzed as well as cases in which intra-individual transitivity is violated. If (transitive) rank order input is used, the program is akin to a metric factor analysis of the preference data.

Carroll and Chang's Generalization of the Coombsian Unfolding Model—Metric and Nonmetric Versions

The Carroll-Chang generalization of the Coombsian unfolding model, PREF-MAP [5], is an extremely versatile program inasmuch as it permits successive fitting of simple to complex models and, in the metric version, a means for testing the improved goodness of fit provided by the introduction of more complex models. Two versions of the program—metric and nonmetric—are available.

Input to the programs consists of a similarities configuration, as obtained (possibly) by a previous multidimensional scaling of the stimuli only; this assumes that all individuals perceive the stimuli similarly. In addition, input data in the form of preference values for each individual are required. The metric version of the program assumes that the preference data are at least interval scaled; the nonmetric version requires only rank order data.

Four models can be fitted to the data. The simplest model is the "vector" model in which preference is related to the projections of each stimulus point on a compensatory vector which weights the basic dimensions. The next model—Coombs' ideal point model—assumes that all subjects weight the axes equally after differential stretching and rotation of the axes according to data of the "average" subject; different ideal point locations are permitted in the common space. The third model allows for both idiosyncratic ideal points and salience weights, while the fourth model permits idiosyncratic rotation of the perceptual space as well. In the metric version statistical tests are provided on the relative adequacy of each model for describing the data.

The nonmetric version starts with the metric solution and then performs a series of monotonic regressions aimed at improving the ordinal fit of the estimated preference values to a data set which is monotone to the original data. After this best fit is obtained, the results are parameterized in the manner described under the metric version.

Carroll and Chang's INDSCAL Program

The INDSCAL program [7] is designed to perform a metric analysis of proximities data that reveals individual differences among subjects in the weights they apply to a common or group space. (The program can be generalized to be "quasi-nonmetric" in the sense of the first stage of the TORSCA programs).

Output of the program consists of the group configuration of stimuli and a plot of subject weights for each dimension. A goodness of fit measure to each individual subject's data is provided and is roughly proportional to the squared distance of the point for that subject from the origin of the subject space. The program is already generalized to handle N-way matrices and, in this respect, can be used in selected types of multi-mode factor analysis and canonical correlation when more than two sets of data are available. By use of the explicit ideal point notion, it can also be used in the development of a joint space of stimuli and ideal points.

ANALYSIS OF QUALITATIVE DATA

The analysis of psychological data often requires routines for "metricizing" responses that are expressed categorically—either dichotomously or multichotomously, ordered classes or not. The scalogram and WAGS programs, described earlier, are illustrations of procedures that may be employed to deal with stimuli, subjects, or both, whose responses are expressed only qualitatively.

Various "traditional" approaches like Lazarsfeld's latent structure analysis [22] have been proposed for such analyses. More recently, Guttman and Lingoes have developed various programs for the multidimensional analysis of categorical data:

1. Multidimensional scalogram analysis—I
2. Multivariate analysis of contingencies—I
3. Multivariate analysis of contingencies—II
4. Multidimensional scalogram analysis—II
5. Multidimensional scalogram analysis—III

Each program is briefly discussed, in turn.

Guttman and Lingoes' Multidimensional
Scalogram Analysis—I

The task of this program [26] is: given an N by k binary matrix of subjects by item categories, transform the coordinates such that for a (categorized) item all subjects falling within a given category will be placed contiguously in a subregion of a derived Euclidean space. Each item represents a partitioning of the space into "boundaries" such that individuals falling in a given category are closer to each other than individuals falling in some other category of the item.

The MSA-I program can handle quantitative (after "degradation" to classificatory) data as well as qualitative responses involving linear as well as nonlinear relationships. Each individual becomes a point in Euclidean space falling in discrete regions representing response categories of the various items. All item categories are assumed to represent nominal scales.

Guttman and Lingoes' Multivariate
Analysis of Contingencies—I and II

The first part of these programs [27] proceeds in a manner similar to the above, leading to an r-dimensional Euclidean space in which each individual is plotted in terms of a chi square metric. Persons "near" each other in the reduced space will exhibit similar binary response profiles.

Version II of these programs embodies an additional feature, however—a a max-min clustering program in which further partitions of the space may be made, based on inter-individual proximity measures (actually, Euclidean distance measures for each pair of individuals). The clustering program uses a threshold distance measure for clustering points within a specified radius criterion. The program proceeds hierarchically by increasing the radius measure. At any given level of clustering a subject appears in only one cluster; no attempt is made at cluster improvement for a specific clustering level. Cluster centroids are computed as well as interpoint distances from each point to the origin and interpoint distances between centroids for all pairs of clusters at a given level of partitioning.

Guttman and Lingoes' Multidimensional Scalogram Analysis—II

This program [26] also starts with a binary attribute matrix of N individuals by k categories. In contrast to MSA-I, however, this program utilizes the reduced space methodology of Guttman and Lingoes' SSA and SSAR series. The objective is to find a space of minimum dimensionality such that the two sets of points (categories and persons) obey certain inequalities on distances, as imposed by the input data.

Guttman and Lingoes' Multidimensional Scalogram Analysis—III

This program [26] also partitions an N by k matrix of subjects by categories. Again, the subjects are represented by points, categories are represented by regions, and items by partitions. Category boundaries in MSA-I can be irregular but are constrained to be circular in MSA-II. In MSA-III, however, the categories are straight-line and parallel. In other respects it is similar to the other two programs of the MSA series.

CLUSTER ANALYTIC ROUTINES

While the main emphasis of our research has been on the utilization of computer algorithms in similarities and preference measurement, several clustering routines have been used as well. As described in Chapter 5, cluster analysis provides ways of partitioning a set of objects (often represented as points in multidimensional space) such that objects within a given cluster are more like each other than they are to objects outside the cluster.

Clustering routines can be useful in a variety of tasks, including the identification of market segments based on commonality of similarities and preference.

Moreover, the combination of reduced space and cluster analysis provides a nonmetric analogue to traditional factor analysis (R and Q techniques).

Clustering programs can be differentiated in three major ways: (a) the type of measure used to portray pairwise proximity, e.g., Euclidean distance, matching coefficients, correlation coefficients, etc.; (b) the way in which objects are grouped, given the proximity measures; and (c) summary measures of each cluster's characteristics. In our research, a number of different computer routines have been used and are described briefly, in turn.

The Day Clustering Routine

This program [11] uses Euclidean distance measures as proximity measures. Input data can consist of standardized characteristics (with equal or *a priori* specified weights), raw data, or factor scores derived from a preliminary factor analysis. A matrix of up to 125 objects and 25 characteristics can be handled.

The program clusters according to the criteria: (a) prespecification of a particular number of points per cluster or (b) use of prespecified threshold cutoff measure. Euclidean distances are computed for all pairs of objects. The object pair with the smallest distance is taken as the node of the first cluster. Points are added to this node according to their closeness to the cluster centroid which is recalculated after each point is added. When some prespecified number of points is clustered, or if the threshold is exceeded, a new cluster is started based on the closest two (unclustered) objects.

The program prints out the centroids of each cluster, the distance of each point to its cluster centroid, average interpoint distances within cluster, and the distance of each cluster centroid to the "grand" centroid of the data.

The Howard-Harris Program

This clustering routine [17] also uses Euclidean distance measures (standardized or unstandardized, equally or unequally weighted characteristics) as proximity measures. The grouping principle is hierarchical and is based on the attainment at each stage of minimal within-cluster variance, summed over all clusters. There are two versions of the routine: (a) the "small" version which handles 120 objects and 16 characteristics and (b) the "large" version which can handle up to 2,000 objects.

The objects are first split into two groups according to the single characteristic displaying the largest variance. Objects are then shifted from cluster to cluster until the minimum variance criterion is satisfied. The cluster containing the larger variance is next split into two clusters and objects are again distributed over clusters in accordance with the minimum variance criterion. The process is then continued until up to 20 groups are formed. Cluster centroids, the distance of each object to its cluster centroid, and a within-variance summary measure of each cluster, are computed. In addition, total, within- and between-variance measures are computed at each stage.

The Ward-Berry-Harris Program

This cluster routine [15] is also hierarchical in nature but proceeds obversely from the one just described. In this program each object starts out in its own cluster. The two closest points (based on minimal within-group variance) are next clustered. At stage three a new object is either added to the preceding two-object cluster or a new cluster of two objects is formed, depending upon the minimum variance criterion. This process is repeated until all objects ultimately appear in one large cluster.

Unlike the Howard-Harris program, this algorithm provides no basis for cluster "improvement"—once an object enters a cluster it remains in that cluster. Both programs are highly metric, however, in that the criterion satisfied is minimum within-cluster variance. Similarly, the Ward-Berry-Harris program computes an "effectiveness" measure at each stage in the hierarchical grouping process as a rough guide to selection of an appropriate level for partitioning the objects.

The Johnson Clustering Program

This cluster routine [18], unlike the preceding ones, is nonmetric in character. Input proximities may be distance measures, correlation coefficients, subjective measures of similarity-dissimilarity, matching coefficients; only a rank order of pairwise proximities is required. The program currently handles up to 185 objects.

This routine is also hierarchical in that each object starts out in its own cluster. At the next stage the program selects that pair of objects which are most similar, as based on the rank order of proximities. Unlike the preceding programs, however, no centroid is computed; rather a "min" (or "max") operator is used to cluster points. In the "diameter" option the program adds a new object to, say, a cluster of two if the minimum value of its proximity with each still exceeds the proximity value of any two (unclustered) objects; otherwise a new cluster of two objects is formed. In the "connectedness" option the program adds a new object to the cluster of two if the maximum value of its proximity with each still exceeds the proximity of any two (unclustered) objects.

In this program, once objects enter a cluster, they remain in the cluster. Eventually the clusters themselves are merged until all objects appear in one large cluster. At each stage an "effectiveness" measure, indicating the proximity value of the clustered object, is printed out. The "diameter" and "connectedness" options are similar to the methods of complete and single linkage, respectively, utilized originally by Sokal and Sneath [39].

The Pruitt Program

The principal feature of this program [35] is the flexibility exhibited in the use of proximity measures. Such proximity measures as the Euclidean and city block metrics, the Tanimoto distance coefficient, Cattell's similarity coefficient, and others are computed, if desired, for up to 100 objects and 45 characteristics.

The program uses a threshold criterion for clustering and the output consists of a taxonomic tree, similar in spirit to the various hierarchical programs commented upon earlier.

The Taxonome Program

Cattell and Coulter's Taxonome program [8] makes use of Cattell's profile similarity coefficient as a proximity measure. The program can handle discrete or measured data. The input matrix of profile similarity coefficients is then converted to an "incidence" matrix of zeros and ones, utilizing a threshold similarity value as an assignment criterion. Subsequent runs may be used in which the threshold level is raised or lowered by the user.

A Boolean algorithm, based on linkage, is used to find the clusters. The cluster sizes are generally not equal. The researcher may then select another threshold level and repeat the linkage process for the (derived) zero-one matrix. The program also contains a feature (similar to the "connectedness" option in the Johnson program) for clustering based on interconnectedness of clusters. In this case, however, the connectedness feature appears at the cluster rather than individual object level. Finally, it should be mentioned that the similarity coefficient itself can be generalized to deal with correlated dimensions and *a priori* weight assignments over different characteristics in the original objects-by-characteristics matrix.

The University of Colorado Program

This computer routine [14] has been designed primarily to perform cluster analysis according to various graph theoretic concepts. The program is hierarchical in nature and, starting out with an undirected graph, the algorithm develops a connectedness measure among the various elements of the set to be clustered. Its use of max and min operators makes it similar in spirit to the Johnson program described earlier.

The Guttman and Lingoes Max-Min
Clustering Program

This program [27], which currently handles up to 100 objects, has been described earlier in relation to the Guttman and Lingoes' Multivariate Analysis of Contingencies-II program. The clustering part of the program may, however, be used separately. It is metric in character and the clustering algorithm is most similar to the Day program in that threshold distance cutoffs are used.

The large amount of research going on in the area of cluster analysis suggests that the above programs are by no means exhaustive of even current cluster routines, let alone new ones expected to appear over the next few years. What appears more urgently needed, however, is a better rationale for clustering and an examination of the statistical properties of the programs' output.

MISCELLANEOUS PROGRAMS

Several other programs have been utilized in our applied research, but are difficult to classify neatly. Some of the programs, falling under the rubric of "conjoint measurement," have been used in the study of evaluation functions, that is, the manner in which partially ordered alternatives are collapsed into simply ordered alternatives in the descriptive study of choice making.

Other programs, e.g., Guttman and Lingoes' Configurational Similarity I and the Cliff-Pennell-Young rotation program, have been used to compare scaling configurations for correspondence.

The Configural Scoring Program

This program [3], called COFIS, enables the researcher to perform a variety of regression analyses when the predictor variable set is categorical, but the criterion variable is interval scaled. In the measurement of evaluation functions, for example, the subject may be given a set of multi-attribute alternatives (e.g., performance characteristics of a hypothetical set of vendors) and for each alternative is asked only to assign an overall "worth" measure. The objective of the researcher is to recover the implicit weights which the subject is assigning to each component of the performance vector.

The configural scoring program will handle up to seven performance characteristics, each expressed dichotomously. All main effects and interaction terms may be computed as well as predictive values for the criterion variable. In addition, the program has provision for fitting other models to the data in which, for example, various interaction coefficients are hypothesized to be zero. The "improvement" of the full configural model over various simplified models can then be ascertained statistically.

Kruskal's Monotone Regression of Data from
Factorial Experiments—MONANOVA

This program [20] can also be utilized in the evaluation function problem but proceeds in a different fashion. It assumes that observations could be scaled (transformed) in such a way that a linear, additive model (no interaction terms) can be found to describe the data. The program finds a function whose values are monotonic with the criterion measure and which permits description of the data by such an additive model. Parameter values of the additive model are also computed.

The program will handle up to four factors, each up to 100 levels, and un-limited replication up to a total of 500 data values; missing observations are permitted. The algorithm is, in part, essentially the same as that used in Kruskal's scaling programs. In addition to its special application in the evaluation function problem, the program may be employed in the analysis of factorial designs where the response measure need only be ordinally scaled.

Guttman and Lingoes' Conjoint Measurement—I

The rationale for this program [28] is similar to that of the preceding one. The researcher is presumed to have a data matrix in which responses are assumed to be an additive combination of row and column effects, such that the values of the additive combinations are as close as possible to being monotone with the response data. The problem is to determine the parameter values of the additive function. In this program the maximum order of either row or column is 50, with a single observation per cell. Functions other than the additive one can be employed as well.

This program can also be used in nonmetric analysis of variance problems, involving two-way designs, as well as in various aspects of scaling.

Guttman and Lingoes' Conjoint Measurement—II

This program [28] may be viewed as a nonmetric version of multiple regression. It assumes a set of predictor variables of orderable scores and a criterion variable which is also orderable. The program finds a set of monotonic transforms of the predictor set and a vector of weights (one for each observation), monotonic with the dependent variable, such that linear correlations between the (transformed) criterion and predictor variables are maximized.

The program will handle up to 25 variables and 200 observation vectors. In objective it is somewhat similar to the Multivariate Analysis of Contingencies programs but, in contrast, obtains a solution which preserves order within each separate variable.

Guttman and Lingoes' Conjoint Measurement—III

This program [28] can be described as a procedure for finding monotone transforms of an $N \times n$ matrix (where the N objects are ordered by the n variables) so as to maximize average correlation among all pairs of variables. It can be used as a preliminary transformation device prior to conducting a metric or nonmetric factor analysis on a set of data that are assumed only to be ordinal scaled.

The AID Program

The Automatic Detection of Interaction program [40] is also relevant to the evaluation function problem but its utility extends beyond this particular application. The AID program, originally developed by Sonquist and Morgan, can be employed in general survey research where one has an interval-scaled criterion variable and a set of nominal-scaled (or values "degraded" to nominal scale) predictor variables. The objective of the program is to develop a nonsymmetrical branching "tree" in which the sample is partitioned into a series of sub-groups (categorized by the predictor variable set) which best account for the variance in the criterion variable. The program selects predictor variables according to their ability to account for maximum (residual) variance in the criterion variable.

The program handles up to 36 predictor variables and 2,500 observations; with fewer predictor variables a larger number of observations may be handled.

Guttman-Lingoes' Configurational Similarity—I

The Guttman-Lingoes' Configurational Similarity—I program [29] is designed to make nonmetric comparisons of data and/or derived configurational matrices. It represents a rank order analogue to the more traditional product moment correlation of interpoint distances. For example, one might obtain similarities maps for two different individuals and wish to find out if their perceptions of the same set of stimuli are common (up to a similarity transform). Or one might wish to find the extent of agreement between the original data matrix and the derived configuration. The Configuration Similarity—I program computes a goodness of fit measure (the Guttman-Lingoes' coefficient of alienation) as a measure of their similarity; in addition, each object is assigned a separate measure of its contribution to the lack of fit.

The program will handle up to an 80 × 80 square matrix of proximities or an 80 × 40 rectangular matrix of (orthogonal) coordinate values.

The Cliff-Pennell-Young Factor Matching Program

This program [9, 33] has as its objective the orthogonal rotation of pairs of factor or scaling solutions to find some best agreement between members of the pair. For example, one might have two different scaling configurations and wish to rotate the solutions to maximal congruence. Or one might have a similarities map and an "objective" matrix of stimulus projections on measurable characteristics of the stimuli. The factor matching program will rotate the (perceived) configuration to best congruence with the target matrix.

The program will handle data matrices up to 50 × 50. The program prints out both the direction cosines of the "best" orthogonal transformation and stimulus projections on the new axes.

The Maximum "r" Rotation Program

This program [32] has as its objective the interpretation of multidimensional scaling solutions by finding directions in perceived space which maximize the linear correlation of property values of a target vector with stimulus projections. The assumption made is that the presumed psychophysical function is linear.

The program uses a multiple regression procedure to obtain the appropriate rotation.

The Carroll-Chang Monotonic Fit Program

This program [5], drawn from the Carroll-Chang generalization of the Coombsian unfolding model, PREF-MAP, has the same objective as the max "r" program. In this case, however, the psychophysical transforms need only be monotonic rather than linear. As such, it can also be used as a monotone multiple regression program, assuming that the set of predictor variables is interval scaled.

The Carroll-Chang Nonlinear Matching Program

This program [6] provides a nonlinear (and possibly non-monotonic) analogue to the above. Using Carroll's kappa criterion, the program finds those directions in psychological space that minimize kappa, Carroll's index of nonlinear correlation. As such, the analyst is not restricted to linear or monotone psychophysical functions relating perceived dimensions to "objective" or property dimensions.

Degerman's Qualitative-Quantitative
Rotation Program

This program [12] takes as its primary objective the interpretation of multidimensional scaling solutions that appear to represent mixtures of class-like and dimensional variables. It attempts to find rotations such that the class-like structure is revealed in a subspace of the original, while dimensional variables constitute a complementary (and orthogonal) subspace.

Input to the program consists of a coordinate matrix obtained from a preliminary multidimensional scaling of proximities data. The program then computes a set of "coefficients of non-planarity" which are used in a clustering stage to reveal class-like structure. A rotation of the space is made which maximally discriminates among clusters, followed by a second rotation which produces orthogonal subspaces of class-like and dimensional structure.

FUTURE PROGRAMS

The above programs, while quite extensive, are not exhaustive of the variety of multidimensional scaling, clustering, and related programs currently available. Moreover, the rate of new algorithm development in these areas shows few signs of tapering off. As more experience is gained with these algorithms, it is to be expected that a number of highly generalized approaches will replace the many specialized programs that now exist.

REFERENCES

1. F. J. Carmone, P. E. Green, and P. J. Robinson, "TRICON–An IBM 360/65 Program for the Triangularization of Conjoint Data," *Journal of Marketing Research*, Vol. 5 (May 1968), pp. 219-20.

2. F. J. Carmone, P. E. Green, and P. J. Robinson, "WAGS–An IBM 360/65 Program for Obtaining Weighted Agreement Scores for Multidimensional Scaling," *Journal of Marketing Research*, Vol. 5 (February 1968), pp. 95-98.

3. F. J. Carmone, P. E. Green, and P. J. Robinson, "COFIS–An IBM 360/65 FORTRAN IV Program for Configural Scoring," *Journal of Marketing Research*, Vol. 5 (August 1968), p. 319.

4. J. J. Chang and J. D. Carroll, "How to use MDPREF, a Computer Program for Multidimensional Analysis of Preference Data," mimeographed, Bell Telephone Laboratories, Murray Hill, N. J., 1969.

5. J. D. Carroll and J. J. Chang, "Relating Preference Data to Multidimensional Scaling Solutions via a Generalization of Coombs' Unfolding Model," mimeographed, Bell Telephone Laboratories, Murray Hill, N. J., 1967.

6. J. D. Carroll and J. J. Chang, "A General Index of Nonlinear Correlation and Its Application to the Interpretation of Multidimensional Scaling Solutions," *American Psychologist*, Vol. 19 (1960), p. 540.

7. J. D. Carroll and J. J. Chang, "A New Method for Dealing with Individual Differences in Multidimensional Scaling," mimeographed, Bell Telephone Laboratories, Murray Hill, N. J., 1969.

8. R. B. Cattell and M. A. Coulter, "Principles of Behavioral Taxonomy and the Mathematical Basis of the Taxonome Computer Program," *British Journal of Mathematical and Statistical Psychology*, Part 2, Vol. 19 (November 1966), pp. 237-69.

9. Norman Cliff, "Orthogonal Rotation to Congruence," *Psychometrika*, Vol. 31 (1966), pp. 33-42.

10. H. A. David, *The Method of Paired Comparisons* (New York: Hafner Publishing Company, 1963).

11. Jerry Day, "An IBM 360 Program for Cluster Analysis," University of Pennsylvania Computer Center, November 1967.

12. Richard Degerman, "Multidimensional Analysis of Complex Structure: Mixtures of Class and Quantitative Variation," unpublished Ph.D. thesis; John Hopkins University, 1968.

13. W. J. Dixon (ed.), "Biomedical Computer Programs," Education and Health Sciences Facility, University of California, Los Angeles, 1965.

14. G. F. Estabrook, "A Mathematical Model in Graph Theory for Biological Classification," *Journal of Theoretical Biology*, Vol. 12 (1966), pp. 297-310.

15. Britt Harris, "An IBM 360 Program for Ward-Berry Hierarchical Grouping," University of Pennsylvania Computer Center, November 1967.

16. J. M. W. Hogan, "STAT-PREF–an IBM 360/65 FORTRAN IV Program Package for Unidimensional Scaling of Preference Data," *Journal of Marketing Research*, Vol. 5 (May 1968), pp. 218-19.

17. Nigel Howard and Britt Harris, "A Hierarchical Grouping Routine–IBM 360/65 FORTRAN IV Program," University of Pennsylvania Computer Center, October 1966.

18. S. C. Johnson, "Hierarchical Clustering Schemes," *Psychometrika*, Vol. 32 (1967), pp. 241-54.

19. J. B. Kruskal, "Multidimensional Scaling by Optimizing Goodness of Fit to a Nonmetric Hypothesis," *Psychometrika*, Vol. 29 (1964), pp. 1-27.

20. J. B. Kruskal, "Analysis of Factorial Experiments by Estimating Monotone Transformations of the Data," *Journal of Royal Statistical Society*, Series B, Vol. 27 (1965), pp. 251-63.

21. J. B. Kruskal, "How to Use M-D-SCAL, a Program to do Multidimensional Scaling and Multidimensional Unfolding" (Version 4 and 4M of M-D-SCAL, all in FORTRAN IV), Bell Telephone Laboratories, Murray Hill, New Jersey, 1968.

22. P. F. Lazarsfeld, *Mathematical Thinking in the Social Sciences* (Glencoe, Ill.: The Free Press, 1954).

23. J. C. Lingoes, "An IBM 7090 Program for Guttman-Lingoes Smallest Space Analysis":

   SSA-I, *Behavioral Science*, Vol. 10 (1965), pp. 183-84
   SSA-II, *Behavioral Science*, Vol. 10 (1965), p. 487
   SSA-III, *Behavioral Science*, Vol. 11 (1966), pp. 75-76
   SSA-IV, *Behavioral Science*, Vol. 11 (1966), p. 407

24. J. C. Lingoes, "An IBM 7090 Program for Guttman-Lingoes Smallest Space Analysis":

   SSAR-I, *Behavioral Science*, Vol. 11 (1966), p. 322
   SSAR-II, *Behavioral Science*, Vol. 11 (1966), p. 323
   SSAR-III, *Behavioral Science*, Vol. 11 (1966), p. 323
   SSAR-IV, *Behavioral Science*, Vol. 12 (1967), pp. 74-75.

25. J. C. Lingoes, "A General Nonparametric Model for Representing Objects and Attributes in a Joint Metric Space," in J. C. Gardin (ed.), *Les Compterendus de Colloque International sur L'emploi des Calculateurs en Archeologie: Problemes Simiologiques et Mathematiques* (Marseilles: Centre National de la Recherche Scientifique, 1969); J. C. Lingoes, "An IBM 360/67 Program for Guttman-Lingoes Smallest Space Analysis—PI," *Behavioral Science*, Vol. 14 (1969), in press.

26. J. C. Lingoes, "An IBM 7090 Program for Guttman-Lingoes Multidimensional Scalogram Analysis, I," *Behavioral Science*, Vol. 11 (1966), pp. 76-78; MSA-II, *Behavioral Science*, Vol. 12 (1967), pp. 268-70; MSA-III, *Behavioral Science*, Vol. 13 (1968), pp. 512-13.

27. J. C. Lingoes, "Multivariate Analysis of Contingencies—An IBM 7090 Program for Analyzing Metric/Nonmetric or Linear/Nonlinear Data," Computation Report, University of Michigan Computing Center, No. 2, June 15, 1963 (Revised August 15, 1966).

28. J. C. Lingoes, "An IBM 7090 Program for Guttman-Lingoes Conjoint Measurement—I," *Behavioral Science*, Vol. 12, (1967), pp. 501-2; CM-II, *Behavioral Science*, Vol. 13 (1968), pp. 85-87; CM-III, *Behavioral Science*, Vol. 13 (1968), pp. 421-22.

29. J. C. Lingoes, "An IBM 7090 Program for Guttman-Lingoes Configurational Similarity—I," *Behavioral Science*, Vol. 12 (1967), pp. 502-3.

30. V. E. McGee, "EMD: A FORTRAN IV Program for Nonmetric (Elastic) Multidimensional Data Reduction," *Journal of Marketing Research*, Vol. 5 (1968), p. 321.

31. V. E. McGee, "Multidimensional Scaling of N Sets of Similarity Measures: A

Nonmetric Individual Differences Approach," *Multivariate Behavioral Research*, Vol. 3 (April 1968), pp. 233-48.

32. J. E. Miller, R. N. Shepard, and J. J. Chang, "An Analytical Approach to the Interpretation of Multidimensional Scaling Solutions," *American Psychologist*, Vol. 19 (1964), pp. 579-80.

33. Roger Pennell and F. W. Young, "An IBM System/360 Program for Orthogonal Least-Squares Matrix Fitting," *Behavioral Science*, Vol. 12 (1967), p. 165.

34. J. P. N. Phillips, "A Procedure for Determining Slater's *i* and All Nearest Adjoining Orders," *British Journal of Mathematical and Statistical Psychology*, Vol. 20 (1967), pp. 217-25.

35. Judy Pruitt, "TAXON—An IBM 360 Numerical Taxonomy Program," University of Pennsylvania Computer Center, November 1967.

36. R. N. Shepard, "The Analysis of Proximities: Multidimensional Scaling with an Unknown Distance Function," Part One, *Psychometrika*, Vol. 27 (1962), pp. 125-39.

37. R. N. Shepard and J. D. Carroll, "Parametric Representation of Nonlinear Data Structures," in P. R. Krishnaiah, *Multivariate Analysis* (New York: Academic Press, 1966), pp. 561–92.

38. Patrick Slater, "Inconsistencies in a Schedule of Paired Comparisons," *Biometrika*, Vol. 48, Nos. 3 and 4 (1961), pp. 303-12.

39. R. R. Sokal and P. H. A. Sneath, *Principles of Numerical Taxonomy* (San Francisco, Cal.: W. H. Freeman & Co., 1963).

40. J. A. Sonquist and J. N. Morgan, "The Detection of Interaction Effects," Monograph No. 35, The University of Michigan, 1964.

41. F. W. Young and W. S. Torgerson, "TORSCA—A FORTRAN IV Program for Shepard-Kruskal Multidimensional Scaling Analysis," *Behavioral Science*, Vol. 12 (1967), p. 498.

42. F. W. Young, "TORSCA, an IBM Program for Nonmetric Multidimensional Scaling," *Journal of Marketing Research*, Vol. 5 (August 1968), pp. 319-21.

43. F. W. Young and R. J. Pennell, "VIEWS, an IBM System/360 Program for 'Points of View' Analysis," *Behavioral Science*, Vol. 12 (March 1967), p. 166.

APPENDIX B

Bibliography

Abelson, R. P., "A Technique and a Model for Multidimensional Attitude Scaling," *Public Opinion Quarterly*, Vol. 18 (1954–55), pp. 405–18.

———— and Sermat, V., "Multidimensional Scaling of Facial Expressions," *Journal of Experimental Psychology*, Vol. 63 (1962), pp. 546–54.

———— and Tukey, J. W., "Efficient Utilization of Non-Numerical Information in Quantitative Analysis: General Theory and the Case of Simple Order," *Annals of Mathematical Statistics*, Vol. 34 (1963), pp. 1347–69.

Ackoff, R. L., *Scientific Method: Optimizing Applied Research Decisions* (New York: John Wiley & Sons, 1962).

Adams, Ernest and Messick, Samuel, "An Axiomatic Formulation and Generalization of Successive Intervals Scaling," *Psychometrika*, Vol. 23 (1958), pp. 355–68.

Anderson, N. H., "Application of an Additive Model to Impression Formation," *Science*, Vol. 138 (1962), pp. 817–18.

Anderson, T. W., "Classification by Multivariate Analysis," *Psychometrika*, Vol. 16 (1951), pp. 31–50.

————, "On Estimation of Parameters in Latent Structure Analysis," *Psychometrika*, Vol. 19 (1954), pp. 1–10.

Andrews, T. J. and Ray, W. S., "Multidimensional Psychophysics: A Method for Perceptual Analysis," *Journal of Psychology*, Vol. 44 (1967), pp. 133–44.

Attneave, F., "A Method of Graded Dichotomies for the Scaling of Judgments," *Psychological Review*, Vol. 56, (1949), pp. 334–40.

————, "Dimensions of Similarity," *American Journal of Psychology*, Vol. 63 (1950), pp. 516–56.

Auerbach Corporation, *Standard EDP Reports* (Philadelphia, Pa.).

Auila, D., "An Inverted Factor Analysis of Personality Distances Between Career- and Homemaking-Oriented Women," *Journal of Educational Research*, Vol. 60 (1967), pp. 416–18.

Balinsky, B., Blum, M. J., and Dutka, S., "The Coefficient of Agreement in Determining Product Preferences," *Journal of Applied Psychology*, Vol. 35 (1951), pp. 348–51.

Ball, G. H., "Data Analysis in the Social Sciences: What About the Details?" Proceedings: Fall Joint Computer Conference, 1965, pp. 539-59. (Obtained from author at Stanford Research Institute.)

_____ and Hall, D. J., "A Clustering Technique for Summarizing Multivariate Data," *Behavioral Science*, Vol. 12 (1967), pp. 154-55.

_____ , "ISODATA, An Iterative Method of Multivariate Data Analysis and Pattern Classification," Proceedings: 1966 IEEE International Communications Conference, pp. 116-17.

_____ , "ISODATA, a Novel Technique for Data Analysis and Pattern Classification," Technical Report (Menlo Park, California: Stanford Research Institute, May, 1965).

_____ "Background Information on Clustering Techniques," working paper, Stanford Research Institute, Menlo Park, California, July 1968.

Banks, A. S. and Gregg, P. M., "Grouping Political Systems: Q-Factor Analysis of a Cross-Policy Survey,"*The American Behavioral Scientist*, Vol. 9 (1965), pp. 3-6.

Bannister, D., "Personal Construct Theory: A Summary and Experimental Paradigm," *Acta Psychologica*, Vol. 1 (1962), pp. 104-20.

Barnett, N. L., "Beyond Market Segmentation," *Harvard Business Review*, Vol. 47 (1969), pp. 152-56.

Bartholomew, D. J., "A Test of Homogeneity for Ordered Alternatives," *Biometrica*, Vol. 46 (1959), pp. 36-48.

Bartlett, M. S., "Multivariate Analysis," *Journal of the Royal Statistical Society*, Vol. 9 (1947), pp. 176-97.

Bass, B. M., "Iterative Inverse Factor Analysis—A Rapid Method for Clustering Persons," *Psychometrika*, Vol. 22 (1957), pp. 105-7.

Beals, Richard W., Krantz, D. H., and Tversky, Amos, "The Foundations of Multidimensional Scaling," MMPP 67-2, Michigan Mathematical Psychology Program, University of Michigan, April 1967.

Bechtel, G. G., "Comparative Scaling of Unidimensional Discrimination and Similarity Data," *Psychometrika*, Vol. 31 (1966), pp. 75-83.

Beckenbach, Edwin and Bellman, Richard, *An Introduction to Inequalities* (New York: Random House, 1961).

Beech, H. R. and Maxwell, A. E. "Differentiation of Clinical Groups Using Canonical Variates," *Journal of Consulting Psychology*, Vol. 22 (1958), pp. 113-21.

Behrman, B. W. and Brown, D. R., Multidimensional Scaling of Form," paper presented at Midwestern Psychological Association, Chicago, May 1967 (mimeographed).

Bennett, J. F., "Determination of the Number of Independent Parameters of a Score Matrix from the Examination of Rank Orders," *Psychometrika*, Vol. 21 (1956), pp. 383-93.

_____ and Hays, W. L., "Multidimensional Unfolding: Determining the Dimensionality of Ranked Preference Data," *Psychometrika*, Vol. 25 (1960), pp. 27-43.

Benson, P. H., "A Short Method for Estimating a Distribution of Consumer Preferences," *Journal of Applied Psychology*, Vol. 46 (1962), pp. 307-13.

_____ and Pilgrim, F. J., "Testing Less Desirable Product Possibilities," *Journal of Marketing*, Vol. 25 (1961), pp. 65-68.

Bentley, M., "Early and Late Metric Uses of the Term 'Distance'," *American Journal of Psychology*, Vol. 63 (1950), p. 619.

Bergmann, G. and Spence, K. W., "The Logic of Psychophysical Measurement," *The Psychological Review*, Vol. 51 (1944), pp. 1–24.

Berkowitz, L., *Advances in Experimental Social Psychology* (New York: Academic Press, 1964).

Birch, D., "A Model for Response Tendency Combination," *Psychometrika*, Vol. 22 (1967), pp. 373–80.

Birdwell, A. E., "A Study of the Influence of Image Congruence on Consumer Choice," *Journal of Business*, Vol. 41 (1968), pp. 76–88.

Birnbaum, A. and Maxwell, A. E., "Classification Procedures Based on Bayes' Formula," Technical Report No. 4, School of Aviation Medicine, Brooks Air Force Base, Texas, 1959.

Black, D., "On the Rationale of Group Decision-Making," *Journal of Political Economy*, Vol. 56 (1958), pp. 23–34.

Bledsoe, W. W., "A Corridor-Projection Method for Determining Orthogonal Hyperplanes for Pattern Recognition," unpublished report, Panoramic Research Corp., Palo Alto, California, 1963.

Block, J., "The Difference Between Q and R," *Psychological Review*, Vol. 63 (1955), pp. 356–58.

————, Levine, L., and McNemar, Q., "Testing for the Existence of Psychometric Patterns," *Journal of Abnormal Social Psychology*, Vol. 46 (1951), pp. 356–59.

Bock, R. D., "The Selection of Judges for Preference Testing," *Psychometrika*, Vol. 21 (1956), pp. 349–66.

Boldt, R. F., "Construction of Some Judgment Spaces," RB-61-18, Educational Testing Service, Princeton, N.J., September 1961.

Bonner, R. E., "On Some Clustering Techniques," *IBM Journal of Research and Development* (January 1964).

Boorman, S. A. and Arabie, Phipps, "Metric Space Analysis of Structural Measures," working paper, Harvard College, May 1969 (mimeographed).

Borgatta, E. F., Cottrell, L. S., Jr., and Meyer, H. J., "On the Dimensions of Group Behavior, *Sociometry*, Vol. 19 (1956), pp. 223–40.

Bottenberg, R. A. and Christal, R. E., "An Iterative Technique for Clustering Criteria which Retains Optimum Predictive Efficiency," WADD-TN-61-30, Air Research and Development Command, U. S. Air Force, Lackland Air Force Base, Texas, March 1961.

Boulding, K. E., *The Image* (Ann Arbor: University of Michigan Press, 1968).

Box, G. E. P. and Cox, D. R., "An Analysis of Transformations," *Journal of the Royal Statistical Society*, Series B, Vol. 26 (1964), pp. 211–52.

Boyd, J. E. and Jackson, D. N., "The Perceived Structure of Social Attitudes and Personality: A Multidimensional Scaling Approach," *Multivariate Behavioral Research*, Vol. 2 (1967), pp. 281–97.

Bradley, R. A., "Incomplete Block Rank Analysis: On the Appropriateness of the Model for a Method of Paired Comparisons," *Biometrics*, Vol. 10 (1954), pp. 375–89.

————, "Some Statistical Methods in Taste Testing and Quality Evaluation," *Biometrics*, Vol. 9 (1953), pp. 23–38.

_____ and Terry, M. E., "Rank Analysis of Incomplete Block Designs," *Biometrics*, Vol. 8 (1952), pp. 324–45.

Bromley, D. B., "Rank Order Cluster Analysis," *The British Journal of Mathematical and Statistical Psychology*, Vol. 19 (1966), pp. 105–23.

Brunk, H. D., "Mathematical Models for Ranking from Paired Comparisons," *Journal of the American Statistical Association*, Vol. 55 (1960), pp. 503–20.

Bruner, J. S., *et al.*, *A Study of Thinking* (New York: John Wiley & Sons, 1966).

Bryan, J. G., "The Generalized Discriminant Function: Mathematical Foundation and Computational Routine," *Harvard Educational Review*, Vol. 21 (1951), pp. 90–95.

Burke, C. J. and Zinnes, J. L., "A Paired Comparison of Paired Comparisons," *Journal of Mathematical Psychology*, Vol. 2 (1965), pp. 53–76.

Burroughs, G. E. R., "Rotation of Axes and Psychological Space," *The British Journal of Statistical Psychology*, Vol. 15 (1962), p. 75.

Burt, C., "Alternative Methods of Factor Analysis," *British Journal of Psychology*, Vol. 40 (1949), pp. 99–121.

_____, "A Comparison of Factor Analysis and Analysis of Variance," *British Journal of Psychology*, Vol. 38 (1947), pp. 3–26.

_____, "Correlations Between Persons," *British Journal of Psychology*, Vol. 28 (1937), pp. 59–96.

_____, "The Relative Merits of Ranks and Paired Comparisons," *British Journal of Statistical Psychology*, Vol. 7 (1954), pp. 112–19.

_____, "Test-Construction and the Scale of Items," *British Journal of Psychology*, Statistical Section, Vol. 4 (1951), pp. 95–129.

_____ and Stephenson, W., "Alternative Views on Correlations Between Persons," *Psychometrika*, Vol. 4 (1939), pp. 269–81.

Campbell, D. T., "The Indirect Assessment of Social Attitudes," *Psychological Bulletin*, Vol. 47 (1949), pp. 15–28.

Carmone, F. J., Green, P. E., and Robinson, P. J., "TRICON–An IBM 360/65 FORTRAN IV Program for the Triangularization of Conjoint Data," *Journal of Marketing Research*, Vol. 5 (1968), pp. 219–20.

_____, "WAGS: An IBM 360/65 FORTRAN IV Computer Program for Obtaining Weighted Agreement Scores for Multidimensional Scaling," *Journal of Marketing Research*, Vol. 5 (1968), pp. 95–98.

_____, "COFIS–An IBM 360/65 Program for Configural Scoring," *Journal of Marketing Research*, Vol. 5 (1968), p. 319.

Carroll, J. B., "Words, Meanings and Concepts," *Harvard Educational Review*, Vol. 34 (1964), pp. 178–202.

Carroll, J. D., "Individual Differences and Multidimensional Scaling," Bell Telephone Laboratories, Murray Hill, N.J., 1969 (mimeographed).

_____, "A Generalization of Canonical Correlation Analysis to Three or More Sets of Variables," Proceedings of 76th Annual Convention of the American Psychological Association, San Francisco, Cal., Vol. 3, 1968, pp. 227–28.

_____, "A General Method for Preference Mapping of Perceptual Space," *Bulletin of the Operations Research Society of America*, Vol. 16 (1968), p. 282.

_____, "Polynomial Factor Analysis," Proceedings of the 77th Annual Convention of the American Psychological Association, Vol. 4, 1969, pp. 103–4.

_____ and J. J. Chang, "A General Index of Nonlinear Correlation and Its Application to the Interpretation of Multidimensional Scaling Solutions," *American Psychologist*, Vol. 19 (1964), p. 540.

_____, "Nonmetric Multidimensional Analysis of Paired Comparisons Data," paper presented at the Joint Meeting of the Psychometric and Psychonomic Societies, Niagara Falls, N.Y., October 1964.

_____, "Analysis of Individual Differences in Multidimensional Scaling via an N-way Generalization of 'Eckart-Young' Decomposition," paper presented at the Spring meeting of the Psychometric Society, Princeton, N.J., April 1969.

_____ and J. J. Chang, "Relating Preference Data to Multidimensional Scaling Solutions via a Generalization of Coombs' Unfolding Model," Bell Telephone Laboratories, Murray Hill, N.J., 1967 (mimeographed).

Cattell, R. B., "A Note on Correlation, Clusters and Cluster Search Methods," *Psychometrika*, Vol. 9 (1944), pp. 169–84.

_____, "The Principal Culture Pattern Discoverable in the Social Dimensions of Existing Nations," *Journal of Social Psychology*, Vol. 32 (1950), pp. 215–53.

_____, "r_p and Other Coefficients of Pattern Similarity," *Psychometrika*, Vol. 14 (1949), pp. 279–98.

_____ and Coulter, M. A., "Principles of Behavioral Taxonomy and the Mathematical Basis of the Taxonome Computer Program," *The British Journal of Mathematical and Statistical Psychology*, Vol. 19 (1966), pp. 237–69.

Cervin, V. B. and Henderson, G. P., "Statistical Theory of Persuasion," *Psychological Review*, Vol. 68 (1961), pp. 157–66.

Chambers, E. G., "Statistical Techniques in Applied Psychology," *Biometrics*, Vol. 33 (1946), pp. 269–73.

Chang, J. J. and Carroll, J. D., "How to Use MDPREF, a Computer Program for Multidimensional Analysis of Preference Data," Bell Telephone Laboratories, Murray Hill, N.J., 1969 (mimeographed).

Claringbold, P. J., "Multivariate Quantal Analysis," *Journal of the Royal Statistical Society*, Vol. 20 (1958), pp. 398–405.

Clark, H. H., "On the Use and Meaning of Prepositions," unpublished Ph.D. Thesis, Johns Hopkins University, 1966.

Cleary, T. Anne, "An Individual Differences Model for Multiple Regression," *Psychometrika*, Vol. 31 (1966), pp. 215–24.

Clevenger, T., Lazier, G. A., and Clark, M. L., "Measurement of Corporate Images by Semantic Differential," *Journal of Marketing Research*, Vol. 2 (1965), pp. 80–82.

Cliff, Norman, "Adverbs as Multipliers," *Psychological Review*, Vol. 66 (1959), pp. 27–44.

_____, "Orthogonal Rotation to Congruence," *Psychometrika*, Vol. 31 (1966), pp. 33–42.

_____, "Analytic Rotation to a Functional Relationship," *Psychometrika*, Vol. 27 (1962), pp. 283–95.

_____ and Pennell, R., "The Influence of Communality, Factor Strength and Loading Size on the Sampling Characteristics of Factor Loadings," *Psychometrika*, Vol. 32 (1967), pp. 309–26.

Cliff, Norman, Pennell, R., and Young, F. W., "Multidimensional Scaling and Cognition I—Relations Among Judgments Obtained Under Varying Conditions," Technical Report No. 1, University of Southern California, February 1967 (mimeographed).

————, "Multidimensional Scaling and Cognition II—The Relation of the Evaluative Dimension of Connotation to the Multidimensional Structure," University of Southern California, February 1967 (mimeographed).

————, "Multidimensional Scaling and Cognition," Final Report, University of Southern California, February 1967 (mimeographed).

Cliff, Norman and Young, F. W., "Multidimensional Scaling and Cognition: Threat Evaluation and Subjective Organization of Simulated Raids," University of Southern California, December 1966 (mimeographed).

————, "On the Relation Between Unidimensional Judgments and Multidimensional Scaling," *Organizational Behavior and Human Performance*, Vol. 3 (1968), pp. 269–85.

Clifton, C. and Odom, Penelope, "Similarity Relations Among Certain English Sentence Constructions," *Psychological Monographs*, Vol. 80 (1966).

Cochran, W. G. and Hopkins, C. E., "Some Classification Problems With Multivariate Qualitative Data," *Biometrics*, Vol. 17 (1961), pp. 10–32.

Cohen, J., Abstract of "A Method of Market Segmentation Based on Multivariate Analysis of Attitude Data," Board Chairman, Abacus Association, New York, N.Y. (undated).

Coleman, J. S., *Introduction to Mathematical Sociology* (Glencoe, Ill.: The Free Press, 1964).

————, "Multidimensional Scale Analysis," *American Journal of Sociology*, Vol. 63 (1957), pp. 253–63.

Comrey, A. L., "An Operational Approach to Some Problems in Psychological Measurement," *Psychological Review*, Vol. 7 (1950), pp. 217–28.

———— and Levonian, Edward, "A Comparison of Three Point Coefficients in Factor Analysis of MMPI Items," *Educational and Psychological Measurement*, Vol. 19 (1958), pp. 739–55.

Conrad, H. S., "Some Principles of Attitude-Measurement: A Reply to 'Opinion-Attitude Methodology'," *Psychological Bulletin*, Vol. 43 (1946), pp. 570–89.

Constantinescu, P., "The Classification of a Set of Elements with Respect to a Set of Properties," *Computer Journal*, Vol. 8 (1966), pp. 352–57.

————, "A Method of Cluster Analysis," *The British Journal of Mathematical and Statistical Psychology*, Vol. 19 (1967), pp. 93–106.

Cook, V. J. and Herniter, J. D., "Preference Measurement in a New Product Demand Situation," in R. L. King (ed.), Proceedings of the Denver Conference of the American Marketing Association (Chicago: American Marketing Association, 1968, pp. 316–22).

Coombs, C. H., "A Theory of Psychological Scaling," *Engineering Research Institute Bulletin*, No. 23 (Ann Arbor: University of Michigan Press, 1952).

————, "A Method for the Study of Interstimulus Similarity," *Psychometrika*, Vol. 19 (1954), pp. 183–94.

————, "An Application of a Nonmetric Model for Multidimensional Analysis of Similarities," *Psychological Reports*, Vol. 4 (1958), pp. 511–18.

————, "Inconsistency of Preferences as a Measure of Psychological Distance," in C. W. Churchman and Ratoosh, P. (eds.), *Measurement: Definition and Theories* (New York, John Wiley & Sons, 1959).

————, "Mathematical Models in Psychological Scaling," *Journal of the American Statistical Association*, Vol. 46 (1951), pp. 480–89.

————, "Psychological Scaling Without a Unit of Measurement," *Psychological Review*, Vol. 57 (1950), pp. 148–58.

————, "Scaling and Data Theory," Psychology Department, University of Michigan, May 1966 (mimeographed).

————, "Some Hypotheses for the Analysis of Qualitative Variables," *Psychological Review*, Vol. 55 (1948), pp. 167–74.

————, "Theory and Methods of Social Measurement," In *Research Methods in the Behavioral Sciences*, L. Festinger and D. Katz (eds.) (New York: The Dryden Press, 1953).

————, *A Theory of Data* (New York: John Wiley & Sons, 1964).

———— and Goode, F. M., "Testing Expectation Theories of Decision Making without Measuring Utility or Subjective Probability," (Supplementary Report), MMPP 65-5, Michigan Mathematical Psychology Program, University of Michigan, October 1965.

————, Greenberg, M., and Zinnes, J., "A Double Law of Comparative Judgment for the Analysis of Preferential Choice and Similarities Data," *Psychometrika*, Vol. 26 (1961), pp. 165–71.

Corcoran, D. W. J., "A Test of Some Assumptions about Psychological Space," *American Journal of Psychology*, Vol. 79 (1966), pp. 531–41.

Cox, D. R., "Note on Grouping," *Journal of the American Statistical Association*, Vol. 52 (1957), pp. 543–47.

Crespi, L., "Use of Scaling Techniques in Surveys," *Journal of Marketing*, Vol. 25 (1961), pp. 69–72.

Cronbach, L. J. and Gleser, G. C., "Assessing Similarity Between Profiles," *Psychological Bulletin*, Vol. 50 (1953), pp. 456–73.

David, H. A., *The Method of Paired Comparisons*. New York: Hafner Publishing Company, 1963.

Davidon, R. S., "Relevance and Category Scales of Judgment," *British Journal of Psychology*, Vol. 53 (1963), pp. 373–80.

Davidon, W. C., "Variance Algorithm for Minimization," *The Computer Journal*, Vol. 11 (1968), pp. 406–10.

Davis, J. M., "The Transitivity of Preferences," *Behavioral Science*, Vol. 3 (1958), pp. 26–33.

Dawes, R. M., "Social Selection Based on Multidimensional Criteria," *Journal of Abnormal and Social Psychology*, Vol. 68 (1964), pp. 104–9.

————, "Towards a General Framework for Evaluation," MMPP 64-7, Michigan Mathematical Psychology Program, University of Michigan, September 1964.

Day, Jerry, "An IBM 360 Program for Cluster Analysis," University of Pennsylvania Computer Center, November 1967.

Day, R. L., "Systematic Paired Comparisons in Preference Analysis," *Journal of Marketing Research*, Vol. 2 (1965), pp. 406–12.

Deese, James, "On the Structure of Associative Meaning," *Psychological Review*, Vol. 69 (1962), pp. 161–75.

Degerman, Richard, "Multidimensional Analysis of Complex Structure: Mixtures of Class and Quantitative Variation," unpublished Ph.D. thesis, Johns Hopkins University, 1968.

Dempsey, P., "The Dimensionality of the MMPI Clinical Scales Among Normal Subjects," *Journal of Consulting Psychology*, Vol. 27 (1963), pp. 492–97.

_____ and Baumhoff, M., "The Statistical Use of Artifact Distributions to Establish Chronological Sequence," *American Antiques*, Vol. 28 (1963), pp. 496–509.

de Leeuw, Jan, "Nonmetric Multidimensional Scaling," RN 010-68, Faculty of Social Sciences, University of Leiden, Netherlands, November 1968.

_____, "Canonical Discriminant Analysis," RN 007-68, Faculty of Social Sciences, University of Leiden, Netherlands, April 1968.

_____, "Nonmetric Discriminant Analysis," RN 006-68, Faculty of Social Sciences, University of Leiden, Netherlands, April 1968.

De Soto, C. B., "The Predilection for Single Orderings," *Journal of Abnormal and Social Psychology*, Vol. 62 (1961), pp. 16–23.

Dichter, E., "Toward an Understanding of Human Behavior," in Robert Ferber and Hugh Wales (eds.), *Motivation and Market Behavior*, (Homewood, Ill.: Richard D. Irwin, 1958).

Diederich, G., "A General Least Squares Solution for Successive Intervals," *Psychometrika*, Vol. 22 (1957), pp. 159–73.

_____, French, J. W., and Carlton, T., "Factors in Judgments of Writing Ability," RB-61-15, Educational Testing Service, Princeton, N.J., August 1961.

Dixon, W. J. (ed.), "Biomedical Computer Programs," Education and Health Sciences Facility, University of California, 1965.

Doehlert, D. H., "Similarity and Preference Mapping: A Color Example," in R. L. King (ed.), Proceedings of the Denver Conference of the American Marketing Association, (Chicago: American Marketing Association, 1968, pp. 250–58).

du Mas, F. M., "A Quick Method of Analyzing the Similarity of Profiles," *Journal of Clinical Psychology*, Vol. 2 (1964), pp. 80–83.

_____, "The Coefficient of Profile Similarity," *Journal of Clinical Psychology*, Vol. 5 (1949), pp. 123–31.

_____, "A Note on the Coefficient of Profile Similarity," *Journal of Clinical Psychology*, Vol. 3 (1950), pp. 300–1.

Duncan, O. D., Ohlin, L. E., Reiss, A. J., Jr., and Stanton, H. R., "Formal Devices for Making Selection Decisions," *American Journal of Sociology*, Vol. 58 (1953), pp. 573–84.

Durbin, J., "Incomplete Blocks in Ranking Experiments," *British Journal of Psychology*, Statistical Section, Vol. 4 (1951), pp. 85–90.

Dwyer, P. S., "Solution of the Personnel Classification Problem by the Method of Optimal Regions," *Psychometrika*, Vol. 18 (1954), pp. 11–26.

Dykstra, O., Jr., "A Note on the Rank Analysis of Incomplete Block Designs—Applications Beyond the Scope of Existing Tables," *Biometrics*, Vol. 12 (1956), pp. 301–6.

Eastlack, J. L., "Consumer Flavor Preference Factors in Food Product Design," *Journal of Marketing Research*, Vol. 1 (1964), pp. 38–42.

Eckart, C. and Young, G., "The Approximation of One Matrix by Another of Lower Rank," *Psychometrika*, Vol. 1 (1936), pp. 211–18.

Edgertown, H. A. and Kolbe, L. E., "The Method of Minimum Variation for the Combination of Criteria," *Psychometrika*, Vol. 1 (1936), pp. 183–87.

Edwards, A. L., *Techniques of Attitude Scale Construction* (New York: Appleton-Century-Crofts, 1957).

Edwards, A. W. F. and Cavalli-Sforza, L. L., "A Method for Cluster Analysis," *Biometrics*, Vol. 21 (1965), pp. 362–75.

Edwards, L. E. and Kilpatrick, F. P., "Scale Analysis and the Measurement of Social Attitudes," *Psychometrika*, Vol. 13 (1948), pp. 99–114.

Eisler, H., "A Note on Treatment of Ratio Setting Data for Construction of Psychological Scales," Report #54, University of Stockholm Psychology Laboratory, undated.

_____, "Similarity in the Continuum of Heaviness with Some Methodological and Theoretical Considerations," *Scandinavian Journal of Psychology*, Vol. 1 (1960), pp. 69–81.

_____ and Ekman, G., "A Mechanism of Subjective Similarity," *Acta Psychologica* (Amsterdam), Vol. 16 (1959), pp. 1–10.

Ekman, G., "Dimensions of Color Vision," *Journal of Psychology*, Vol. 38 (1954), pp. 467–74.

_____, "Measurement of Moral Judgment: A Comparison of Scaling Methods," *Perceptual and Motor Skills*, Vol. 15 (1962), pp. 3–9.

_____, "Dimensions of Emotion," *Acta Psychologica*, Vol. 11 (1955), pp. 279–88.

_____, "Two Generalized Ratio Scaling Methods," *Journal of Psychology*, Vol. 45 (1958), pp. 287–95.

_____, "Weber's Law and Related Functions," *Journal of Psychology*, Vol. 47 (1959), pp. 343–52.

_____, "A Direct Method for Multidimensional Ratio Scaling," *Psychometrika*, Vol. 28 (1963), pp. 33–41.

_____, "Two Methods for the Analysis of Perceptual Dimensionality," *Perceptual and Motor Skills*, Vol. 20 (1965), pp. 557–72.

_____, Eisler, H., and Kunnapas, T., "Brightness Scales for Monochromatic Light," *Scandinavian Journal of Psychology*, Vol. 1 (1960), pp. 41–48.

_____, Engen, T., Kunnapas, T., and Lindman, R., "A Quantitative Principle of Qualitative Similarity," *Journal of Experimental Psychology*, Vol. 68 (1964), pp. 530–36.

_____, Goude, G., and Waern, Y., "Subjective Similarity in Two Perceptual Continua," *Journal of Experimental Psychology*, Vol. 61 (1961), pp. 222–27.

_____ and Sjoeberg, L., "Scaling," *Annual Review of Psychology*, Vol. 16 (1965), pp. 451–74.

_____ and Waern, Y., "A Second Order Ratio Scale," *Acta Psychologica*, Vol. 47 (1959), pp. 343–52.

Ellis, B., *Basic Concepts of Measurement* (Cambridge: Cambridge University Press, 1962).

Ellson, D. G., "A Method for Identifying Pattern Clusters in Test Score Profiles," *American Psychologist*, Vol. 2 (1947), p. 425. (Abstract)

Eriksen, C. W. and Hake, H. W., "Multidimensional Stimulus Differences and Accuracy of Discrimination," *Journal of Experimental Psychology*, Vol. 50 (1955), pp. 154–60.

Estabrook, G. F., "A Mathematical Model in Graph Theory for Biological Classification," *Journal of Theoretical Biology*, Vol. 12 (1966), pp. 297–310.

Estes, W. K., "The Problem of Inference from Curves Based on Group Data," *Psychological Bulletin*, Vol. 53 (1956), pp. 134–40.

Eysenck, H. J., "The Appreciation of Humour: An Experimental and Theoretical Study," *British Journal of Psychology*, Vol. 32 (1942), pp. 295–300.

Eysenck, H. J., "The General Factor in Aesthetic Judgments," *British Journal of Psychology*, Vol. 31 (1940), pp. 94–102.

_____, "The Logical Basis of Factor Analysis," *American Psychologist*, Vol. 8 (1953), pp. 105–14.

_____, "Psychiatric Diagnosis as a Psychological and Statistical Problem," *Psychological Reports*, Vol. 1 (1955), pp. 3–17.

_____, "Type Factors in Aesthetic Judgments," *British Journal of Psychology*, Vol. 31 (1941), pp. 262–70.

_____, "Uses and Abuses of Factor Analysis," *Applied Statistics*, Vol. 1 (1952), pp. 45–49.

_____ and Crown, S., "National Stereotypes: An Experimental and Methodological Study," *International Journal of Opinion and Attitude Research*, Vol. 3 (1948), pp. 26–39.

Fagen, R., "Some Contributions of Mathematical Reasoning to the Study of Politics," *American Political Science Review*, Vol. 55 (1961), pp. 888–900.

Fagot, R. F., "A Model for Ordered Metric Scaling by Comparison of Intervals," *Psychometrika*, Vol. 24 (1959), pp. 157–68.

Fechner, G. T., *Elements der Psychophysik* (reprint) (Leipzig: Breitkopf and Hartel, 1889).

Ferber, R. and Wales, H. G., *Motivation and Market Behavior* (Homewood, Ill.: Richard D. Irwin, 1958).

Ferguson, G. A., "The Concept of Parsimony in Factor Analysis," *Psychometrika*, Vol. 19 (1954), pp. 281–90.

_____, "The Factorial Interpretation of Test Difficulty," *Psychometrika*, Vol. 6 (1941), pp. 323–29.

Festinger, L., "The Treatment of Qualitative Data by 'Scale Analysis'," *Psychological Bulletin*, Vol. 44 (1947), pp. 149–61.

Fishbein, M., "An Investigation of the Relationships Between Beliefs About an Object and the Attitude Toward that Object," *Human Relations*, Vol. 16 (1963), pp. 233–39.

Fishburn, P. C., "On the Prospects of a Useful Unified Theory of Value for Engineering," *IEEE Transactions on Systems Science and Cybernetics*, Vol. 2 (1966), pp. 27–34.

_____, "Conjoint Measurement in Utility Theory with Incomplete Product Sets," *Journal of Mathematical Psychology*, Vol. 4 (1967), pp. 104–19.

_____, "Methods of Estimating Additive Utilities," *Management Science*, Vol. 13 (1967), pp. 435–53.

_____, "A Note on Recent Developments in Additive Utility Theories for Multiple-Factor Situations," *Operations Research*, Vol. 14 (1966), pp. 1143–48.

Fisher, W. D., "On Grouping for Maximum Homogeneity," *Journal of American Statistical Association*, Vol. 53 (1958), pp. 789–98.

Fishman, J. A., "An Examination of the Process and Function of Social Stereotyping," *Journal of Social Psychology*, Vol. 43 (1956), pp. 27–64.

Fletcher, R. and Powell, M. J. D., "A Rapidly Convergent Descent Method for Minimization," *Computer Journal*, Vol. 6 (1963), pp. 163–68.

Foa, U. G., "The Foreman-Worker Interaction: A Research Design," *Sociometry*, Vol. 18 (1955), pp. 226–44.

————, "New Developments in Facet Design and Analysis," *Psychological Review*, Vol. 72 (1965), pp. 262–74.

Forgy, E. W., "Detecting 'Natural' Clusters of Individuals," paper presented at the Western Psychological Association Meetings, 1963.

Fortier, J. J. and Solomon, H., "Clustering Procedures," Technical Report 7, Stanford University, 1964.

————, "Clustering Procedures," paper presented at the International Symposium on Multivariate Analysis, University of Dayton, June 1965.

Frank, R. E. and Green, P. E., "Numerical Taxonomy in Marketing Analysis: A Review Article," *Journal of Marketing Research*, Vol. 5 (1968), pp. 83–94.

Gaier, E. L. and Lee, M. C., "Pattern Analysis: The Configural Approach to Predictive Measurement," *Psychological Bulletin*, Vol. 50 (1953), pp. 140–48.

Generelli, J. A., "A Method for Detecting Subgroups in a Population and Specifying Their Membership," *Journal of Psychology*, Vol. 55 (1963), pp. 457–68.

Gerard, H. B., "Determining the Degree of Inconsistency in a Set of Paired Comparisons," *Psychometrika*, Vol. 23 (1958), pp. 33–46.

Ghiselli, E. E., "Differentiation of Tests in Terms of the Accuracy with Which They Predict for a Given Individual," *Educational and Psychological Measurement*, Vol. 20 (1960), pp. 675–84.

Gibson, W. A., "An Extension of Anderson's Solution for the Latent Structure Equations," *Psychometrika*, Vol. 20 (1955), pp. 69–73.

————, "Three Multivariate Models: Factor Analysis, Latent Structure Analysis and Latent Profile Analysis," *Psychometrika*, Vol. 24 (1959), pp. 229–52.

————, "A Latent Structure for the Simplex," *Psychometrika*, Vol. 32 (1967), pp. 35–46.

Glass, V., "Factors in Teachers' Perceptions of Students," *Journal of Educational Measurement*, Vol. 4 (1967), pp. 87–93.

Gleason, T. C., "A General Model for Nonmetric Multidimensional Scaling," MMPP 67-3, Michigan Mathematical Psychology Program, University of Michigan, June 1967.

————, "Multidimensional Scaling of Sociometric Data," Research Center for Group Dynamics, Institute for Social Research, University of Michigan, 1969.

Goldstein, K. M., Blackman, S., and Collins, D. J., "Relationship Between Sociometric and Multidimensional Scaling Methods," *Perceptual and Motor Skills*, Vol. 23 (1966), pp. 639–42.

Goodman, L. A., "Simple Statistical Methods for Scalogram Analysis," *Psychometrika*, Vol. 24 (1959), pp. 29–43.

———— and Kruskal, W. H., "Measures of Association for Cross Classifications," *Journal of the American Statistical Association*, Vol. 59 (1964), pp. 732–64.

Goodstein, L., Guertin, W. H. and Blackburn, H. L., "Effects of Social Motivation Variables on Choice Reaction Time of Schizophrenics," *Journal of Abnormal and Social Psychology*, Vol. 62 (1961), pp. 24–27.

Gower, J. C., "Multivariate Analysis and Multidimensional Geometry," *The Statistician*, Vol. 17 (1967), pp. 13–28.

————, "Some Distance Properties of Latent Root and Vector Methods in Multivariate Analysis," *Biometrica*, Vol. 53 (1966), pp. 315–28.

Green, B. F., Jr., "The Computer Revolution in Psychometrics," *Psychometrika*, Vol. 31 (1966), pp. 437–45.

————, "A General Solution for the Latent Class Model of Latent Structure Analysis," *Psychometrika*, Vol. 16 (1951), pp. 151–66.

————, "Latent Structure Analysis and its Relation to Factor Analysis," *Journal of the American Statistical Association*, Vol. 47 (1952), pp. 71–76.

————, "The Orthogonal Approximation of an Oblique Structure in Factor Analysis," *Psychometrika*, Vol. 17 (1952), pp. 429–40.

Green, P. E. and Carmone, F. J., "A Reduced Space and Cluster Analysis of Physicians' Media Reading Habits," working paper, University of Pennsylvania, September 1967.

————, "Advertisement Perception and Evaluation: An Empirical Application of Multidimensional Scaling," working paper, University of Pennsylvania, May 1968.

————, "Cross Techniques Study: Computer Model Clustering," working paper, University of Pennsylvania, August 1967.

————, "Marketing Journal Images: How Are Our Professional Journals Perceived?" working paper, University of Pennsylvania, May 1967.

————, "Multidimensional Scaling: An Introduction and Comparison of Nonmetric Unfolding Techniques," *Journal of Marketing Research*, Vol. 6 (1969), pp. 330–41.

————, "Perceptual and Preference Mapping of Professional Journals," working paper, University of Pennsylvania, May 1967.

————, "Perceptual Structure of Graduate Business Schools—An Application of Multidimensional Scaling," working paper, University of Pennsylvania, June 1967.

————, *Selected Studies in Multidimensional Scaling and Cluster Analysis* (Cambridge: Marketing Science Institute, August 1968).

————, Structural Characteristics of the Computer Market—An Application of Reduced Space and Cluster Analysis," working paper, University of Pennsylvania, July 1967.

————, "The Performance Structure of the Computer Market: A Multivariate Approach," *Economics and Business Bulletin*, Vol. 21 (1968), pp. 1–11.

———— and Robinson, P. J., "A Comparison of Perceptual Mapping via Confusions Data and Direct Similarity Judgments," in R. L. King (ed.), Proceedings of the Denver Conference of the American Marketing Association (Chicago: American Marketing Association (1968), pp. 323–34).

————, "Nonmetric Scaling Methods: An Exposition and Overview," *Wharton Quarterly*, Vol. 2 (1968), pp. 27–41.

Green, P. E., Carmone, F. J. and Fox, L. B., "Television Similarities: an Application of Subjective Clustering," *Journal of the Market Research Society*, Vol. 11 (1969), pp. 70–90.

Green, P. E. and Maheshwari, A., "A Note on the Multidimensional Scaling of Conditional Proximity Data," *Journal of Marketing Research*, Vol. 7 (February 1970), pp. 106–10.

————, "Common Stock Perception and Preference: An Application of Multidimensional Scaling," *Journal of Business*, Vol. 42 (October 1969), pp. 439–57.

———— and Rao, V. R., "Self Concept and Brand Preference: An Empirical Application of Multidimensional Scaling," *Journal of the Market Research Society*, Vol. 11 (1969), pp. 343–60.

————, "Dimensional Interpretation and Configuration Invariance in Multi-dimensional Scaling: An Empirical Study," *Multivariate Behavioral Research*, Vol. 6 (1969), pp. 159–80.

Green, P. E. and Morris, T. W., "Individual Differences Models in Multidimensional Scaling: An Empirical Comparison," working paper, University of Pennsylvania, April 1969.

———— and Rao, V. R., "A Note on Proximity Measures and Cluster Analysis," *Journal of Marketing Research*, Vol. 6 (1969), pp. 359–64.

————, "A Note on the Sensitivity of Multidimensional Scaling Solutions to Departures in Monotonicity," working paper, University of Pennsylvania, February 1969.

————, "Configuration Invariance in Multidimensional Scaling: An Empirical Study," Proceedings of the Cincinnati Conference of the American Marketing Association, Cincinnati, Ohio (Chicago: American Marketing Association, 1969).

Green, P. E. and Tull, D. S., *Research for Marketing Decisions* (Englewood Cliffs, N. J., Prentice-Hall, Inc., 1966).

Greenberg, M. G., "A Method of Successive Cumulations for the Scaling of Pair-Comparison Preference Judgments," *Psychometrika*, Vol. 30 (1965), pp. 441–48.

————, "A Modification of Thurstone's Law of Comparative Judgment to Accommodate a Judgment Category of 'Equal' or 'No Difference'," *Psychological Bulletin*, Vol. 64 (1965), pp. 108–12.

————, "A Variety of Approaches to Nonmetric Multidimensional Scaling," paper presented at the 16th International Meeting of The Institute of Management Sciences, New York, March 1969.

Greenhouse, S. W. and Geisser, S., "On Methods in the Analysis of Profile Data," *Psychometrika*, Vol. 24 (1959), pp. 95–112.

Gregson, R. A. M., "Fitting a Linear Trace Decay Model to Taste Comparisons and Preferences," *British Journal of Statistical Psychology*, Vol. 17 (1964), pp. 137–51.

————, "Theoretical and Empirical Multidimensional Scalings of Taste Mixture Matchings," *British Journal of Mathematical and Statistical Psychology*, Vol. 19, (1966), pp. 59–76.

————, "Representations of Taste Mixture Cross-Modal Matching in a Minkowski R-Metric," *Australian Journal of Psychology*, Vol. 17 (1965), pp. 195–204.

———— and Russell, R. M., "Problems and Results in the Scaling of Intermodal and Intramodal Complex Taste Similarities by D* Metrics," Research Report No. 7, Psychology Department, University of Canterbury, Christchurch, N.Z., 1965.

Gross, I., *Symposium on Sociological Theory* (New York: Harper & Row, 1959).

Guilford, J. P., "The Phi Coefficient and Chi Square as Indices of Item Validity," *Psychometrika*, Vol. 6 (1941), pp. 11–19.

————, *Psychometric Methods* (New York: McGraw-Hill, 1954).

Gulliksen, H., "Intercultural Attitude Comparisons and Introductory Remarks at a Princeton University Conference on Preference Analysis and Subjective Testing," RM-60-8, Educational Testing Service, Princeton, N.J., June 1960.

————, "Mathematical Solutions for Psychological Problems," *American Scientist*, Vol. 47 (1959), pp. 178–201.

Gulliksen, H., "Linear and Multidimensional Scaling," *Psychometrika*, Vol. 26, (1961), pp. 9–25.

————, "Measurement of Subjective Values," *Psychometrika*, Vol. 21 (1956), pp. 229–44.

————, "Measuring and Comparing Values for Different National Groups," RM-61-7, Educational Testing Service, Princeton, N. J., September 1961.

————, "Paired Comparisons and the Logic of Measurement," *Psychological Review*, Vol. 35 (1938), pp. 199–213.

———— and Messick, S. (eds.), *Psychological Scaling* (New York: John Wiley and Sons, 1960).

———— and Tucker, L. R., "A General Procedure for Obtaining Paired Comparisons from Multiple Rank Orders," *Psychometrika*, Vol. 26 (1961), pp. 173–83.

Guttman, L., "A Basis for Scaling Qualitative Data," *American Sociological Review*, Vol. 9 (1944), pp. 139–50.

————, "The Principal Components of Scale Analysis," in S. A. Stouffer, *et al.* (eds.), *Measurement and Prediction* (Princeton, N. J.: Princeton Press, 1950), Chapter 6.

————, "Image Theory for the Structure of Quantitative Variates," *Psychometrika*, Vol. 18 (1953), pp. 227–96.

————, "A New Approach to Factor Analysis: The Radex," in P. F. Lazarsfeld (ed.), *Mathematical Thinking in the Social Sciences* (Glencoe, Ill.: The Free Press, 1954), pp. 258–345.

————, "A Generalized Simplex for Factor Analysis," *Psychometrika*, Vol. 20 (1955), pp. 173–92.

————, "An Additive Metric from all the Principal Components of a Perfect Scale," *British Journal of Statistical Psychology*, Vol. 8 (1955), pp. 17–24.

————, "The Matrices of Linear Least-Squares Image Analysis," *British Journal of Statistical Psychology*, Vol. 13 (1960), pp. 109–18.

————, "The Cornell Technique for Scale and Intensity Analysis," *Educational and Psychological Measurement*, Vol. 7 (1947), pp. 247–79.

————, "Empirical Verification of the Radex Structure of Mental Abilities and Personality Traits," *Educational and Psychological Measurement*, Vol. 17 (1957), pp. 391–407.

————, "A General Nonmetric Technique for Finding the Smallest Coordinate Space for a Configuration of Points," *Psychometrika*, Vol. 33 (1968), pp. 469–506.

————, "General Theory and Methods for Matrix Factoring," *Psychometrika*, Vol. 9 (1944), pp. 1–16.

————, "Introduction to Facet Design and Analysis," Proceedings of 15th International Conference on Psychology, Brussels, 1959, pp. 130–33.

————, "Measuring the True State of Opinion," in R. Ferber and H. Wales (eds.), *Motivation and Market Behavior* (Homewood, Ill.: Richard D. Irwin, 1958).

————, "Metricizing Rank-Ordered or Unordered Data for a Linear Factor Analysis," *Sankhya*, Vol. 21 (1958), pp. 257–67.

————, "An Outline of Some New Methodology for Social Research," *Public Opinion Quarterly*, Vol. 18 (1954–55), pp. 395–404.

————, "The Nonmetric Breakthrough for the Behavioral Sciences," Automatic Data Processing Conference of the Information Processing Association of Israel, Jerusalem, 1966, pp. 1–16.

————, "A Structural Theory for Intergroup Beliefs and Action," *American Sociological Review*, Vol. 24 (1959), pp. 318–28.

————, "What Lies Ahead for Factor Analysis? *Educational and Psychological Measurement*, Vol. 18 (1958), pp. 497–515.

————, "The Development of Nonmetric Space Analysis: A Letter to Professor John Ross," *Multivariate Behavioral Research*, Vol. 2 (1967), pp. 71–82.

———— and Foa, U. G., "Social Contact and an Intergroup Attitude," *Public Opinion Quarterly*, Vol. 15 (1951), pp. 43–53.

Guttman, N. and Kalish, H. I., "Discriminability and Stimulus Generalization," *Journal of Experimental Psychology*, Vol. 51 (1956), pp. 79–88.

Guttman R. and Guttman, L., "A New Approach to the Analysis of Growth Patterns: The Simplex Structure of Intercorrelations of Measurements," *Growth*, Vol. 29 (1965), pp. 219–32.

Haggard, E. A., Chapman, J. P., Isaacs, K. S., and Dickman, K. W., "Intraclass Correlation versus Factor Analytic Techniques for Determining Groups of Profiles," *Psychological Bulletin*, Vol. 56 (1959), pp. 48–57.

Hammersley, J. M., "The Distribution of Distance in a Hypersphere," *Annals of Mathematical Statistics*, Vol. 21 (1950), pp. 447–52.

Handel, S., "Classification and Similarity of Multidimensional Stimuli," *Perceptual and Motor Skills*, Vol. 24 (1967), pp. 1191–1203.

Hanson, G., "A Factorial Investigation of Speech Sound Perception," *Scandinavian Journal of Psychology*, Vol. 4 (1963), pp. 123–28.

Harris, B., "Outline of Harris Modifications of the Howard Grouping Algorithm," Institute for Environmental Studies, University of Pennsylvania, May 1967 (mimeographed).

————, "An IBM 360 Program for Ward-Berry Hierarchical Grouping," University of Pennsylvania Computer Center, November 1967.

Harris, C. W., "Characteristics of Two Measures of Profile Similarity," *Psychometrika*, Vol. 20 (1955), pp. 289–97.

————, "A Factor Analysis of Selected Senate Roll Calls, 80th Congress," *Educational and Psychological Measurement*, Vol. 4 (1948), pp. 583–91.

Harris, D., "Predicting Consumer Reaction to Product Designs," *Journal of Advertising Research*, Vol. 4 (1964), pp. 34–37.

Hays, D. G. and Borgatta, E. F., "An Empirical Comparison of Restricted and General Latent Distance Analysis," *Psychometrika*, Vol. 19 (1954), pp. 271–79.

Hays, W. L. and Bennett, J. R., "Multidimensional Unfolding: Determining Configuration from Complete Rank Ordering of Preference Data," *Psychometrika*, Vol. 26 (1961), pp. 221–38.

Heerman, E. F., "Comments on Overall's Multivariate Methods for Profile Analysis," *Psychological Bulletin*, Vol. 63 (1965), p. 128.

Helm, C. D., "A Multidimensional Ratio Scaling Analysis of Color Relations," Office of Naval Research Report, Princeton University and Educational Testing Service, 1959.

————, "A Multidimensional Ratio Scaling Analysis of Perceived Color Relations," *Journal of the Optical Society of America*, Vol. 54 (1964), pp. 256–62.

Helm, C. D., Messick, Samuel, and Tucker, L. R., "Psychological Methods for Relating Discrimination and Magnitude Estimation Scales," *Psychological Review*, Vol. 68 (1961), pp. 167–77.

_____ and Tucker, L. R., "Individual Differences in the Structure of Color Perception," *American Journal of Psychology*, Vol. 75 (1962), pp. 437–44.

Helmstadter, G. C., "An Empirical Comparison of Methods for Estimating Profile Similarity," *Educational and Psychological Measurement*, Vol. 17 (1957), pp. 71–82.

Henrickson, A. E., "Choice Behavior and Advertising: A Theory and Two Models," paper read at the Admap World Advertising Workshop, Southampton, England, October 18–22, 1967. (Obtain from Admap, London, England.)

Henry, A. F., "A Method of Classifying Non-Scale Response Patterns in a Guttman Scale," *Public Opinion Quarterly*, Vol. 16 (1952), pp. 95–106.

Herman, L. M. and Dollinger, M. B., "Predicting Effectiveness of Bayesian Classification Systems," *Psychometrika*, Vol. 31 (1966), pp. 341–49.

Hoffman, P. J., "The Paramorphic Representation of Clinical Judgment," *Psychological Bulletin*, Vol. 57 (1960), pp. 116–31.

Hogan, J. M. W., "STAT-PREF—An IBM 360/65 FORTRAN IV Program Package for Unidimensional Scaling of Preference Data," *Journal of Marketing Research*, Vol. 5 (1968), pp. 218–19.

_____ , "An IBM 7040 Program for Thurstonian Scaling," University of Pennsylvania Computer Center, May 1967.

Holland, J. L., *et al.*, "The Classification of Occupations by Means of Kuder Interest Profiles: I. The Development of Interest Groups," *Journal of Applied Psychology*, Vol. 37 (1953), pp. 263–369.

Holzinger, K. J., "Factoring Test Scores and Implications for the Method of Averages," *Psychometrika*, Vol. 9 (1944), pp. 155–67.

_____ , "A Synthetic Approach to Factor Analysis," *Psychometrika*, Vol. 5 (1940), pp. 235–50.

Horan, C. B., "Multidimensional Scaling: Combining Observations When Individuals Have Different Perceptual Structures," *Psychometrika*, Vol. 34 (1969), pp. 139–65.

Horst, P., "Generalized Canonical Correlations and Their Applications to Experimental Data," *Journal of Clinical Psychology*, Vol. 14 (1961), pp. 331–47.

_____ , "Least Squares Multiple Classification for Unequal Subgroups," *Journal of Clinical Psychology*, Vol. 12 (1956), pp. 309–15.

_____ , "Multiple Classification by the Method of Least Squares," *Journal of Clinical Psychology*, Vol. 12 (1956), pp. 3–16.

_____ , "Pattern Analysis and Configural Scoring," *Journal of Clinical Psychology*, Vol. 10 (1954), pp. 1–11.

_____ , "Relations Among m Sets of Measures," *Psychometrika*, Vol. 26 (1961), pp. 129–49.

_____ , "Short Articles and Notes," *Journal of Social Psychology*, Vol. 6 (1935), pp. 369–75.

Hotelling, H., "Analysis of a Complex of Statistical Variables into Principal Components," *Journal of Educational Psychology*, Vol. 24 (1933), pp. 499–520.

————, "Relations Between Two Sets of Variates," *Biometrica*, Vol. 28 (1936), pp. 321–77.

————, "The Relations of the Newer Multivariate Statistical Methods to Factor Analysis," *British Journal of Statistical Psychology*, Vol. 10 (1957), pp. 69–79.

Householder, A. S. and Young, G., "Matrix Approximation and Latent Roots," *American Mathematical Monthly*, Vol. 45 (1938), pp. 165–71.

Howard, J. A. and Sheth, J. N., *The Theory of Buyer Behavior* (New York: John Wiley & Sons, 1969).

Howard, K. I. and Aiesenhaus, H. I., "Direction of Measurement and Profile Similarity," *Multivariate Behavioral Research*, Vol. 2 (1967), pp. 225–37.

Howard, Nigel and Harris, Britt, "A Hierarchical Grouping Routine, IBM 360/65 FORTRAN IV Program," University of Pennsylvania Computer Center, Philadelphia, Pa., October 1966.

Hurst, P. M. and Siegel, S., "Prediction of Decisions from a Higher Ordered Metric Scale of Utility," *Journal of Experimental Psychology*, Vol. 52 (1967), pp. 138–44.

Hyman, R. and Well, A., "Judgments of Similarity and Spatial Models," *Perception and Psychophysics*, Vol. 2 (1967), pp. 233–48.

Indow, T. and Kanazawa, K., "Multidimensional Mapping of Munsell Colors Varying in Hue, Chroma, and Value," *Journal of Experimental Psychology*, Vol. 59 (1960), pp. 330–36.

———— and Shiose, T., "An Application of the Method of Multidimensional Scaling to Perception of Similarity or Difference in Colors," *Japanese Psychological Research*, Vol. 3 (1956), pp. 45–64.

———— and Uchizono, T., "Multidimensional Mapping of Munsell Colors Varying in Hue and Chroma," *Journal of Experimental Psychology*, Vol. 59 (1960), pp. 321–29.

Jackson, D. N. and Messick, S. J., "Individual Differences in Social Perception," *British Journal of Social and Clinical Psychology*, Vol. 2 (1963), pp. 1–10.

———— and Solley, C. M., "A Multidimensional Scaling Approach to the Perception of Personality," *The Journal of Psychology*, Vol. 44 (1957), pp. 311–18.

Jackson, J. E. and Fleckenstein, M., "An Evaluation of Some Statistical Techniques Used in the Analysis of Paired Comparison Data," *Biometrics*, Vol. 13 (1957), pp. 51–64.

Jarrett, R. F., "Rotation and Psychological Space: A Reply," *British Journal of Statistical Psychology*," Vol. 15 (1962), pp. 161–62.

Jenkins, J. J. and Russell, W. A., "An Atlas of Semantic Profiles for 360 Words," *American Journal of Psychology*, Vol. 71 (1958), pp. 688–99.

Johnson, P. E., "Some Psychological Aspects of Subject-Matter Structure," *Journal of Educational Psychology*, Vol. 58 (1967), pp. 75–83.

Johnson, P. O., "The Quantification of Qualitative Data in Discriminatory Analysis," *Journal of the American Statistical Association*, Vol. 45 (1950), pp. 65–76.

Johnson, R. M., "Market Segmentation—A Comparison of Techniques," paper presented at the 16th International Meeting of The Institute of Management Sciences, New York, March 27, 1969.

Johnson, S. C., "Hierarchical Clustering Schemes," *Psychometrika*, Vol. 32 (1967), pp. 241–54.

Jonckheere, A. R., "A Test of Significance for the Relationship between *m* Rankings and Ranked Categories," *British Journal of Statistical Psychology*, Vol. 7 (1954), pp. 93–100.

Jones, M. B., "Practice as a Process of Simplification," Research Report, U. S. Naval School of Aviation Medicine, Pensacola, Florida, October 3, 1961.

Joreskoy, "Some Contributions to Maximum Likelihood Factor Analysis," *Psychometrika*, Vol. 32 (1967), pp. 443–82.

Jurgensen, C. E., "Table for Determining Phi Coefficients," *Psychometrika*, Vol. 12 (1947), pp. 17–29.

Kaskey, G., *et al.*, "Cluster Formation and Diagnostic Significance in Psychiatric Symptom Evaluation," Proceedings of the Fall Joint Computer Conference, 1962, p. 285.

Katz, M. M. and Cole, J. O., "A Phenomenological Approach to Classification of Schizophrenic Disorders," *Journal of Disorders of the Nervous System*, Vol. 24 (1963), pp. 147–54.

Keats, J. A., "A Method of Treating Individual Differences in Multidimensional Scaling," *British Journal of Statistical Psychology*, Vol. 27 (1964), pp. 37–50.

Kelly, G. A., *Psychology of Personal Constructs* (New York: Norton Publishing, 1955).

Kelley, H. H., Hovland, C. I., Schwartz, M., and Abelson, R. P., "The Influence of Judges' Attitudes in Three Methods of Attitude Scaling," *The Journal of Social Psychology*, Vol. 42 (1955), pp. 147–58.

Kendall, M. G., *A Course in Multivariate Analysis* (New York: Hafner Publishing, 1947).

———, "Discrimination and Classification," in P. R. Krishnaiah (ed.), *Multivariate Analysis* (New York: Academic Press, 1966), pp. 165–85.

———, "Further Contributions to the Theory of Paired Comparisons," *Biometrics*, Vol. 11 (1955), pp. 43–62.

———, *Rank Correlation Methods* (London: Griffen Publishing, 1948).

——— and Smith, B. B., "Factor Analysis," *Journal of the Royal Statistical Society*, Vol. 12 (1950), pp. 60–73.

——— "On the Method of Paired Comparisons," *Biometrica*, Vol. 31 (1940), pp. 324–44.

Kernan, J. B., "Choice Criteria, Decision Behavior and Personality," *Journal of Marketing Research*, Vol. 5 (1968), pp. 155–64.

Klahr, David, "A Monte Carlo Investigation of the Statistical Significance of Kruskal's Nonmetric Scaling Procedure," *Psychometrika*, Vol. 34 (1969), pp. 319–33.

———, "Decision Making and Search in Multidimensional Environments," paper presented at The Institute of Management Sciences, April 16, 1967. (Obtained from author at Carnegie-Mellon University.)

Klemmer, E. T. and Shrimpton, N. W., "Preference Scaling via a Modification of Shepard's Proximity Analysis Method," *Human Factors*, Vol. 5 (1963), pp. 163–68.

Klingberg, F. L., "Studies in Measurement of the Relations Among Sovereign States," *Psychometrika*, Vol. 6 (1941), pp. 335–52.

Koch, S. (ed.), *Psychology: A Study of a Science* (New York: McGraw-Hill, 1963), seven volumes.

Krantz, D. H., "Conjoint Measurement: The Luce-Tukey Axiomization and Some Extensions," *Journal of Mathematical Psychology*, Vol. 1 (1964), p. 249.

————, "Extensive Measurement in Semiorders," MMPP 66–6, Michigan Mathematical Psychology Program, University of Michigan, December, 1966.

————, "A Survey of Measurement Theory," MMPP 67–4, Michigan Mathematical Psychology Program, University of Michigan, June 1967.

————, "The Scaling of Small and Large Color Differences," unpublished Ph.D. thesis, University of Pennsylvania, 1964.

————, "Rational Distance Functions for Multidimensional Scaling," *Journal of Mathematical Psychology*, Vol. 4 (1967), pp. 226–45.

———— and Tversky, Amos, "A Critique of the Applicability of Cardinal Utility Theory," MMPP 65–4 Michigan Mathematical Psychology Program, University of Michigan, July 1965.

Kruskal, J. B., "Analysis of Factorial Experiments by Estimating Monotone Transformations of the Data," *Journal of the Royal Statistical Society*, Series B, Vol. 27 (1965), pp. 251–63.

————, "How to Use M-D-SCAL, a Program to do Multidimensional Scaling and Multidimensional Unfolding," (Version 4 and 4M of M-D-SCAL, all in FORTRAN IV), Bell Telephone Laboratories, Murray Hill, N. J., March 1968 (mimeographed).

————, "Nonmetric Multidimensional Scaling: A Numerical Method," *Psychometrika*, Vol. 29 (1964), pp. 115–29.

————, "A Systematic Approach to Multidimensional Scaling," Bell Telephone Laboratories, Murray Hill, N. J., 1963 (mimeographed).

————, "Multidimensional Scaling by Optimizing Goodness of Fit to a Nonmetric Hypothesis," *Psychometrika*, Vol. 29 (1964), pp. 1–27.

————, "Toward a Practical Method Which Helps Uncover the Structure of a Set of Multivariate Observations by Finding the Linear Transformation Which Optimizes a New 'Index of Condensation'," paper presented at the Conference in Statistical Computation, Madison, Wisconsin, April 30, 1969 (mimeographed).

———— and Carroll, J. D., "Geometrical Models and Badness of Fit Functions," paper presented at International Symposium on Multivariate Analysis, University of Dayton, June 1968.

———— and Hart, R. E., "A Geometric Interpretation of Diagnostic Data from a Digital Machine: Based on a Study of the Morris, Illinois Electronic Central Office, *Bell System Technical Journal*, (October 1966), pp. 1299–1338.

Kunnapas, T., "Visual Memory of Capital Letters: Multidimensional Ratio Scaling and Multidimensional Similarity," Stockholm Laboratory Report No. 215, 1966.

————, "Acoustic Perception and Acoustic Memory of Letters," Stockholm Laboratory Report No. 218, 1966.

————, "Visual Memory of Capital Letters: Multidimensional Ratio Scaling and Multidimensional Similarity," Stockholm Laboratory Report No. 215, 1966.

————, Maelhammar, G., and Svensson, O., "Multidimensional Ratio Scaling and Multidimensional Similarity of Geometric Figures," *Scandinavian Journal of Psychology*, Vol. 5 (1964), pp. 249–56.

Kuno, U. and Suga, Y., "Multidimensional Mapping of Piano Pieces," *Japanese Psychological Research*, Vol. 8 (1966), pp. 99–124.

Laird, D. A., "How the Consumer Estimates Quality by Subconscious Sensory Impressions," *Journal of Applied Psychology*, Vol. 16 (1932), pp. 241–46.

Laumann, E. O. and Guttman, L., "The Relative Associational Contiguity of Occupations in an Urban Setting," *American Sociological Review*, Vol. 31 (1966), pp. 169–78.

Lawley, D. N. and Maxwell, A. E., *Factor Analysis as a Statistical Method* (London: Butterworth, 1963).

Lazarsfeld, P. F., *Mathematical Thinking in the Social Sciences* (Glencoe, Ill.: The Free Press, 1954).

_____ , "Recent Developments in Latent Structure Analysis," *Sociometry*, Vol. 18 (1955), pp. 647–59.

_____ and Rosenberg, M., *The Language of Social Research* (Glencoe, Ill.: The Free Press, 1955).

Levy, L. H., "A Factorial Study of Personal Constructs," *Journal of Consulting Psychology*, Vol. 20 (1956), pp. 53–57.

Lienau, C. C., "Discrete Bivariate Distributions in Certain Problems of Statistical Order," *American Journal of Hygiene*, Vol. 33 (1964), pp. 65–85.

Lingoes, J. C., "MINISSA-I: A FORTRAN IV (G) Program for the Smallest Space Analysis of Square Symmetric Matrices," *Behavioral Science*, Vol. 14 (1969), in press.

_____ , "An IBM 360/67 Program for Guttman-Lingoes Smallest Space Analysis-PI," *Behavioral Science*, Vol. 14 (1969), in press.

_____ , "An IBM 7090 Program for Guttman-Lingoes Smallest Space Analysis":

> SSA-I, *Behavioral Science*, Vol. 10 (1965), pp. 183–84
> II, *Behavioral Science*,   10 (1965), p. 487
> III, *Behavioral Science*,   11 (1966), pp. 75–76
> IV, *Behavioral Science*,   11 (1966), p. 407
> RI, *Behavioral Science*,   11 (1966), p. 322
> II, *Behavioral Science*,   11 (1966), p. 323
> III, *Behavioral Science*,   11 (1966), p. 323
> IV, *Behavioral Science*,   12 (1967), pp. 74–75

_____ , "An IBM 7090 Program for Guttman-Lingoes Configurational Similarity," *Behavioral Science*, Vol. 12 (1967), pp. 502–3.

_____ , "An IBM 7090 Program for Guttman-Lingoes Conjoint Measurement":

> I, *Behavioral Science*, Vol. 12 (1967), pp. 501–2
> II, *Behavioral Science*,   13 (1968), pp. 85–87
> III, *Behavioral Science*,   13 (1968), pp. 421–23

_____ , "An IBM 7090 Program for Guttman-Lingoes Multidimensional Scalogram Analysis":

> I, *Behavioral Science*, Vol. 11 (1966), pp. 76–78
> II, *Behavioral Science*,   12 (1967), pp. 268–70
> III, *Behavioral Science*,   13 (1968), pp. 512–13

_____ , "Multiple Scalogram Analysis: A Set-Theoretic Model for Analyzing Dichotomous Items," *Educational and Psychological Measurement*, Vol. 23 (1963), pp. 501–24.

_____ , "Multivariate Analysis of Contingencies: An IBM 7090 Program for

Analyzing Metric/Nonmetric or Linear/Nonlinear Data," Computation Report, University of Michigan Computing Center, No. 2, June 15, 1963 (Revised August 15, 1966).

————, "The Multivariate Analysis of Qualitative Data," paper presented at Conference on Cluster Analysis of Multivariate Data, New Orleans, December 1966.

————, "New Computer Developments in Pattern Analysis and Nonmetric Techniques," Proceedings of the IBM Symposium: Computers in Psychological Research (Blaricum: Gauthier-Villars, Paris, 1967).

————, "Recent Computational Advances in Nonmetric Methodology for the Behavioral Sciences," in Proceedings of the International Symposium on Mathematical and Computational Methods in Social Sciences (Rome: International Computation Centre, 1967).

————, "A General Nonparametric Model for Representing Objects and Attributes in a Joint Metric Space," in J. C. Garden (ed.), *Les Compte-rendus de Colloque International sur L'emploi des Calculateurs en Archeologie: Problemes Semiologiques et Mathematiques* (Marseilles: Centre National de la Recherche Scientifique, 1969).

———— and Guttman, Louis, "Nonmetric Factor Analysis: A Rank Reducing Alternative to Linear Factor Analysis," *Multivariate Behavioral Research*, Vol. 2 (1967), pp. 485–505.

Linhart, H., "Techniques for Discriminating Analysis with Discrete Variables," *Metrika*, Vol. 2 (1959), pp. 138–49.

Lirtzman, S., "The Computer and Procedures for Scaling Attitudes," in Lee Adler and Irving Crespi (eds.), *Attitude Research at Sea* (Chicago: The American Marketing Association, 1966).

Loevinger, J., "The Technique of Homogeneous Tests Compared with Some Aspects of 'Scale Analysis' and Factor Analysis," *Psychological Bulletin*, Vol. 45 (1948), pp. 507–29.

Lord, F. M. and Novick, M. R., *Statistical Theories of Mental Test Scores* (Reading, Mass.: Addison-Wesley, 1968).

Lorr, M. and Radhakrishnan, B. K., "A Comparison of Two Methods of Cluster Analysis," *Educational and Psychological Measurement*, Vol. 27 (1967), pp. 47–53.

Lubin, A., "Linear and Nonlinear Discriminating Functions," *British Journal of Psychology*, Vol. 3 (1950), pp. 90–103.

———— and Osburn, H. G., "A Theory of Pattern Analysis for the Prediction of a Quantitative Criterion," *Psychometrika*, Vol. 22 (1957), pp. 63–73.

Luce, R. D., "A Choice Theory Analysis of Similarity Judgments," *Psychometrika*, Vol. 26 (1961), pp. 325–32.

———— and Tukey, J. W., "Simultaneous Conjoint Measurement: A New Type of Fundamental Measurement," *Journal of Mathematical Psychology*, Vol. 1 (1964), pp. 1–27.

Lunn, J. A., "Psychological Classification," *Commentary*, Vol. 8 (1966), pp. 161–73.

Lykken, D. T., "A Method of Actuarial Pattern Analysis," *Psychological Bulletin*, Vol. 53 (1956), pp. 102–8.

MacDiarmid, J. A., "An Application of Multidimensional Scaling to Advertising Evaluation," unpublished MBA thesis, Wharton School of Finance and Commerce, April 1968.

MacNaughton-Smith, P., "Some Statistical and Other Numerical Techniques for Classifying Individuals," Publication No. 6 on Studies in the Causes of Delinquency and the Treatment of Offenders, Her Majesty's Stationery Office, London, 1964.

MacQueen, J. B., "Some Methods for Classification and Analysis of Multivariate Observations," working paper No. 96, University of California, March 1966.

Main, T. H., "The Perception of and Preference for Graduate Business Schools: An Application of Multidimensional Scaling," unpublished MBA thesis, Wharton School of Finance and Commerce, University of Pennsylvania, April 1968.

Marimont, R. B., "A New Method of Checking the Consistency of Precedence Matrices," *Journal of Association for Computing Machines*, Vol. 6 (1959), pp. 164–71.

Marks, E., "Student Perceptions of College Persistence and Their Intellective Personality and Performance Correlates," *Journal of Educational Psychology*, Vol. 58 (1967), pp. 210–21.

Massarik, F. and Ratoosh, P. (eds.), *Mathematical Explorations in Behavioral Science* (Homewood, Ill.: Richard D. Irwin, 1965).

Mattson, R. L. and Damman, J. E., "A Technique for Determining and Coding Subclasses in Pattern Recognition Problems," *IBM Journal of Research and Development*, Vol. 9 (1965), pp. 294–302.

Maung, K., "Measurement of Association in a Contingency Table with Special Reference to the Pigmentation of Hair and Eye Colours of Scottish School Children," *Annals of Eugenics*, Vol. 2 (1942), pp. 189–223.

Maxwell, A. E., "Canonical Variate Analysis When the Variables are Dichotomous," *Educational and Psychological Measurement*, Vol. 21 (1961), pp. 259–71.

May, K. O., "Intransitivity, Utility and the Aggregation of Preference Patterns," *Econometrica*, Vol. 22 (1954), pp. 1–13.

McCracken, R. F., "Multidimensional Scaling and the Measurement of Consumer Perception: A Description and Sensitivity Analysis," unpublished MBA thesis, Wharton School of Finance and Commerce, May 1968.

————, "The Parametric Mapping of Second Order Distance," informal notes, University of Pennsylvania, August 1968.

McDonald, R. P., "A Unified Treatment of the Weighting Problem," *Psychometrika*, Vol. 33 (1968), pp. 351–81.

McElwain, D. W. and Keats, J. A., "Multidimensional Unfolding—Some Geometric Solutions," *Psychometrika*, Vol. 26 (1961), pp. 325–33.

McGee, V. E., "CEMD/DEMD: Nonmetric Individual Differences Model for (Elastic) Multidimensional Data Reduction—to Handle N Sets of Multivariate Data," *Journal of Marketing Research*, Vol. 5 (1968), p. 322.

————, "Elastic Multidimensional Scaling: A Hybrid Technique," International Symposium on Mathematical and Computational Methods in Social Sciences, Rome, Italy, July 4, 1966. (Obtained from author at Dartmouth).

————, "EMD: A FORTRAN IV Program for Nonmetric (Elastic) Multidimensional Data Reduction," *Journal of Marketing Research*, Vol. 5 (1968), p. 321.

————, "The Multidimensional Analysis of 'Elastic' Distances," *British Journal of Mathematical and Statistical Psychology*, Vol. 19 (1966), pp. 181–96.

————, "Multidimensional Scaling of N Sets of Similarity Measures: A Nonmetric Individual Differences Approach," *Multivariate Behavioral Research*, Vol. 3 (1968), pp. 233–48.

———— and Carleton, W. T., "Piecewise Regression," Amos Tuck School of Business, Dartmouth College, 1969 (mimeographed).

McNemar, Q., "Opinion-Attitude Methodology," *Psychological Bulletin*, Vol. 43 (1946), pp. 289–374.

McQuitty, L. L., "Best Classifying Every Individual at Every Level," *Educational and Psychological Measurement*, Vol. 23 (1963), pp. 337–45.

————, "Capabilities and Improvements of Linkage Analysis as a Clustering Method," *Educational and Psychological Measurement*, Vol. 24 (1964), pp. 441–56.

————, "Comprehensive Hierarchical Analysis," *Educational and Psychological Measurement*, Vol. 22 (1960), pp. 805–16.

————, "Hierarchical Linkage Analysis for the Isolation of Types," *Educational and Psychological Measurement*, Vol. 22 (1962), pp. 513–31.

————, "Rank Order Typal Analysis," *Educational and Psychological Measurement*, Vol. 23 (1963), pp. 55–61.

————, "A Novel Application of the Coefficient of Correlation in the Isolation of Both Typal and Dimensional Constructions," *Educational and Psychological Measurement*, Vol. 27 (1967), pp. 591–99.

————, "Multiple Rank Order Typal Analysis for the Isolation of Independent Types," *Educational and Psychological Measurement*, Vol. 26 (1966), pp. 3–11.

————, "Similarity Analysis by Reciprocal Pairs for Discrete and Continuous Data," *Educational and Psychological Measurement*, Vol. 26 (1966), pp. 825–31.

————, "Single and Multiple Hierarchical Classification by Reciprocal Pairs and Rank Order Types, *Educational and Psychological Measurement*, Vol. 26 (1966), pp. 253–65.

————, "A Conjunction of Rank Order Typal Analysis and Item Selection," *Educational and Psychological Measurement*, Vol. 25 (1965), pp. 949–61.

————, "Typal Analysis," *Educational and Psychological Measurement*, Vol. 21 (1961), pp. 677–96.

————, "Hierarchical Syndrome Analysis," *Educational and Psychological Measurement*, Vol. 20 (1960), pp. 293–304.

————, "Elementary Linkage Analysis for Isolating Orthogonal and Oblique Types and Typal Relevancies," *Educational and Psychological Measurement*, Vol. 17 (1957), pp. 207–29.

————, "Agreement Analysis: Classifying Persons by Predominant Patterns of Responses," *British Journal of Psychology*, Statistical Section, Vol. 16 (1956), pp. 68–73.

————, "Pattern Analysis Illustrated in Classifying Patients and Normals," *Educational and Psychological Measurement*, Vol. 14 (1954), pp. 598–604.

McRae, D., "Direct Factor Analysis of Sociometric Data," *Sociometry*, Vol. 23 (1960), pp. 360–71.

————, "An Exponential Model for Assessing Fourfold Tables," *Sociometry*, Vol. 19 (1956), pp. 84–93.

Meehl, P. E., "Configural Scoring," *Journal of Consulting Psychology*, Vol. 14 (1950), pp. 165–71.

Mellinger, J., "A Comparison of Multidimensional Scaling and Similarity Analysis," *American Psychologist*, Vol. 13 (1958), p. 375. (Abstract)

—————, "An Investigation of Psychological Color Space," unpublished Ph. D. thesis, University of Chicago, 1956.

—————, "Psychological Color Space," *American Psychologist*, Vol. 11 (1956), p. 398.

Messick, S. J., "Dimensions of Social Desirability," *Journal of Consulting Psychology*, Vol. 24 (1960), pp. 279–87.

—————, "An Empirical Evaluation of Multidimensional Successive Intervals," *Psychometrika*, Vol. 21 (1956), pp. 367–75.

—————, "The Perceived Structure of Political Relationships," *Sociometry*, Vol. 24 (1961), pp. 270–78.

—————, "The Perception of Social Attitudes," *Journal of Abnormal and Social Psychology*, Vol. 52 (1956), pp. 57–66.

—————, "The Perception of Attitude Relationships: A Multidimensional Scaling Approach to the Structuring of Social Attitudes," unpublished Ph. D. thesis, Princeton, 1954.

————— and Abelson, R. P., "Research Tools: Scaling and Measurement Theory," *Review of Educational Research*, Vol. 27 (1957), pp. 387–97.

—————, "The Additive Constant Problem in Multidimensional Scaling," *Psychometrika*, Vol. 21 (1956), pp. 1–15.

————— and Fritzky, F. J., "Dimensions of Analytic Attitude in Cognition and Personality," *Journal of Personality*, Vol. 31 (1963), pp. 346–70.

————— and Kogan, N., "Personality Consistencies in Judgment: Dimensions of Role Constructs," *Multivariate Behavioral Research*, Vol. 1 (1966), pp. 165–75.

Messick, S. J. and Ross, J. *Measurement in Personality and Cognition* (New York: John Wiley & Sons, 1962).

Michener, C. D. and Sokal, R. R., "A Quantitative Approach to a Problem in Classification," *Evolution*, Vol. 2 (1957), pp. 130–62.

Miller, C. R., Eyman, R. K., and Dingman, H. F., "Factor Analysis, Latent Structure Analysis and Mental Typology," *British Journal of Statistical Psychology*, Vol. 14 (1961), pp. 29–34.

Miller, J. E., Shepard, R. N., and Chang, J. J., "An Analytical Approach to the Interpretation of Multidimensional Scaling Solutions," *American Psychologist*, Vol. 19 (1964), pp. 579–80.

Mindak, W. A., "Fitting the Semantic Differential to the Marketing Problem," *Journal of Marketing*, Vol. 25 (1961), pp. 28–33.

Mori, T., "Structure of Motivations for Becoming a Teacher," *Journal of Educational Psychology*, Vol. 56 (1965), pp. 175–88.

Morris, Charles and Jones, L. V., "Value Scales and Dimensions," *Journal of Abnormal and Social Psychology*, Vol. 51 (1955), pp. 523–35.

Morrison, Donald F., *Multivariate Statistical Methods* (New York: McGraw-Hill, 1967).

Morrison, D. G., "Measurement Problems in Cluster Analysis," *Management Science*, Vol. 13 (1967), B-755-80.

Norton, A. S., "Similarity as a Determinant of Friendship: A Multidimensional Study," Technical Report, Educational Testing Service, Princeton, N. J. (Ph. D. thesis, Princeton, 1959).

Mosier, C. I., "Determining a Simple Structure When Loadings for Certain Tests Are Known," *Psychometrika*, Vol. 4 (1939), pp. 149–62.

———, "A Psychometric Study of Meaning," *The Journal of Social Psychology*, Vol. 13 (1941), pp. 123–40.

Muldoon, J. F. and Ray, R. S., "A Comparison of Pattern Similarity as Measured by Six Statistical Techniques and Eleven Clinicians," *Educational and Psychological Measurement*, Vol. 18 (1958), pp. 775–81.

Munsinger, Harry, "Multivariate Analysis of Preference for Variability," *Journal of Experimental Psychology*, Vol. 71 (1966), pp. 889–95.

Myers, J. G. and Nicosia, F. M., "On the Study of Consumer Typologies," *Journal of Marketing Research*, Vol. 5 (1968), pp. 182–93.

———, "Consumer Image and Attitude," Institute of Business and Economic Research, University of California at Berkeley, 1968 (monograph).

Needham, R. M., "The Theory of Clumps, II," Report No. 139, Cambridge Language Research Unit, Cambridge, England, 1961.

Neidell, L. A., "Physicians' Perception and Evaluations of Selected Ethical Drugs: An Application of Nonmetric Multidimensional Scaling to Pharmaceutical Marketing," unpublished Ph. D. thesis, University of Pennsylvania, December 1968.

Noble, C. E., "Psychology and the Logic of Similarity," *Journal of General Psychology*, Vol. 57 (1957), pp. 23–43.

Nunnally, J., "The Analysis of Profile Data," *Psychological Bulletin*, Vol. 59 (1962), pp. 311–19.

Nurimen, Anna-Marja, "Evaluation of a Technique for Measuring Subjective Similarity," *Scandinavian Journal of Psychology*, Vol. 6 (1965), pp. 209–19.

Odesky, S. H., "Handling the Neutral Vote in Paired Comparison Product Testing," *Journal of Marketing Research*, Vol. 4 (1967), pp. 199–201.

Olans, J. L., "Dimensionality of Selected TAT Cards," unpublished Ph.D. thesis, George Washington University, 1965.

Osburn, H. G. and Lubin, A., "The Use of Configural Analysis for the Evaluation of Test Scoring Methods," *Psychometrika*, Vol. 22 (1957), pp. 359–71.

Osgood, C. E., "Studies on the Generality of Affective Meaning Systems," *American Psychologist*, Vol. 17 (1962), pp. 10–28.

——— and Suci, G. J., "A Measure of Relation Determined by Both Mean Difference and Profile Information," *Psychological Bulletin*, Vol. 49 (1952), pp. 251–62.

——— and Tannenbaum, P. H., *The Measurement of Meaning* (Urbana, Ill.: University of Illinois Press, 1957).

Overall, J. E., "Note on Multivariate Methods for Profile Analysis," *Psychological Bulletin*, Vol. 61 (1964), pp. 195–98.

——— and Hollister, L. E., "Computer Procedures for Psychiatric Classification," *Journal of the American Medical Association*, Vol. 187 (1964), pp. 583–88.

Parker-Rhodes, A. F., "Contributions to the Theory of Clumps," Report No. 138, Cambridge Language Research Unit, Cambridge, England, 1961.

Pearson, W. H., "Estimation of a Correlation Coefficient from an Uncertainty Measure," *Psychometrika*, Vol. 31 (1966), pp. 421–33.

Pennell, R. J. and Young, F. W., "An IBM System 360 Program for Orthogonal Least-Squares Matrix Fitting," *Behavioral Science*, Vol. 12 (1967), p. 165.

Phillips, J. P. N., "On a Certain Type of Partial Higher-Ordered Metric Scaling," *British Journal of Mathematical and Statistical Psychology*, Vol. 19 (1966), pp. 77–86.

————, "A Procedure for Determining Slater's *i* and All Nearest Adjoining Orders," *British Journal of Mathematical and Statistical Psychology*, Vol. 20 (1967), pp. 217–55.

Pollatsek, A., "On the Relation Between Subjectively Expected Utility and the Psychophysics of Gambling," MMPP 66–1 Report, Michigan Mathematical Psychology Program, University of Michigan, 1966.

Proceedings of Invitational Conference on Testing Problems, Educational Testing Service, Princeton, N. J., October 28, 1961.

Pruitt, Judy, "TAXON–An IBM 360 Numerical Taxonomy Program," University of Pennsylvania Computer Center, November 1967.

Ramsay, J. O., "Some Statistical Considerations in Multidimensional Scaling," *Psychometrika*, Vol. 34 (1969), pp. 167–82.

Rao, C. R., "Estimation and Tests of Significance in Factor Analysis," *Psychometrika*, Vol. 20 (1955), pp. 93–111.

————, "Tests of Significance in Multivariate Analysis," *Biometrica*, Volume 35 (1948), pp. 58–79.

————, "The Utilization of Multiple Measurements in Problems of Biological Classification," *Journal of the Royal Statistical Society*, Series B, Vol. 10 (1948), pp. 159–93.

Rapoport, Ammon, "Undirected Graphs and the Structural Analysis of Proximity Matrices," Report No. 33, Psychometric Laboratory, University of North Carolina, July 1967.

————, "A Comparison of Two Tree-Construction Methods for Obtaining Proximity Measures Among Words," *Journal of Verbal Learning and Verbal Behavior*, Vol. 6 (1967), pp. 884–90.

Ray, W. S., "Multidimensional Psychophysics and Verbal Associations," unpublished Ph. D. thesis, University of Maryland, 1953.

Reeb, M., "How People See Jobs: A Multidimensional Analysis," *Occupational Psychology*, Vol. 33 (1959), pp. 1–17.

Reiser, R. J., "Why New Products Fail, Why Old Products Falter," a Discussion of Market Segmentation, speech before ANA Workshop on Advertising Planning and Evaluation, December 13, 1966. (Obtained from the Association of National Advertisers, New York).

Remage, Russell, Jr. and Thompson, W. A., Jr., "Maximum-Likelihood Paired Comparison Rankings," *Biometrica*, Vol. 53 (1966), pp. 143–49.

Restle, F., *Psychology of Judgment and Choice* (New York: John Wiley and Sons, 1961).

Richards, E. A., "A Commercial Application of Guttman Scaling Techniques," *Journal of Marketing*, Vol. 22 (1952), pp. 166–73.

Richardson, M. W., "Multidimensional Psychophysics," *Psychological Bulletin*, Vol. 35 (1938), pp. 659–60.

Rickard, T. E., Triandis, H. C., and Patterson, C. H., "Indices of Employer Prejudice Toward Disabled Applicants," *Journal of Applied Psychology*, Vol. 47 (1963), pp. 52–55.

Rigney, J. W. and DeBow, C. H., "Multidimensional Scaling Analysis of Decision Strategies in Threat Evaluation," *Journal of Applied Psychology*, Vol. 51 (1967), pp. 305–10.

Rimoldi, H. J. A., "Prediction of Scale Values for Combined Stimuli," *The British Journal of Statistical Psychology*, Vol. 9, Part I (1956), pp. 29–40.

———— and Grib, T. F., "Pattern Analysis," *British Journal of Statistical Psychology*, Vol. 13, Part 2 (1960), pp. 137–49.

Robinson, W. S., "Ecological Correlations and the Behavior of Individuals," *American Sociological Review*, Vol. 15 (1950), pp. 351–57.

Rodgers, C. R. and Dymond, R. F. (eds.), *Psychotherapy and Personality Change, Coordinated Studies in the Client-Centered Approach* (Chicago: University of Chicago Press, 1954).

Rogers, D. J. and Tanimoto, T. T., "A Computer Program for Classifying Plants," *Science*, Vol. 132 (1960), pp. 1115–18.

Root, R. T., "A Multidimensional Scaling Analysis of Meaning," *Dissertation Abstracts*, Vol. 28 (1963), p. 2979. (Abstract)

Rosenberg, S., Nelson, O., and Vivekananthan, P., "A Multidimensional Approach to the Structure of Personality Impressions," Rutgers University, New Brunswick, 1967 (mimeographed).

Roskam, E. E., *Metric Analysis of Ordinal Data in Psychology* (Voorschoten, Holland: University of Leiden Press, 1968).

Ross, J., "A Remark on Tucker and Messick's 'Points of View' Analysis," *Psychometrika*, Vol. 31 (1966), pp. 27–31.

Rowan, T. C., "Some Developments in Multidimensional Scaling Applied to Semantic Relationships," unpublished Ph.D. thesis, University of Illinois, 1954.

Rulon, P. J., "Distinctions Between Discriminant and Regression Analysis and a Geometric Interpretation of the Discriminant Function," *Harvard Educational Review*, Vol. 21 (1951), pp. 80–92.

Runkel, P. J., "Cognitive Similarity in Facilitating Communication," *Sociometry*, Vol. 19 (1956), pp. 178–91.

Russell, P. N. and Gregson, R. A. M., "A Comparison of Intermodal and Intramodal Methods in the Multidimensional Scaling of Three-Component Taste Mixtures," *Australian Journal of Psychology*, Vol. 18 (1966), pp. 244–54.

Saffir, M. A., "A Comparative Study of Scales Constructed by Three Psychophysical Methods," *Psychometrika*, Vol. 2 (1937), pp. 179–98.

Sakoda, J. M., "Osgood and Suci's Measure of Pattern Similarity and Q Technique Factor Analysis," *Psychometrika*, Vol. 19 (1954), pp. 19–38.

Sanai, M., "An Experimental Study of Politico-Economic Attitudes," *International Journal of Opinion and Attitude Research*, Vol. 4 (1950), pp. 563–77.

————, "An Experimental Study of Social Attitudes," *Journal of Social Psychology*, Vol. 34 (1951), pp. 235–64.

Sarbin, T. R., "A Contribution to the Study of Actuarial and Individual Methods of Prediction," *American Journal of Sociology*, Vol. 48 (1942), pp. 593–602.

Saunders, D. R., "Moderator Variables in Prediction," *Educational and Psychological Measurement*, Vol. 16 (1956), pp. 209–22.

Sawrey, W. L., Keller, L., and Conger, J. J., "An Objective Method of Grouping Profiles by Distance Functions and Its Relation to Factor Analysis," *Educational and Psychological Measurement*, Vol. 20 (1960), pp. 651–73.

Schiffman, H. and Messick, S., "Scaling and Measurement Theory," in *Review of Educational Research*, Vol. 33 (1963), pp. 533–42.

Schoeffler, M. S., "Probability of Response to Compounds of Discriminated Stimuli," *Journal of Experimental Psychology*, Vol. 48 (1954), pp. 323–29.

Schubert, G., "The 1960 Term of the Supreme Court: A Psychological Analysis," *American Political Science Review*, Vol. 56 (1962) pp. 90–107.

Scott, Dana and Suppes, Patrick, "Foundational Aspects of Theories of Measurement," *Journal of Symbolic Logic*, Vol. 23 (1958), pp. 113–28.

Shapiro, M. B., "A Method of Measuring Psychological Changes Specific to the Individual Psychiatric Patient," *British Journal of Medical Psychology*, Vol. 34 (1961), pp. 151–55.

Shelly, M. W. and Bryan, G. L. (eds.), *Human Judgments and Optimality* (New York: John Wiley & Sons, 1964).

Shepard, R. N., "Analysis of Proximities as a Technique for the Study of Information Processing in Man," *Human Factors*, Vol. 5 (1963) pp. 33–48.

————, "The Analysis of Proximities: Multidimensional Scaling with an Unknown Distance Function," Part One, *Psychometrika*, Vol. 27 (1962), pp. 125–39.

————, "The Analysis of Proximities," Part Two, *Psychometrika*, Vol. 27 (1962), pp. 219–46.

————, "Attention and the Metric Structure of the Stimulus," *Journal of Mathematical Psychology*, Vol. 1 (1964), pp. 54–87.

————, "Metric Structures in Ordinal Data," *Journal of Mathematical Psychology*, Vol. 3 (1966), pp. 287–315.

————, "A Note Concerning the Computer Programs for Extracting Multidimensional Structure from Nonmetric Data That Have Been Developed at the Bell Telephone Laboratories," Murray Hill, N.J., March 1967 (mimeographed).

————, "Polynomial Fitting in the Analysis of Proximities," Proceedings of the 17th International Congress of Psychology (Amsterdam: North Holland Publishing Co., 1964), pp. 345–46. (Abstract)

————, "Stimulus and Response Generalization: A Stochastic Model Relating Generalization to Distance in Psychological Space," *Psychometrika*, Vol. 22 (1957), pp. 325–45.

————, "On Subjectively Optimum Selection Among Multiattribute Alternatives," in G. L. Bryon and N. W. Shelley (eds.), *Human Judgments and Optimality* (New York: John Wiley & Sons, 1964), pp. 257–81.

————, "Similarity of Stimuli and Metric Properties of Behavioral Data," in H. Gulliksen and S. Messick (eds.), *Psychological Scaling: Theory and Applications* (New York: John Wiley & Sons, 1960).

————, "Stimulus and Response Generalization: Tests of a Model Relating Generalization to Distance in Psychological Space," *Journal of Experimental Psychology*, Vol. 55 (1958), pp. 509–23.

————, "Some Principles and Prospects for the Spatial Representation of Behavioral Science Data," working paper, Stanford University, June 1969 (mimeographed).

———— and Carroll, J. D., "Parametric Representation of Nonlinear Data Structures," in P. R. Krishnaiah (ed.), *Multivariate Analysis* (New York: Academic Press, 1966), pp. 561–92.

———— and Chang, J. J., "Stimulus Generalization in the Learning of Classifications," *Journal of Experimental Psychology*, Vol. 65 (1963), pp. 94–102.

_____ and Kruskal, J. B., "Nonmetric Methods for Scaling and for Factor Analysis," *American Psychologist*, Vol. 19 (1964), pp. 557–58. (Abstract)

Sherman, C. R. and Young, F. W., "Nonmetric Multidimensional Scaling: A Monte Carlo Study," Proceedings of 76th Annual Convention of the American Psychological Association, 1968, pp. 207–8.

Shiose, T., "An Application of the Method of Multidimensional Scaling to the Perception of Similarity of Difference in Colors," *Japanese Journal of Psychology*, Vol. 28 (1958), pp. 375–85. (English summary)

Sidman, M., "A Note on Functional Relations Obtained from Group Data," *Psychological Bulletin*, Vol. 49 (1952), pp. 263–69.

Siegal, A. I. and Smith, R., "A Multidimensional Scaling Analysis of the Job of Civil Defense Director," Office of Civil Defense, Department of Army, Contract OCD-PS-LO4-30, 1965.

Siegel, S., "A Method for Obtaining an Ordered Metric Scale," *Psychometrika*, Vol. 21 (1956), pp. 207–16.

_____ , *Nonparametric Statistics* (New York: McGraw-Hill, 1956).

Simpson, G. G., "Numerical Taxonomy and Biological Classification, *Science*, Vol. 144 (1964), pp. 712–13.

Skager, R. W., Klein, S. P., and Schultz, C. B., "The Prediction of Academic and Artistic Achievement at a School of Design," *Journal of Educational Measurement*, Vol. 4 (1967), pp. 105–17.

_____ , Schultz, C. G., and Klein, S. P., "The Multidimensional Scaling of a Set of Artistic Drawings: Perceived Structure of Scale Correlates," *Multivariate Behavioral Research*, Vol. 1 (1966), pp. 425–36.

Slater, Patrick, "The Analysis of Personal Preferences," *British Journal of Statistical Psychology*, Vol. 13 (1960), pp. 119–35.

_____ , "Inconsistencies in a Schedule of Paired Comparisons," *Biometrica*, Vol. 48 (1961), pp. 303–12.

Small, V. H., "Judged Similarity of Visual Form as Functions of Selected Stimulus Dimensions," unpublished Ph. D. thesis, Purdue University, 1961.

Smith, Kay H., Pederson, D. M., and Lewis, R. E., "Dimensions of Inter-Personal Perception in a Meaningful On-Going Group," *Perceptual and Motor Skills*, Vol. 22 (1966), pp. 867–80.

Sneath, P. H. A., "The Application of Computers to Taxonomy," *Journal of General Microbiology*, Vol. 17 (1957), pp. 201–26.

Snell, E. J., "A Scaling Procedure for Ordered Categorical Data," *Biometrica*, Vol. 20 (1964), pp. 592–607.

Sokal, R. R. and Michener, C. D., "A Statistical Method for Evaluating Systematic Relationships," *University of Kansas Science Bulletin*, March, 1958.

_____ and Sneath, P. H. A., *Principles of Numerical Taxonomy* (San Francisco: W. H. Freeman, 1963).

Solomon, H., *Studies in Item Analysis and Prediction* (Stanford, Cal.: Stanford University Press, 1961).

_____ and Rosner, B., "Factor Analysis," *Review of Educational Research*, Vol. 24 (1954), pp. 421–38.

Sonquist, J. A. and Morgan, J. N., "The Detection of Interaction Effects," Monograph No. 35, The University of Michigan, 1964.

Spang, H. A., "A Review of Minimization Techniques for Nonlinear Functions," *Society for Industrial and Applied Mathematics*, Vol. 4 (1962), pp. 343–65.

Spector, A. J., "Basic Dimensions of Corporate Image," *Journal of Marketing*, Vol. 23 (1961), pp. 47–51.

Stefflre, V. J., "Market Structure Studies: New Products for Old Markets and New Markets (Foreign) for Old Products," in F. M. Bass, C. W. King, and E. A. Pessemier (eds.), Proceedings of the Purdue Symposium: *Application of the Sciences in Marketing Management* (New York: John Wiley and Sons, 1968), pp. 251–68.

————, "Simulation of People's Behavior Toward New Objects and Events," *American Behavioral Scientist*, Vol. 8 (1965), pp. 12–15.

Stenson, H. H., "The Psychophysical Dimension of Similarity Among Random Shapes," *Perception and Psychophysics*, Vol. 3 (1968), pp. 201–14.

———— and Knoll, R. L., "Goodness of Fit for Random Rankings in Kruskal's Nonmetric Scaling Procedure," *Psychological Bulletin*, Vol. 71 (1969), pp. 122–26.

Stephenson, W., "Some Observations on Q Technique," *Psychological Bulletin*, Vol. 49 (1952), pp. 483–98.

————, *The Study of Behavior* (Chicago: University of Chicago Press, 1953).

Stevens, S. S., "Mathematics, Measurement and Psychophysics," in S. S. Stevens (ed.), *Handbook of Experimental Psychology* (New York: John Wiley and Sons, 1962).

Stringer, P., "Cluster Analysis of Non-Verbal Judgments of Facial Expressions," *British Journal of Mathematical and Statistical Psychology*, Vol. 20 (1967), pp. 71–79.

Stone, M., "Subjective Discrimination as a Statistical Method," *British Journal of Statistical Psychology*, Vol. 14 (1961), pp. 25–28.

Stouffer, S. A. (ed.), *Measurement and Prediction* (Princeton, N. J.: Princeton University Press, 1950).

Strodtbeck, F. L. and Harmon, H. L., "The Social Dimensions of a Twelve-man Jury Table," *Sociometry*, Vol. 24 (1961), pp. 397–415.

Suchman, E. A., "The Logic of Scale Construction," *Educational and Psychological Measurement*, Vol. 10 (1950), pp. 79–83.

Suppes, P., *Introduction to Logic* (New York: Van Nostrand, 1957).

Swed, F. S. and Eisenhart, C., "Tables for Testing Randomness of Grouping in a Sequence of Alternatives," *Annals of Mathematical Statistics*, Vol. 14 (1943), pp. 66–87.

Tanaka, Y., "A Cross-Culture and Cross-Concept Study of the Generality of Semantic Spaces," *Journal of Verbal Learning and Verbal Behavior*, Vol. 2 (1963), pp. 392–405.

Tannenbaum, P. H., "Initial Attitude Toward Source and Concept as Factors in Attitude Change Through Communication," *Public Opinion Quarterly*, Vol. 20 (1956), pp. 413–25.

Tate, M. W. and Clelland, R. C., *Nonparametric and Shortcut Statistics*. (Danville, Ill.: Interstate Printers and Publishers, 1957).

Tatusuoka, M. M. and Tiedeman, D. V., "Statistics as an Aspect of Scientific Method in Research on Teaching," in N. L. Gage (ed.), *Handbook of Research on Teaching*, (Chicago: Rand McNally, 1963), pp. 142–70.

Taylor, J. R., "An Empirical Evaluation of Coombs Unfolding Theory," unpublished Ph.D. thesis, University of Minnesota, July 1967.

————, "The Meaning and Structure of Data Related to Scaling Models," paper presented at the Denver Meeting of the Education Division of the American Marketing Association, August 1968.

————— , "Alternative Methods for Collecting Similarities Data," paper presented to the American Marketing Association, Cincinnati, Ohio, August 1969.

Thompson, W. A., Jr. and Singh, J., "Models for Paired Comparisons," *Florida State University Statistics Report M115*, Tallahassee, Florida, June 1966.

————— , "The Use of Limit Theorems in Paired Comparison Model Building," *Florida State University Statistics Report M111*, Tallahassee, Florida, June 1966.

Thurstone, L. L., *The Measurement of Values* (Chicago: The University of Chicago Press, 1959).

————— , "Theory of Attitude Measurement," *Psychological Review*, Vol. 36 (1929), pp. 222–41.

Tolman, E. C., "Principles of Performance," *Psychological Review*, Vol. 62 (1955), pp. 315–26.

Torgerson, W. S., "Multidimensional Scaling: I—Theory and Method," *Psychometrika*, Vol. 17 (1952), pp. 401–19.

————— , "Multidimensional Scaling of Similarity," *Psychometrika*, Vol. 30 (1965), pp. 379–93.

————— , *Theory and Methods of Scaling* (New York: John Wiley and Sons, 1960).

————— , "Multidimensional Representation of Similarity Structures," paper presented at Conference on the Role and Methodology of Classification in Psychiatry and Psychopathology, Washington, D. C., 1965.

————— , "Varieties of Similarity," paper presented at Symposium on Multidimensional Analysis of Similarity Data," Congress on Psychology, Washington, D. C., 1963.

————— , "A Theoretical and Empirical Investigation of Multidimensional Scaling," unpublished Ph.D. thesis, Princeton, 1951.

Triandis, H. C., "Differential Perception of Certain Jobs and People by Managers, Clerks and Workers in Industry," *Journal of Applied Psychology*, Vol. 43 (1959), pp. 221–25.

————— , "Exploratory Factor Analyses of the Behavioral Component of Social Attitudes," *Journal of Abnormal and Social Psychology*, Vol. 68 (1964), pp. 420–30.

————— and Fishbein, M., "Cognitive Interaction in Person Perception," *Journal of Abnormal and Social Psychology*, Vol. 67 (1963), pp. 446–53.

Tryon, R. C., "Cumulative Communality Cluster Analysis," *Educational and Psychological Measurement*, Vol. 18 (1958), pp. 3–35.

————— , "General Dimensions of Individual Differences: Cluster Analysis vs. Multiple Factor Analysis," *Educational and Psychological Measurement*, Vol. 18 (1958), pp. 477–95.

————— , "Domain Sampling Formulation of Cluster and Factor Analysis," *Psychometrika*, Vol. 24 (1959), pp. 113–35.

————— , "Communality of a Variable: Reformulation from Cluster Analysis," *Psychometrika*, Vol. 22 (1957), pp. 241–60.

————— , "Social Areas from Cluster Analysis," University of California, *Publications in Psychology*, Vol. 8 (1955), pp. 1–100.

————— , *Cluster Analysis* (Ann Arbor: Edwards Brothers, 1939).

Tucker, L. R., "Cluster Analysis and the Search for Structure Underlying Individual Differences in Psychological Phenomena," paper presented at Conference on Cluster Analysis of Multivariate Data, New Orleans, December 1966.

————— , "Description of Paired Comparison Preference Judgments by a Multidimensional Vector Model," RM-55-7, Educational Testing Service, Princeton, N. J., 1960.

————— , "Dimensions of Preference," RM-60-7, Educational Testing Service, Princeton, N. J., 1960.

————— , "The Extension of Factor Analysis to Three-Dimensional Matrices," in N. Frederiksen and H. Gulliksen (eds), *Contributions to Mathematical Psychology*, (New York: Holt, Rinehart and Winston, 1964), pp. 109–27.

————— , "Factor Analysis of Double Centered Score Matrices," RM 56-3, Educational Testing Service, Princeton, N. J., October 1956.

————— , "Intra-Individual and Inter-Individual Multidimensionality," in H. Gulliksen and S. Messick (eds.), *Psychological Scaling: Theory and Applications* (New York: John Wiley and Sons, 1960).

————— , "Individual Differences in Multidimensional Scaling," RM-60-15, Educational Testing Service, Princeton, N. J., 1960.

————— and Coffman, W. E., "A Factor Analytic Study of Judged Relevance of Test Items," RM-59-11, Educational Testing Service, Princeton, N. J., October 1959.

————— and Messick, S., "An Individual Differences Model for Multidimensional Scaling," *Psychometrika*, Vol. 28 (1963), pp. 333–67.

Tukey, J. W., "The Future of Data Analysis," *Annals of Mathematical Statistics*, Vol. 33 (1962), pp. 1-67.

Tversky, Amos, "Additivity Analysis of Choice Behavior: A Test of Utility Theory," MMPP 62-2, Michigan Mathematical Psychology Program, University of Michigan, May 1965.

————— , "Additivity, Utility and Subjective Probability," *Journal of Mathematical Psychology*, Vol. 4 (1967), pp. 175–201.

————— , "Finite Additive Structures," MMPP 64-6, Michigan Mathematical Psychology Program, University of Michigan, August 1964.

————— , "A General Theory of Conjoint Measurement," MMPP 65-1, Michigan Mathematical Psychology Program, University of Michigan, April 1965.

————— , "A General Theory of Polynomial Conjoint Measurement," *Journal of Mathematical Psychology*, Vol. 4 (1967), pp. 1–20.

————— , "Intransitivity of Preferences," *Psychological Review*, Vol. 76 (1969), pp. 31–48.

————— , "A Note on Additivity and One-Dimensional Unfolding," MMPP 65-3, Michigan Mathematical Psychology Program, University of Michigan, July 1965.

————— , "The Dimensional Representation and the Metric Structure of Similarity Data," Harvard University: Center for Cognitive Studies, 1966 (mimeographed).

————— and Krantz, David, "The Dimensional Representation and the Metric Structure of Similarity Data," MMPP 69-7, Michigan Mathematical Psychology Program, University of Michigan, 1969.

Tyler, F. T., "Some Examples of Multivariate Analysis in Educational and Psychological Research," *Psychometrika*, Vol. 17 (1952), pp. 289–96.

Van de Geer, J. P., "Matching *k* Sets of Configurations," RN 005-68, Faculty of Social Sciences, University of Leiden, Netherlands, August 1968.

Von Ende, E., "A Cluster Analysis of Judaic-Christian Religious Belief and of Prejudice," unpublished MA thesis, University of California, 1955.

Wallach, M. A., "On Psychological Similarity," *Psychological Review*, Vol. 65 (1958), pp. 103–16.

Walters, H. A. and Jackson, D. N., "Group and Individual Regularities in Trait Inference: A Multidimensional Scaling Analysis," *Multivariate Behavioral Research*, Vol. 1 (1966), pp. 145–63.

Wang, C. K. A., "Suggested Criteria for Writing Attitude Statements," *Journal of Social Psychology*, Vol. 3 (1932), pp. 367–73.

Warburton, F. W., "Analytic Methods of Factor Rotation," *British Journal of Statistical Psychology*, Vol. 16 (1963), pp. 165–74.

Ward, J. H., Jr., "Hierarchical Grouping to Optimize an Objective Function," *Journal of the American Statistical Association*, Vol. 58 (1963), pp. 236–44.

Ward, J. H., Jr. and Hook, M. E., "Application of a Hierarchical Grouping Procedure to a Problem of Grouping Profiles," *Educational and Psychological Measurement*, Vol. 23 (1963), pp. 69–82.

Warren, R. M., "Are Loudness Judgments Based on Distance Estimates?" *Journal of the Acoustical Society of America*, Vol. 35 (1963), pp. 613–14.

Watanabe, Satosi, "Information Theoretical Analysis of Multivariate Correlation," *IBM Journal* (January 1960), pp. 66–82.

Watson, G. S., "A Study of the Group Screening Method," *Technometrics*, Vol. 3 (1961), pp. 371–87.

Watson, H. E., "Agreement Analysis: A Note on Professor McQuitty's Articles," *British Journal of Statistical Psychology*, Vol. 9 (1956), pp. 17–20.

Webster, H., "A Note on Profile Similarity," *Psychological Bulletin*, Vol. 49 (1952), pp. 538–39.

Weitzenhoffer, A. M., "Mathematical Structures and Psychological Measurements," *Psychometrika*, Vol. 16 (1951), pp. 387–406.

Werner, R. A., "A FORTRAN Program for Guttman and Other Scalogram Analyses," *Educational and Psychological Measurement*, Vol. 27 (1967), p. 203.

Wherry, R. J. and Gaylord, R. H., "Factor Pattern of Test Items and Tests as a Function of the Correlation Coefficient, Content, Difficulty and Constant Error Factors," *Psychometrika*, Vol. 9 (1944), pp. 237–46.

Wiggins, Nancy and Hoffman, P. J., "Dimensions of Profile Judgments as a Function of Instructions, Cue-Consistency and Individual Differences," *Multivariate Behavioral Research*, Vol. 3 (1968), pp. 3–20.

Wilks, S. S., "Weighting System for Linear Functions of Correlated Variables When There is No Dependent Variable," *Psychometrika*, Vol. 3 (1938), pp. 23–40.

Williams, E. J., "Use of Scores for the Analysis of Association in Contingency Tables," *Biometrica*, Vol. 39 (1952), pp. 274–89.

Williams, W. T. and Lance, G. M., "Choice of Strategy in the Analysis of Complex Data," *The Statistician*, Vol. 18 (1968), pp. 31–43.

Wilson, K. V., "Multidimensional Analysis of Confusions of English Consonants," *American Journal of Psychology*, Vol. 76 (1963), pp. 89–95.

————, "Multidimensional Scaling Obtained by the Method of Triads," Control Systems Laboratory, University of Illinois, 1955 (mimeographed).

Wind, Yoram, Green, P. E., and Robinson, P. J., "The Determinants of Vendor Selection: The Evaluation Function Approach," *Journal of Purchasing*, Vol. 4 (1968), pp. 29–41.

Wirth, M., Estabrook, G. F., and Rogers, D. J., "A Graph Theory Model for Systematic Biology, with an Example for the Oncidinae (Orchidaceae)," *Systematic Zoology*, Vol. 15 (1966), pp. 59–69.

Wish, M., "A Facet-Theoretic Approach for Morse Code and Related Signals," MMPP 65-6, Michigan Mathematical Psychology Program, 1965.

Wish, M., Deutsch, M., and Rogers, L. B., "Individual Differences in Nation Perception," Bell Telephone Laboratories, Murray Hill, N. J. June 1969 (mimeographed).

Wiskoff, M. F., "A Multidimensional Representation of Psychologists' Perception of Psychologists," unpublished Ph.D. thesis, Maryland University, 1963.

Wolfe, D., "Diversity of Talent," *The American Psychologist*, Vol. 15 (1960), pp. 535–45.

Wolfe, J. H., "A Computer Program for the Maximum Likelihood Analysis of Types," Technical Bulletin, 65-15, U. S. Naval Personnel Research Activity, San Diego, California, 1965.

Wrigley, C., "Objectivity in Factor Analysis," *Educational and Psychological Measurement*, Vol. 18 (1958), pp. 463–76.

Xhignesse, L. V. and Osgood, C. E., "Bibliographical Citation Characteristics of the Psychological Journal Network in 1950 and 1960," *American Psychologist*, Vol. 22 (1967), pp. 778–91.

Yntema, D. B. and Torgerson, W. S., "Man-Computer Cooperation in Decisions Requiring Common Sense," *IRE Transactions of Human Factors in Electronics*, March, 1961, pp. 20–26.

Yoshida, M., "Similarity Among Different Kinds of Taste Near the Threshold of Concentration," *Japanese Journal of Psychology*, Vol. 34 (1963), pp. 25–35.

Young, F. W., "TORSCA, An IBM Program for Nonmetric Multidimensional Scaling," *Journal of Marketing Research*, Vol. 5 (August 1968), pp. 319–21.

————, "Nonmetric Multidimensional Scaling: Development of an Index of Metric Determinancy," Report No. 68, Psychometric Laboratory, University of North Carolina, August 1968.

————, "Polynomial Conjoint Analyses of Similarities: A Model for Constructing Polynomial Conjoint Measurement Algorithms," Report No. 74, Psychometric Laboratory, University of North Carolina, April 1969.

————, "A Computer-Administered Multidimensional Psychophysics Experiment," Psychometric Laboratory, University of North Carolina, April 1969 (mimeographed).

———— and Torgerson, W. S., "A FORTRAN IV Program for Nonmetric Multidimensional Scaling on the IBM 360/75 Computer," (obtained from Dr. Young at the University of North Carolina).

————, "TORSCA, A FORTRAN IV Program for Shepard-Kruskal Multidimensional Scaling Analysis," *Behavioral Science*, Vol. 12 (1967), p. 498.

Young, G. and Householder, A. S., "A Note on Multidimensional Psychophysical Analysis," *Psychometrika*, Vol. 6 (1941), pp. 331–33.

———— , "Discussion of a Set of Points in Terms of Their Mutual Distances," *Psychometrika*, Vol. 3 (1938), pp. 19–22.

Zubin, J. A., "A Technique for Measuring Like-Mindedness," *Journal of Abnormal Social Psychology*, Vol. 33 (1938), pp. 508–16.

———— , "Socio-biological Types and Methods for Their Isolation," *Psychiatry*, Vol. 1 (1938), pp. 237–47.

———— , "A Technique for Pattern Annalysis," *Psychological Bulletin*, Vol. 33 (1936), p. 733. (Abstract)

Index

A

Ackoff, R. L. (see Churchman-Ackoff)
Additive constant, 11, 34, 45
Advertisements, 10, 17, 54, 91
Aggregation problem, 132-133
AID (Automatic Detection of Inter-
   action) program, 155
Algorithm, 12, 33, 37-38, 40, 42, 45,
   48-51, 97, 113, 123, 135, 138
  aspects, 53, 68, 128
  computer, 12-13, 21, 35, 38
  development, 10, 35, 125
AMC Javelin (see 1968 car models)
Analogues, 62, 87
Analysis:
  direct similarities, 88
  "points of view," 78, 88
  results, 15-18, 61, 67
Association measures, 56, 62, 113
Attitude statements, 29, 35
Attneave, F., 134, 135
Attributes, 10, 13, 78, 86, 131
  levels, 10, 22-23, 59
Axes, 15, 58-59, 66, 131
  differential stretching, 63, 79, 81
  uniform stretching, 36, 57, 66
  rotation of, 43, 57; see also Rotation
Axis:
  horizontal, 12, 59
  interpretation, 57-58
  labeling, 12-13
  vertical, 12, 59

B

Beckenbach, E., and Bellman, R., 26
Behavioral data, 21, 40
  measure, 54
  response, 53
Bellman, R. (see Beckenbach, E.)
Bennett, J. F., and Hays, W. L., 11,
  35, 87
Brand:
  competitive position, 16
  switching research, 18
Buick (see 1968 car models)

C

Carnegie-Mellon University, 12, 87
Carroll, J. D., and Chang, J. J.:
  generalization of the unfolding model
   (*ill.*), 80, 91, 148, 157
  ideal point concept, 78
  individual differences model (*ill.*),
   64-65
  INDSCAL, 67, 131, 148-149
  M-D-PREF model, 76, 147-148

Carroll, J. D., and Chang, J. J.: *(cont.)*
  model, 61, 63, 66, 81-82, 131, 133
  parametric mapping program, 45,
    47, 147
  "shared space" model, 61, 63
Cattell, R. B., 153
  similarity coefficient, 153
  Taxonome program, 153
Cell values, 44, 46-47, 73, 98
Chang, J. J. (see Carroll, J. D.)
Chevrolet (see 1968 car models)
Chicago Business School, 12, 87
Churchman-Ackoff value measure, 86
Chrysler (see 1968 car models)
Circumference, 26
City block metric, 26-27, 40, 152
Classification system, 53
Cliff, N. (see Cliff-Pennell-Young
    program)
Cliff-Pennell-Young program, 127, 156
Cluster, 62-63, 66, 117-118, 150-154
  analysis, 32, 97, 103-104, 119-121,
    123, 150-154
  composition class 1 machines *(chart)*,
    117-118
Clusters, 91, 93, 110-111, 113, 116,
    120, 150-154
  ideal point, 18
Clustering procedures, 97, 109, 112-
    113
  techniques, 55, 62, 118, 119-123
COFIS (Configural Scoring Program),
    154
Columbia Business School, 12, 87
Commentary (see Professional journals)
Comparisons:
  interpersonal, 32
  paired, 84-85
Compensatory distance model, *(ill.)*, 71
Component space, 62
Computer:
  processing, 36
  programs, 26, 32, 36-37, 109, 112,
    117, 141-157
  models, 112-113, 115, 118, 141-157
Conceptual structure, 42, 71
Configuration, 12, 16, 19, 34-38, 46,
    62, 89, 110, 121, 127-128, 131,

  134, 136, 154, 156
  axes of, 36, 43
  fixing the, 55, 83
  interpretation, 61, 68, 86
  joint-space, 82, 84, 86, 92
  original used in scaling analysis *(ill.)*,
    48
  "recovered" under noisy data condi-
    tions *(ill.)*, 51
  "recovered" under error-free condi-
    tions *(ill.)*, 50, 126
  two-space, 12, 59, 82
Confusions data, 45, 54
Conjoint comparisons, 53, 55
  data, 45, 55
  measurement, 10
Consonance, 22, 24, 28
Constraints, 32, 36-37, 55, 72, 81, 83
Constructs:
  pre-specified, 56, 58-59, 84
Continuum, 10, 19, 22-23, 87
Coombs, C. H., 11, 21, 29, 35, 77
Coombsian classification system, 28,
    32, 40
  data theory, 30
  concept of ideal point, 78-79; see
    also ideal point
Cook, V. J., and Herniter, J. D., 93
Coordinates, 25-26, 34, 36
  values, 36, 45, 58, 89
Core set methods, 47, 67
Coulter, M. A., 153

D

Data, 10, 15, 22, 46, 122
  analysis, 48, 119
  base, 112-113
  classification, 21; see also Coombs
  collection, 42, 45, 68, 71, 85
  collection methods, 43, 46, 53, 84,
    129
  interval scaled, 8, 34, 45
  "upgrading," 10, 57
Day, J., 151
Decreasing similarity, 31, 54
Degeneracy, 46-47, 81, 128
Degerman, R., 121-122, 157

Descriptors, 28, 53, 72
Difference:
  absolute, 24, 26, 43
  square, 24, 26
Dimension, 24, 27, 58, 97
Dimensionality:
  lowest, 11, 37, 39, 76, 122
  specified, 36-37
Dimensions, 15, 30, 66, 86, 97, 122
Discriminant analysis, 62, 111
Disjoint data, 54-55
  comparisons, 53-54
Dissimilarities, 21, 31-32, 43
  between pairs of car models, 33
Distance, 24, 43, 120, 129
Distance functions, 21, 26, 37, 41,
  135
  properties of, 24; see also Euclidean
Distance models, 42-43, 68, 71-73,
  78
Distances, 21, 36-37, 46-47, 120,
  128
  adding error, 51
  between, 22, 26, 38
  ratio-scaled, 10-11, 34-35
Dominance, 22, 24, 28, 32, 40

                      E

Element, 30, 32, 43
Empirical applications, 47-57
Empirical problems, 42, 53, 66, 71,
  78, 87, 129, 132, 138
Error-free conditions (see Configuration)
Euclidean distance function, 25, 127,
  135, 151
  models, 66, 127
Euclidean measure, 56-57, 105-106,
  151, 152
  metric, 26-27, 40, 43, 72, 131, 135
  space, 34-35, 82, 131, 149
Euclidean distances, 21, 24, 26, 34,
  151
Evaluation function, 16-17, 71
"Explicit ideal," 77
  point formulation, 78, 84
  ratings, 86

                      F

Factor analysis, 30, 34, 45-46, 56, 99,
  119, 123, 128, 154
  approach, 11, 40, 46
Fit measure, 38, 52, 79
Fords (see 1968 car models)
Fully metric, 11, 21, 34-35, 40
  method, 33, 37, 41, 45
  scaling solution, 34

                      G

Geometric space, 21-22
Gleason, T. C., 37, 128
Gower, J. C., 100
Graduate Business Schools, 11-12,
  87
  similarities map of (ill.), 12
Greenberg, M., 56
Guttman, L. (see Guttman-Lingoes
    programs, Guttman scalogram,
    Guttman's lambda)
Guttman-Lingoes programs, 45, 47, 49,
    56, 73, 87, 114, 119, 126, 145-146,
    149-150, 154, 155
  Max-Min Clustering program,
    153
  phi coefficient, 50, 156
  SSA-I program, 49, 52, 102
  SSAR-I program, 73, 145
  SSAR-II program, 47, 73, 87, 103,
    119, 146
Guttman scalogram, 29, 142, 149-
  150
Guttman's lambda measure, 114
Guy (see Magazines)

                      H

Hays, W. L. (see Bennett, J. F.)
Herniter, J. D. (see Cook, V. J.)
Householder, A. S. (see Young, G.)
Howard-Harris program, 151

                      I

Ideal point, 15-16, 23, 71, 78, 81, 93,
  132, 148

Ideal point *(cont.)*
  anti-ideal, 81
  generalization, 78
  model, 79, 148
Index of fit, 38; see also fit measurement
Individual differences, 57, 79
  models, 42
INDSCAL (see Carroll, J.D.)
Infinity, 26-27, 76-77, 79
Information, 32-33, 35-36, 85
  "lost," 101
Input data, 11, 33-35, 37-38, 40, 46,
  48, 55, 73, 98, 121, 130
  nonmetric, 11, 13
  original, 40, 103
  rank order, 35-36
  ranks, 38-39
Input "distances," 11, 35
Interpoint distances, 11, 23, 26-27,
  32, 34, 36, 40, 43, 46, 49-51, 67,
  89, 115, 128, 151
  all pairs of points, 35, 48, 55, 82
  monotone, 37-38
  rank order, 36, 66, 82
Isopreference curve *(ill.)*, 72, 75
Interstimulus, 56, 77, 87
Interval scale, 8, 43, 72, 76, 109, 118
Isosimilarity contours *(ill.)*, 27, 40

                      J

Jaguar (see 1968 car models)
Johnson Clustering program, 152
Journal of Advertising Research (see
  Professional Journals)
Journal of Business (see Professional
  Journals)
Journal of Marketing (see Professional
  Journals)
Journal of Marketing Research (see
  Professional Journals)

                      K

Kelly, G. A., 58
Kendall, M. G., 85
Klingberg, F. L., 11

Kruskal, J. B.:
  M-D-SCAL programs, 45, 113, 144-
    145
  M-D-SCAL IV program, 46, 73, 88,
    126, 128, 130, 145
  stress, 38, 49, 76, 127, 129
  MONANOVA program, 154-155

                      L

Labeling, 130
Lazarsfeld, P., 119, 149
Lincoln (see 1968 car models)
Linear function, 8, 46, 156
Lingoes, J. C. (see Guttman-Lingoes)
Local minima:
  problems of, 81
  types of, 46
Local optima, 47

                      M

McDonald, R. P., 119
McGee, V. E.:
  procedures, 61
  programs, 45-46, 146-147
Magazines, 75, 91
Management Science (see Professional
  Journals)
Market segmentation, 15-16, 61
Marketing problems, 7, 14
Marketing research, 7-8, 19, 29, 68, 86
Marketing Science Institute, 13
Matrices, 21, 47, 120
  off-diagonal proximity, 32, 88
  multiway, 42, 67-68
Matrix, 43, 45-46, 56-57, 100-101, 120
  off-diagonal, conditional, 43, 73-76,
    83
  off-diagonal, unconditional, 43, 74
Max "r" procedure, 58, 156-157
Maximum frequencies, 114
Men Today (see Magazines)
Messick, S. J. (see Tucker, L. R.)
M-D-SCAL IV program, 28, 46-53, 82-
    83, 87-88, 113, 126; see also
    Kruskal
Mercury (see 1968 car models)

Methodology, 7, 11, 97, 125, 133, 137
Metric:
    major technique, 99
    methods, 48, 128
    reduction, 99
    solutions, 35, 81
    space, 24, 28
Miller, J. E., 131
Minkowski p-metrics, 24, 26-27, 40,
    57, 127, 146; see also Isosimilarity
    contours
MIT (Massachusetts Institute of Tech-
    nology) Business School of, 12, 87
MONANOVA program, 154-155
Monotone, 37, 47, 128, 154-155, 157
    function, 40, 46-47, 49-50, 52
    "regression," 39, 47, 58, 81, 154-
    155, 157
Monte Carlo:
    analysis of synthetic data, 57
    comparative studies, 37, 135
    techniques, 126, 136
Multidimensional scaling methods, 17-
    19, 71, 128-129, 137
    techniques, 9, 11, 15, 119; see also
    Scaling, multidimensional
"Nonmetric," 8, 21, 129
    methods, 10-11, 17, 43, 48
    multidimensional scaling, 10, 32, 34-
    36
    solution, 46
Nonstationary models, 135-136
Numerical values, 34, 84

O

Output data, 35
Objective scales, 59
Objects by variables, 98-99
Ordering methods, 85
Ordinal, 48, 84
    approaches, 46
Ordinal scaled (see "nonmetric")
Orientation, 43, 50-51, 57, 59
Origin, 26, 36, 43, 77, 81

P

Pairs of points, 10, 72, 102
Parametric mapping, 17, 47, 73, 88,
    127, 147, 154; see also Carroll and
    Chang
"Passive cells," 32, 40, 46
Pennell, R., 127, 156
Perceptual dimensions, 43, 54, 81, 86,
    156
Perception, 42-43, 72, 79
Performance profiles, 56
Phillips, J. P. N., 47
Pilot study, 7, 13, 91
Plymouth (see 1968 car models)
Point projections, 35
Points, 22, 36, 43, 48, 82
    configuration, 11, 37
    pairs of pairs, 23-24, 28-30
Popular Mechanics (see Magazines)
Precursor approaches, 10, 35
Preference, 71, 73, 81, 84
Preference data, 22, 29, 77, 79, 81-82,
    84-85, 87-88, 93
    analysis of, 13, 71-72, 91, 134-135
    function, 15, 73, 81
    judgment, 71, 79, 87
    values, 75-76
Preferences, 18, 90, 134, 136-137
Procedures, 57, 85
Product life cycle, 14-15
Professional Journals:
    ideal point and similarities configura-
    tion of (ill.), 14
    pilot study, 13
Programs, combining, 46-47, 55-103
Property fitting:
    illustration of, 59
    procedures, 58
Proximities, 32, 35, 40, 45, 47, 54,
    73, 83, 152, 156, 157
Proximity matrices, 45, 47, 109, 156
    major types of, 31, 43, 68
Pruitt program, 152
Psychogalvanometer, 54

Psychological data, 24, 28
  "distances," 28-29, 31-32, 53
  theory, 43
Psychometricians, 72
Public Opinion Quarterly (see Professional Journals)
Pythagorean theorem, 24

Q

Q-technique factor analysis, 32
Q-type component analysis, 62, 106-107, 109, 146
Quadrant data, 28-30, 32, 40
"Quasi-nonmetric," 46, 63, 68, 146, 148

R

Rank order, 12, 35, 37, 46-47, 84-85, 102
  data, 36-37, 76
Reduced space, 40, 101-103
Relations, 22-23; see also dominance and consonance
Researcher:
  expertise, 57, 61
  judgments, 57-58
Respondents, 61, 82, 130
Response, 43, 45, 54-55, 71
  amplitude, 54
Restle, F., 134
Richardson, M. W., 11
Roskam, E. E., 76-77
Rotation:
  principal components (*ill.*), 101
  problem, 130-131
  programs, 156-157
Rotational "freedom," 27
  invariance, 26-27

S

Salience configuration (*ill.*), 64-65
Saliences:
  different dimensions, 15, 63, 72, 89
  respective, 17
Salient:

attributes, 28
dimension, 59
Scalar:
  multiplier, 27
  products, 32, 45-46
Scaling:
  analyses of original configuration (*ill.*), 48
  applications, 7, 36, 45
  multidimensional, 7, 10-11, 14, 16, 19, 21, 28-30, 40, 57, 83, 87, 97, 125, 130-131; see also multidimensional, scaling methods
  nonmetric, 10, 36-37, 43
  results, 49
  solutions, 42-43, 59, 68
  techniques, 21, 28, 30
Scenario influences, 42, 66-67, 90-91, 129
"Scores," 17, 53, 56, 72, 97, 100
Second choice models, 136
Semantic differential scales, 56, 59
  configuration and vectors (*ill.*), 60
Shepard, R. N., 33, 35, 36, 76, 122, 126, 131, 134, 146
  scatter plot, 40
Sherman, C. R., and Young, F. W., 127
Similarities data, 30, 43, 53-54, 68, 84, 87, 91, 156
  analysis of, 42, 61, 67; see also Analysis
  procedures for collecting, 53
  judgments, 11-13
Similarities and preference data, 78, 87, 131
  analysis, 13, 18, 134-135
  illustration of space (*ill.*), 23
  joint space configuration (*ill.*), 90
  model utilizing, 77
Simple aggregation, 61
Slater, P., 85
Solution interpretation, 42, 71
  joint space, 86
  uniqueness of, 126
Sport (see magazines)
Squares:
  sum of, 38, 78-79
Stanford:

Stanford: *(cont.)*
  Business School of, 12, 87
  Research Institute, 122
STAT-PREF package, 142
Stimulus "bundles," 65, 87
  points, 70-71, 73
  set, 56, 59, 61, 67, 129-130
Stress:
  formula, 38, 53
  procedures, 61, 129-130
Synthetic data, 42, 77, 82-83
  analysis of, 48, 71, 74
  "unfold" solutions applied to (*ill.*),
    84

T

Tanimoto coefficient, 108, 153
Taxonome program, 153
Thurstone, L. L.:
  Case V, 86, 142
  model, 30
  scaling judgment, 29-30, 76
Time changes, 137
Torgerson, W. F., 11, 120, 128, 134,
    146; see also TORSCA programs
TORSCA programs, 37, 40, 45-46, 49-
    52, 73, 82-83, 87-89, 102, 126-
    127, 146
Transformation:
  linear and monotonic, 8, 34, 76, 89,
    128, 154, 155, 157
  permissible, 8-9
Triangle inequality, 24, 26-27
TRICON programs, 85, 143
True (see Magazines)
Tucker, L.R., 67, 74-76; see also
  Tucker, L.R., and Messick, S.J.

Tucker, L. R., and Messick, S. J.:
  models, 61-63, 74-76, 133, 144
  points of view analysis, 62

U

Unidimensional scales, 19, 22-23, 29-
    30
University of Colorado program, 153
Utility function (*ill.*), 73, 78

V

Varimax sub-routine, 57
Vectors:
  illustrative, 75, 86, 103
  model, 74-76, 79

W

WAGS program, 143, 149
Ward-Berry-Harris program, 152
Wharton School of Finance and Com-
    merce, 12, 87
Women's World (see Magazines)

Y

Young, F. W., 127, 146, 156; see also
    TORSCA programs
Young, G., and Householder, A. S., 11

Z

Zero:
  a mean of, 51, 85, 106, 113
  weight, 15, 63, 72, 75-76